INSTRUCTOR'S GUIDE TO
TEXT AND MEDIA FOR

Biology

Campbell • Reece

Seventh Edition

Joan Sharp
Simon Fraser University

PEARSON

Benjamin
Cummings

San Francisco   Boston   New York
Cape Town   Hong Kong   London   Madrid   Mexico City
Montreal   Munich   Paris   Singapore   Sydney   Tokyo   Toronto

Editorial Director: Frank Ruggirello
Editor in Chief: Beth Wilbur
Project Editor: Joan Keyes, Dovetail Publishing Services
Biology Marketing Manager: Jeff Hester
Managing Editor, Production: Erin Gregg
Production Supervisor: Vivian McDougal
Production Services: TechBooks/GTS
Cover Designer: Stacy Wong
Manufacturing Buyer: Stacy Wong
Printer: Von Hoffmann Graphics

ISBN 0-8053-7148-6

2 3 4 5 6 7 8 9 10—BRG—07 06 05

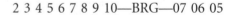

www.aw-bc.com

PEARSON

Benjamin
Cummings

About This Book

This *Instructor's Guide to Text and Media* is designed to help you organize and integrate the many different student and instructor resources that are available with Campbell/Reece *BIOLOGY*, Seventh Edition. The following sections are included for each chapter:

- The **Teaching Objectives** list the key teaching and learning goals for each main section of the chapter.

- The **Student Misconceptions** section is provided to advise teachers about how they can best help their students avoid content confusion and misunderstandings.

- The **Chapter Guide to Teaching Resources** provides a list, organized by the main heads in each chapter, of the instructor's resources available in the different components of the supplements package. These include the following:

  - *Transparency Acetates,* which include all the art and tables from the book, to help you prepare for lecture.

  - *The Instructor and Student Media Resources* list provides a quick reference to all of the digital instructor and student resources available in *The Campbell Media Manager,* Instructor Resources on the Campbell *BIOLOGY* website (www.campbellbiology.com), and course management systems (CourseCompass™, Blackboard, and WebCT).

- **Key Terms** is a convenient list of all boldfaced terms that appear in the text. The key terms are also on the Campbell *BIOLOGY* CD-ROM and website, where they are linked to the glossary.

- **Word Roots** includes key word roots for each chapter, giving the meaning of each root and an example of a term from the text. The Word Roots are also on the Campbell *BIOLOGY* CD-ROM and website.

Note to Instructors

Student Misconceptions

University and college students come to first-year biology courses with a wide range of prior knowledge and preconceptions. Biology is inherently interesting, and students are familiar with many biological terms and concepts from high school biology courses, from nature shows on television, and from outside reading.

A general biology course can be intimidating for a first-year student. There is an enormous specialized vocabulary. To master each new term, students must do far more than merely learn a definition. They must master the concept underlying the term, understand how the concept relates to other new concepts that they have learned, recognize and interpret specific examples that relate to the new concept, and apply the new concept to solve problems. The sheer volume of information and new ideas can be overwhelming.

Students are trying to build meaningful biological knowledge in their first-year class. There are many possible sources of student error, factors that can lead to misunderstanding and confusion rather than to meaningful knowledge.

- Students bring misconceptions with them, from earlier courses or from outside sources.

- Many biological terms have everyday meanings that are related to their biological meaning, but are different in significant ways.

- Some biological concepts are inherently difficult. Some important biological ideas are counterintuitive.

- The meaning of many biological terms has changed over time, as our understanding increases. Even expert knowledge is incomplete and rapidly changing.

- Many students are most comfortable with memorization as a learning tool. Such students may fail to understand the significance of the details they are learning and may not build connections between concepts.

How can a biology instructor help students to recognize, confront, and correct their misunderstandings? The first step is to gain awareness of possible sources of student confusion and misunderstandings. Talk to your students as much as possible. Structured and focused conversation can be a very useful tool to probe student understanding and misunderstanding of concepts. Ask questions—in conversation and on examinations—that will give you insight into student misunderstandings. Delve into the excellent education literature on student misconceptions in biology, especially in the areas of evolution and genetics. Once you are aware of student misconceptions, address them directly. Point out and correct common misunderstandings in lectures, in conversation, and in answer keys to examinations. Expect and require your students to understand the relationships between concepts, to provide suitable examples, and to make predictions and solve problems using the concepts they have learned.

Encourage your students to become biologists as soon as possible. If there are opportunities at your institution for students to volunteer in labs or to conduct undergraduate research, bring them to your students' attention and urge them to take advantage of these opportunities. As your students become biologists, the concepts you are teaching them will become meaningful and real.

Supplements for Instructors

Campbell Media Manager (set of 8 CD-ROMs) (0-8053-7153-7)

The Campbell Media Manager combines all the instructor and student media for Campbell/Reece *BIOLOGY* into one chapter-by-chapter resource. It includes eight CD-ROMs, one for each unit in the text. Instructor media includes PowerPoint Lectures, PowerPoint TextEdit Art, PowerPoint Active Lecture Questions, and the Image Library—1,600 photos, all art from the book with and without labels, selected art layered for step-by-step presentation, tables, 85 videos, and more than 100 animations. Also included are Lecture Outlines in Word format for each chapter. The Campbell Media Manager also includes printed thumbnail-sized images for easy viewing of all the resources in the Image Library and a convenient fold-out Quick Reference Guide.

Campbell Biology Website (www.campbellbiology.com)

The Instructor Resources section of the Campbell *BIOLOGY* website includes the resources listed above for the Campbell Media Manager. Suggested answers to

Lab Report questions from the Investigations are also available, as is the Instructor's Guide to *Biological Inquiry: A Workbook of Investigative Cases*. For access to the website, refer to the insert in the Professional copy of Campbell/Reece *BIOLOGY*, Seventh Edition.

Lecture Outlines

Joan Sharp, Simon Fraser University

Chapter lecture outlines are available in Word format on the Campbell Media Manager and in the Instructor Resources section at www.campbellbiology.com.

Transparency Acetates (0-8053-7149-4)

Approximately 1,000 acetates include all full-color illustrations and tables from the text, many of which incorporate photos. In addition, selected figures illustrating key concepts are broken down into layers for step-by-step lecture presentation.

Printed Test Bank (0-8053-7154-0)
Computerized Test Bank (0-8053-7153-2)

Edited by William Barstow, University of Georgia

Thoroughly revised and updated, the Seventh Edition test bank also includes optional questions from the book's Self-Quiz and questions related to the media to encourage students to use these resources. Available in print, on a cross-platform CD-ROM, and in the instructor section of CourseCompass™, Blackboard, and WebCT.

PowerPoint Lectures

Chris C. Romero, Front Range Community College, Larimer Campus

PowerPoint Lectures are provided for each chapter and include the art, photos, tables, and an editable lecture outline. The PowerPoint Lectures can be used as is or customized for your course with your own images and text and/or additional photos, videos, and animations from the Campbell Media Manager.

PowerPoint TextEdit Art

All the art, photos, and tables are provided on the Campbell Media Manager. Selected figures are layered for step-by-step presentation. The PowerPoint TextEdit Art can be used as is or labels can be edited in PowerPoint as needed.

New! *Biological Inquiry: A Workbook of Investigative Cases, Instructor's Guide* (0-8053-7177-X)

The Instructor's Guide provides specific and detailed suggestions on how to effectively use each case study, outlining links to specific content in *BIOLOGY,* Seventh Edition, and other supplements, providing direction on how to facilitate problem-based learning, and listing suggested answers and opportunities for extended investigations.

Practicing Biology, Instructor's Version,
Second Edition (0-8053-8184-2)

The instructor's version is available online at http://suppscentral.aw.com.

Course Management Systems

The content from the Campbell *BIOLOGY* website is also available in these popular course management systems: CourseCompass™, Blackboard, and WebCT. Visit http://cms.aw.com for more information.

Classroom Response Systems

Invigorate lectures with Active Lecture Questions. These multiple-choice questions are adapted from various sources, including the end-of-chapter questions, Student Study Guide, Test Bank, and *Biomath: Problem Solving for Biology* by Robert W. Keck and Richard R. Patterson. The questions are available in PowerPoint format via Supplements Central or preloaded on H-ITT and EduCue Personal Response System (PRS). Sources and answers are located in the PowerPoint Notes field. One or two questions in each chapter will have additional Discussion Points added as suggestions for the instructor.

Supplements for Students

Campbell *BIOLOGY* Student CD-ROM and Website
(www.campbellbiology.com)

The CD-ROM and website that accompany each book include 230 interactive Activities, 85 Videos, and 55 Investigations. New graphing exercises help students learn how to build and interpret graphs. The CD-ROM and website are fully integrated with the text, reinforcing students' focus on the big ideas. The media organization mirrors that of the textbook, with all the Activities, Videos, and Investigations for a given chapter correlated to the key concepts from the book.

There are three separate quizzes per chapter: a Pre-Test, a Chapter Quiz, and an Activities Quiz. A new electronic Gradebook automatically records students' quiz scores. Another new feature of the Seventh Edition, *Cumulative Test,* allows students to build a self-test with questions from more than one chapter. Feedback is provided to students on all quizzes and tests in the media, which have been upgraded in level of difficulty.

New Flashcards help students master terminology, along with Key Terms linked to the Glossary and Word Roots. Students can also access Art from the book with and without labels, the Glossary with audio pronunciations, the Campbell *BIOLOGY* Interviews from previous editions, an E-Book, the Biology Tutor Center, Web Links, News, and Further Readings.

New! *Biological Inquiry: A Workbook of Investigative Cases*
(0-8053-7176-1)

Margaret Waterman, Southeast Missouri State University, and Ethel Stanley, Beloit College

This new workbook offers eight investigative cases, one for each unit of the textbook. In order to understand the science in each case, students will pose questions, analyze data, think critically, examine the relationship between evidence and conclusions, construct hypotheses, investigate options, graph data, interpret results, and communicate scientific arguments. Students will actively engage in the experimental nature of science as they gain new insight into how we know what we know. For example, in *Donor's Dilemma* (the Unit 3 case) students explore the concepts of protein synthesis, viral genomes, and transmission pathways while investigating a blood donor who may have been exposed to the West Nile virus. Web links and other online resources referred to in the investigative cases are provided on the Campbell *BIOLOGY* website.

Student Study Guide (0-8053-7155-9)

Martha R. Taylor, Cornell University

This popular study guide offers an interactive approach to learning, providing framework sections to orient students to the overall picture, concept maps to complete or create for most chapters, chapter summaries, word roots, chapter tests, and a variety of interactive questions, including multiple choice, short-answer essay, labeling art, and interpreting graphs.

Practicing Biology: A Student Workbook, Second Edition
(0-8053-8184-2)

Jean Heitz, University of Wisconsin, Madison

This workbook's hands-on activities emphasize key ideas, principles, and concepts that are basic to understanding biology. Suitable for group work in lecture, discussion sections, and/or lab, the workbook includes class-tested Process of Science activities, concept map development, drawing exercises, and modeling activities.

New! Test Preparation Guide to MCAT/GRE for Campbell *BIOLOGY*, 7e (0-8053-7178-8)

Exclusively available with *BIOLOGY*, Seventh Edition, this new guide includes sample questions and answers from the Kaplan test preparation guides correlated to specific pages in this edition of *BIOLOGY*.

Art Notebook (0-8053-7183-4)

This resource contains all the line art from the text without labels with plenty of room for students to take notes.

BIOLOGY—Basic Concepts Study Card (0-8053-7175-3)

Useful as a quick reference guide, this fold-out card summarizes the basic concepts and content covered in *BIOLOGY*, Seventh Edition.

Biology Tutor Center (www.aw.com/tutorcenter)

This center provides one-to-one tutoring for college students in four ways—phone, fax, email, and the Internet—during evening hours and on weekends. Qualified college instructors are available to answer questions and provide instruction regarding self-quizzes and other content found in *BIOLOGY*, Seventh Edition. Visit the website for more information.

The Benjamin Cummings Special Topics Booklets

- Understanding the Human Genome Project (0-8053-6774-8)
- Stem Cells and Cloning (0-8053-4864-6)
- Biological Terrorism (0-8053-4868-9)
- The Biology of Cancer (0-8053-4867-0)

The Chemistry of Life CD-ROM, Second Edition (0-8053-3063-1)

Robert M. Thornton, University of California, Davis

This CD-ROM helps biology students grasp the essentials of chemistry with animations, interactive exercises, and quizzes with feedback.

An Introduction to Chemistry for Biology Students, Eighth Edition (0-8053-3970-1)

George I. Sackheim, University of Illinois, Chicago

This printed workbook helps students master all the basic facts, concepts, and terminology of chemistry that they need for their life science course.

Biomath: Problem Solving for Biology Students (0-8053-6524-9)

Robert W. Keck and Richard R. Patterson

A Short Guide to Writing About Biology, Fourth Edition (0-321-07843-8)

Jan A. Pechenik, Tufts University

Spanish Glossary (0-8053-7182-6)

Supplements for the Lab

Investigating Biology, Fifth Edition (0-8053-7196-6)

Judith Giles Morgan, Emory University, and M. Eloise Brown Carter, Oxford College of Emory University

With its distinctive investigative approach to learning, this laboratory manual encourages students to practice science. Students are invited to pose hypotheses, make predictions, conduct open-ended experiments, collect data, and then apply the results to new problems.

Investigating Biology, Annotated Instructor's Edition, Fifth Edition (0-8053-7180-X)

Teaching information, added to the original Student Edition text, includes margin notes with hints on lab procedures, additional art, and answers to in-text and end-of-chapter questions from the Student Edition. Also featured is a detailed Teaching Plan at the end of each lab with specific suggestions for organizing labs, including estimated time allotments and suggestions for encouraging independent thinking and collaborative discussion.

Preparation Guide for Investigating Biology, Fifth Edition (0-8053-7181-8)

Guides lab coordinators in ordering materials as well as in planning, setting up, and running labs.

New! Designs for Bio-Explorations (0-8053-7229-6)

Janet Lanza, University of Arkansas at Little Rock

Eight inquiry-based laboratory exercises offer students creative control over the projects they undertake. Students are provided background information that enables them to design and conduct their own experiments.

New! Designs for Bio-Explorations, Instructor's Version (0-8053-7228-8)

The instructor's version is available online at http://suppscentral.aw.com.

Symbiosis Book Building Kit—Customized Lab Manuals (0-201-72142-2)

Build a customized lab manual, choosing the labs you want, importing artwork from our graphics library, and even adding your own material, and get a made-to-order black-and-white lab manual. Visit http://www.pearsoncustom.com/database/symbiosis.html for more information.

Biology Labs On-Line (www.biologylabsonline.com)

Twelve on-line labs enable students to expand their scientific horizons beyond the traditional wet lab setting and perform potentially dangerous, lengthy, or expensive experiments in an electronic environment. Each experiment can be repeated as often as necessary, employing a unique set of variables each time. The labs are available for purchase individually or in a 12-pack with the printed Student Lab Manual.

Student Lab Manual for Biology Labs On-Line (0-8053-7017-X)

Instructor's Lab Manual for Biology Labs On-Line (0-8053-7018-8)

Contents

Effective Uses of Instructional Technologies in Teaching Introductory Biology

By Eric J. Simon
New England College
Email: esimon@nec.edu

Technology is a funny thing. During the last decade, methods of teaching and learning have changed faster than during any time in the history of organized education. What is responsible for this rapid reformulation? Technology, of course. As educators, we hear about it all the time. The myriad benefits of instructional technologies have been stated and restated so many times that they are approaching mantra, if not dogma.

Yet, almost every educator has a favorite story about how technology can be overemphasized, inappropriately glorified, or just plain misused. Here is mine. A few years ago, my wife and I were in Hawaii (she on business, me as the grateful spouse). We decided to visit the observatories at the top of Mauna Kea, nearly 14,000 feet above the sea. The trip to the top is precarious enough to require a 4-wheel-drive jeep, so we rented one for the occasion. On our way down the mountain, when we returned to paved road, I needed to take the jeep out of 4-wheel drive and back into 2-wheel drive for the highway. My efforts failed and caused a terrible grinding of the gears. In a flash of inspiration, I decided to check the driver's manual. I opened the glove compartment, smiling at my cleverness. Inside, however, I found no driver's manual. What I found was an instructional video.

I could just imagine a committee patting each other on the back for the excellent way they had used technology to help jeep drivers. But at the top of a Hawaiian mountain, I was less impressed. The point was clearly noted: Technology should not be haphazardly applied across the whole spectrum of educational situations, but should be used in a thoughtful manner that always supports preestablished learning objectives.

BIOLOGY, Seventh Edition, by Neil Campbell and Jane Reece, has a number of technology supplements for students and instructors. First, every new copy of the book includes a student CD-ROM and an access code to the Campbell *BIOLOGY* website (www.campbellbiology.com). The website includes the same materials that are on the CD-ROM plus additional web-only content. Instructors also have the option of establishing an online course website for their students using Campbell/Reece-specific content in a course management system. CourseCompass™, provided by Pearson Education, is a nationally hosted course management system. Alternatively, instructors can download a Campbell/Reece Blackboard course or WebCT course for local hosting. All of these websites are password-protected and contain the same content that is on the Campbell *BIOLOGY* website. Students who purchase a new copy of the textbook receive an access code card for the online course with their textbook. Students who buy a used book can purchase access to a website separately.

The purpose of this introduction is to present ways that these instructional technology tools for students can be used to enhance teaching and learning in introductory biology courses that use *BIOLOGY,* Seventh Edition. I will present issues to consider and ideas gained from my own experience. In keeping with the lesson cited above, this introduction also discusses the possible pitfalls of technology use. Most importantly, this guide to technology is firmly grounded in one fundamental learning objective: teaching introductory biology using *BIOLOGY,* Seventh Edition.

A quick word on what this introduction does not cover. This introduction will not discuss details of implementation. Visit http://cms.aw.com for information on specific course management systems (CourseCompass™, Blackboard, and WebCT). The ideas presented in this introduction are general enough to apply to multiple course management systems and related technologies such as CD-ROMs, the Campbell *BIOLOGY* website, and e-books. The purpose of this introduction is to stimulate thought and provide ideas on how any instructor might gain the advantages of technology use in the classroom while, hopefully, avoiding the types of inappropriate uses that form the basis of so many apocryphal tales.

General Considerations

This section will discuss some general issues related to the use of instructional technologies in the introductory biology classroom.

The most important general point to be made about using technology tools is the one already stated: Don't let the technology tail wag the learning dog. Before implementing any specific technology, make sure to pause and ask yourself a few questions: Is this technology appropriate for my classroom? Is the proposed use firmly grounded in one or more of my course objectives? Will the technology under consideration enhance my ability to teach and/or the students' ability to learn? If the answer to any of these questions is "no," then perhaps using the new technologies under consideration should be reconsidered or saved for another course or semester.

Today's students are, in general, technology literate. We've all heard the cliché of a young child teaching his/her parents how to use a VCR or computer, and many classroom instructors may feel that the students are as comfortable (or more) with particular technologies as they are. While this may often be true, instructors need to acknowledge that some students may be very uncomfortable, perhaps even functionally illiterate, with certain technological learning aids. In particular, adults or returning students, international students, and economically disadvantaged students might be behind their peers in experience with new technologies. In addition, no matter how good they are at certain specific uses of the Internet, nearly every student needs guidance on the proper use of technology as an educational tool.

Thus, it is important for the instructor to introduce technology to the students and to carefully evaluate if it is serving all students. This introduction and evaluation can be accomplished in several ways. First, circulate a questionnaire to determine the level of computer literacy and comfort among your students. If you plan to make heavy use of instructional technologies during your course, poll your students on the first day of class to determine their comfort level. These polls and questionnaires can help guide the instructor regarding the pace of introducing new technologies, indicating which technologies the students are very comfortable with (e.g., email), and which might require more training or supervision (e.g., presentation software). The polls can also be used to establish teams of students by pairing less savvy students with those who are more competent. Figure I-1 (page I-15) contains a sample technology questionnaire that can serve as the basis for your own.

A similar poll can be used at the end of the course (or at the end of the first semester of a two-semester course) to evaluate the technology experience of your students. This poll can provide helpful information to the instructor regarding adapting the technologies for future courses or semesters. I have often found the students' comments to be insightful with respect to how the technologies were used and any perceived benefits and drawbacks. Figure I-2 (page I-16) contains a sample end-of-semester technology questionnaire.

A useful method for introducing students to the technologies you plan to use is to create assignments that combine course material with technology usage. For example, ask students to track down certain specific information on the Internet (e.g., "How many organisms have had their genomes sequenced?" or "How many different species of mammal have been cloned?"). Require students to provide both the answer and a proper citation for their source. This assignment will help to familiarize students with Web-based biology resources and can also turn into a sophisticated lesson on how to critically evaluate Internet sources, a crucial skill as the Internet gains prominence as a scholarly tool. Other possible assignments can be based on the content provided on the *BIOLOGY* CD-ROM and website. In each case, the assignment serves a dual purpose: to guide the students in a biology-related inquiry, and to ensure their proper use of the technology involved.

Many students, particularly those less familiar with technology, will experience two learning curves in a technology-heavy course: one for the curricular material itself and another for the technologies. Students can thus benefit from the stepwise introduction of instructional technologies into the classroom. A recommended approach is to use a series of assignments that gradually introduce the different instructional technologies. The first technology-related assignment should use an easy and familiar resource, such as e-mail. Future assignments should build upon each other with respect to the technologies required. A second assignment, for example, might involve e-mailing a report, thus combining e-mail and word processing skills. Future assignments can involve the course bulletin board, Internet, CD-ROMs, websites, and other resources. A capstone assignment for the course might involve creating a multimedia presentation on some relevant subject, requiring skills in presentation software, word processing, graphics, Internet searches, etc. The important point is to make sure that no particular assignment introduces more than one new technology component at a time and that the assignments build upon each other with respect to both curricular and technology content.

A final general piece of advice is to use both incentives ("carrots") and requirements ("sticks") to encourage students to participate in the technology components of the course. Assignments are a great way to ensure that every student is benefiting from the technologies, but remember to toss out some carrots as well. I have found that the prompt posting of grades to an online gradebook provides incentive for students to access the course website, particularly for once-a-week courses or at the end of the semester. Providing hints for an exam (through, for example, a virtual chat study session or postings to a bulletin board) is an excellent way of increasing participation. Providing fun links to multimedia such as videos, cartoons, and songs is another way to capture student interest. For example, point students toward content-related songs (such as Weird Al Yankovic's "I Think I'm a Clone Now" or Pearl Jam's "Do the Evolution"—email me for a list of dozens of biology-related popular songs) available as free samples on some retail websites (e.g., http://amazon.com). Or provide links to movie websites that connect to the curriculum, such as those for the *Jurassic Park* movies or *Gattaca.* I often allow students to earn extra credit by completing small technology projects, such as creating a slide for my in-class PowerPoint presentations or compiling and critically evaluating a list of Web links related to a course topic. Remember that to be used to its maximum potential, the technology, like the material itself, must be both informative and interesting to the students.

Technology alternatives to standard media have many potential benefits to the teaching and learning processes. Some of these benefits include:

- Multimedia capabilities
- Improved assessment
- Ability to present timely material
- Improved communication
- Customization of curriculum
- Portability

The following sections will discuss each of these advantages in detail. Specific suggestions will be made on using course management systems and related technologies to gain each advantage. In addition, tips on avoiding certain pitfalls of technology use will also be discussed.

Multimedia

One of the most obvious and powerful advantages that technology offers over the printed medium is the ability to display multimedia such as video, animation, hyperlinks, and sound. Movement is one of the characteristics of life, and explaining certain complex biological processes using only static visuals often proves difficult. Metabolic pathways, anatomical configurations, ecological systems, pronunciations of difficult words, and cell cycles are just a few of the topics that benefit from multimedia exposition.

BIOLOGY, Seventh Edition, comes loaded with multimedia supplements. They fall into two general categories: those for the students and those for the instructor. Each chapter in this *Instructor's Guide to Text and Media* includes a list of the media assets available for that chapter.

Student Media

Multimedia student materials can be found on the CD-ROM, Campbell *BIOLOGY* website, and Campbell course management websites. The student media include the following:

- Each chapter opens with a Chapter Guide, which clearly lays out all the media resources available within each chapter.
- The E-Book gives students quick access to the textbook contents while they are using the Campbell website. The E-Book includes text, art, tables, and photos organized by the key concepts in each chapter.

- There are over 230 Activities containing animations, interactive exercises, audio, and digital video to convey key concepts. More than 55 Investigations involve students in interactive laboratory activities that teach them to follow the scientific method by making observations, formulating a hypothesis, designing and performing an experiment, collecting data, and drawing conclusions. Investigations include a Lab Notebook for recording data and Questions, which students can answer and email to their instructors. Students can also link to Biology Labs On-Line, twelve extensive virtual labs. (For more information, see www.biologylabsonline.com.) Assignments for Biology Labs On-Line can also be emailed.

- There are over 80 videos available for student viewing. Videos are in easy-view Flash format and include video scripts.

- Each chapter contains three different multiple-choice quizzes: a Pre-Test to diagnose current knowledge, an Activities Quiz that tests understanding of the media Activities in the chapter, and a comprehensive Chapter Quiz. Each quiz contains hints and immediate feedback. Pre-Test and Chapter Quiz questions provide concept number references as well as hyperlinks to concepts in the E-Book. Results from each quiz can submitted to an electronic, online gradebook. A Cumulative Test allows students to build their own multiple-choice self-assessment test on any or all chapters by selecting questions from any chapter. Questions include concept number references and hints, and offer immediate feedback.

- With Graph It!, students can manipulate real data while learning the art of graphing through nine Graph It! interactive activities.

- Art from the book is provided both with labels and without labels. Students can print out the art to take to class for note-taking, and they can use the version without labels as a self-quiz.

- Word Study Tools for each chapter include Word Roots and Key Terms to improve vocabulary skills. Key Terms also include selected audio pronunciations. A Flashcards game allows students to practice terms, definitions, and word roots.

- The Glossary includes every boldface term from Campbell/Reece *BIOLOGY*, Seventh Edition, with audio pronunciations of selected terms. Terms in the Activities and E-Book are linked to the Glossary, and students can also access the Glossary independently.

- The Web Links and References section includes links to news stories that present recent developments related to the chapter content, and also to further readings. Students can research topics further through the Research Navigator, which offers unlimited access to scientific journals, websites, and the *New York Times* database of news articles.

- The Campbell *BIOLOGY* Interviews section contains discussions with specialists from a variety of fields, including many well-known scientists. Every interview includes text and photos. The interviews can help students personalize the curriculum and research experience.

- About the Book provides more information about *BIOLOGY,* Seventh Edition, the authors, and the supplements.

Instructor Media

Nothing captures student interest during lengthy lectures more than lively presentations with informative multimedia elements. The Campbell Media Manager, available as a set of eight instructor CD-ROMs and via the Instructor

Resources section of the *BIOLOGY* website, aids the instructor in improving classroom lectures and presentations. This chapter-by-chapter visual archive of over 2700 images is for the exclusive use of adopters of Campbell/Reece *BIOLOGY,* Seventh Edition. All of the diverse images—art and tables, photos, videos, and animations—are organized by chapter. All file formats have been thoroughly tested in large lecture halls. The Media Manager includes:

- 1600 photos, including the photos from the text, plus additional photos collected from a variety of sources that have been especially chosen to match the content of each chapter.
- All the art and tables from the text. Art figures are provided both with and without labels for maximum flexibility in lecture presentations. The version without labels can be customized for lecture, used to create a quiz, or used to create step-by-step presentations. All of the art and tables have been reformatted to be larger and clearer when used for lecture presentation.
- Selected art figures are layered for step-by-step presentation.
- PowerPoint Slides. All of the photos, art, and tables have been imported into PowerPoint.
- PowerPoint Active Lecture Questions. These questions, drawn from book content, can increase interactivity during lecture by testing student comprehension of key topics.
- More than 80 video clips. Instructors can enhance their lectures with videos on a variety of biological concepts. Scripts are provided for background information. The videos are available in large (640 × 480) and small (320 × 240) formats.
- Over 100 animations. Animations can be used in lecture to help students understand key biological concepts.
- Lecture Outlines. Available in Microsoft Word format, these outlines can be edited, printed, and distributed electronically to help students focus on important study goals.
- A Quick Reference Guide summarizes all available resources in a fold-out format.

Fully prepared PowerPoint Lectures with lecture outlines, art, tables, and photos are also available. The PowerPoint Slides or Lectures can be customized for an instructor's course. If desired, the PowerPoint files can be printed out and duplicated for students to use for taking notes during lecture. Customized lecture notes can be published through Pearson Custom Publishing. (See www.pearsoncustom.com for more information.)

Assessment

One of the most challenging and time-consuming aspects of teaching is creating and grading tests and quizzes. Many teachers find it to be the most frustrating aspect of the job, from keeping track of old exam questions to calculating and recording grades. Technology can alleviate some of this frustration by doing what computers do best: repetitive tasks. There are also, however, some interesting problems that arise when using technology-based assessment tools.

The assessment tools available with *BIOLOGY,* Seventh Edition, fall into two basic categories: those intended to help students test their knowledge of the material, and those intended to aid the instructor in the assessment process. For the students, the CD-ROM and the Campbell *BIOLOGY* website include multiple self-assessment aids organized by chapter. Every chapter includes a Pre-Test of ten multiple choice questions which can be used by the instructor to gauge student understanding before lecture. A Chapter Quiz of 30–50 multiple-choice questions helps students test their new knowledge. Each quiz has hints and feedback for students, and answers can be submitted to an online gradebook.

The Cumulative Test is a feature new to *BIOLOGY*, Seventh Edition. It is a Flash-based multiple-choice self-assessment test that allows students to choose the chapter or chapters they would like to be tested on and the number of questions. Each question includes feedback and hints. At the end of their test, students receive their personal score as well as a list of the concepts that may require further study.

Several of the features included on the Campbell CD-ROM and website have their own internal assessment tools. The multimedia Activities section associated with each chapter, for example, includes a multiple-choice quiz of 15–25 questions, many of which include graphics from the activities themselves. This quiz reinforces the materials presented in that chapter's Activities, thereby reinforcing important curricular concepts. Assigning the Activities Quiz is a good way to ensure that students successfully complete the Activities section. Answers can be submitted to an online gradebook. Also, student understanding of the Investigations can be measured by requiring students to email their responses. Suggested answers to the Questions can be found in the Instructor Resources section of the Campbell website. For instructors who assign any of the Biology Labs On-Line (www.biologylabsonline.com), students can email responses to assignments from within the Campbell *BIOLOGY* website.

The Computerized Test Bank for instructors includes 50–60 multiple-choice questions per chapter that students do not have access to. In addition, the Test Bank includes the book's multiple-choice Self-Quiz questions and five multiple-choice questions on the Media Activities so that instructors can encourage students to use these features by including questions on tests if they would like to.

All of these same assessment tools from the *BIOLOGY* website are included in the CourseCompass™, Blackboard, and WebCT course management systems, giving the instructor great flexibility in preparing and presenting quizzes and tests. The Assessment Manager tools (in CourseCompass™/Blackboard) control the pre-written quizzes for each chapter: Self-Quiz, Essay Questions, Pre-Test, Activities Quiz, and Chapter Quiz (all taken from the Campbell *BIOLOGY* website) and Test Bank questions (taken from the Instructor's Computerized Test Bank). In each case, the instructor has the ability to preview, modify, or remove the pre-loaded question set. The modifications that an instructor can make are quite extensive. Every question can be altered to include text, images, or links. The number of answer choices can be set and the text and image for each answer modified. The specific feedback given upon a correct or incorrect answer can be changed for each question. The questions can be grouped into categories for easier selection. The instructor can use all of the questions provided or a subset of them, and the instructor can add original questions and answers.

Once a quiz/test has been created, the instructor has many options for making the quiz available to the students. The instructor controls when to make the quiz/test available to students. The correct answer can be revealed or not, depending on whether the instructor wishes the students to take a quiz multiple times. The customized feedback can be displayed or not. Students may be permitted multiple attempts at each question. A time limit can be set for the quiz, and it can be password-protected. All of these options allow the instructor to tailor each quiz to a particular learning goal. Taken together, these assessment tools provide great convenience in managing the creation and distribution of quizzes and tests while also providing great flexibility.

Once quizzes are made available to students, the Assessment Manager (in CourseCompass™/Blackboard) makes grading very convenient for the instructor. The students submit their answers electronically. The quizzes can be automatically graded, with grades sent to the instructor and/or recorded in the online gradebook. The instructor has the ability to view each student's quiz results from anywhere with Internet access, removing the requirement of physical proximity to the office. The online gradebook can calculate averages and create a variety of reports, and is exportable to spreadsheet programs. Students also have access to their own grades on the website so that they can easily keep track of their standing in the course.

No matter which quiz format is being used, online assessment always involves issues of security. Secure online testing is one of the most vexing problems currently facing instructors who deliver courses electronically, and I know of no solution that is fully satisfactory for every teaching situation. The course management Assessment Manager (in CourseCompass™/Blackboard) does include some security features. A timer can be set to limit the amount of time a student has to complete a quiz. Setting the timer to a sufficiently low value can reduce the chances that a student can consult non-permitted materials (i.e., the book) but obviously does not eliminate that possibility. A password can be associated with each quiz, thereby controlling access, starting from the time the instructor makes that password available and ending when the instructor removes access to the quiz. Neither of these features allows for total confidence, however. Probably the most secure method of online testing can be found in schools with a testing center, i.e., a computer facility with a proctor. Such a facility gives students great flexibility of when to take their quiz while also ensuring a high level of security. Some distance learning formats allow students to visit a testing center at a local institution, or with a previously established proctor. Some day, I can imagine secure online testing being achieved through the use of Web cameras that will allow students to take a quiz at home under the scrutiny of an electronic eye that keeps them honest.

Another way to avoid the issue of test security is to design assessments that preclude cheating. For example, I have moved to a format of weekly online quizzes. I prepare a set of 30–50 questions using the electronic Test Bank and import them to my class website (part of the Blackboard course management system). When students take the quiz, they are assigned ten questions at random from the larger pool. This ensures that every student takes the quiz independently, since each student receives a different set of questions. I allow students access to all available study materials during the quizzes. At the end of the quiz, students receive their score only, no indication of which questions were answered correctly/incorrectly, and no hints or correct answers. Students may then repeat the quiz as many times as they like, but they will receive a different set of ten questions each time. Only the grade of the final attempt is recorded, so students may repeat the quiz as often as they like until they achieve their desired score. Besides mitigating questions of test security, this method provides some interesting insights into students' goals (e.g., which students are happy to stop at a 70, and which will take the quiz eight times to raise a 90 to a 100?).

Timeliness

No subject in the curriculum is more affected by recent advances than biology. We live in a time when biology seems to be in the news every day. Recent advances in cloning, genetically engineered foods, stem cells, genomes, fertility, and DNA technologies easily capture student attention. In addition to being very interesting, students see the relevance of these topics to their lives. Students, particularly introductory students, always appreciate when connections are made between the subject matter at hand and current events or popular culture. Biology instructors are uniquely positioned to take advantage of our current biology-centric society to improve the climate of learning in their classrooms.

Several technology resources available with *BIOLOGY*, Seventh Edition, allow for the introduction of timely material. The Campbell *BIOLOGY* website contains several timely content areas, and nearly identical materials are also built into the pre-loaded online course for *BIOLOGY*, Seventh Edition, in the three course management systems. Even better, the timely materials available on each of these resources (the website and course management system offerings) are pre-sorted by the relevant *BIOLOGY* textbook chapter, making it easy for the instructor to incorporate current events into classroom activities.

The website that comes with the printed text and the course management websites contain three sets of particularly timely materials: News Links that cover recent advances, Web Links that point to timely Internet resources, and the Research Navigator, which offers unlimited access to scientific journals, websites, and the *New York Times* database of news articles. There is at least one relevant News Link associated with every chapter. On average, each chapter has about ten Web Links, with descriptions of the sites. In the course management systems, instructors can also add their own News Links and Web Links.

An advantage of using the online resources for recent news is that it avoids any copyright conflict. Most instructors know that photocopying articles and handing them out in class raises issues of copyright violation. Reprinting an article electronically on a course website raises identical issues. The Internet offers a way to avoid this potential problem through News Links and Web Links. A local link to a remote article that has been publicly posted by the producer poses no risk of copyright violation. Instructors can thus provide access to online versions of recent news articles without the possibility of recrimination.

Communication

Effective communication is important in every classroom. There are several avenues of communication that must be maintained: between professor and student, student and student, and student and teaching assistant. Many introductory biology courses have large enrollments, thus making effective communication simultaneously more important and more difficult.

Computer resources have the potential to vastly improve communication among all participants. Many instructors have found that the nature of the electronic medium encourages some students to speak up who otherwise might not. Students who may be intimidated to participate during lecture are often more comfortable participating via email and online discussions wherein they can compose and edit their comments before submitting them. The asynchronous nature of these forms of electronic communication (email and bulletin boards) provides greater access for all students but is particularly helpful for part-time or nontraditional students who are not on campus as often as their traditional peers. Multiple forms of electronic communication can also be used to create a sense of community and overcome the somewhat impersonal nature of the electronic medium. Creating a learning community is particularly helpful when teaching distance learning courses that lack the close in-person contact of the classroom environment. Students and instructors also benefit from the more global nature of electronic communication. Outside experts, colleagues, and other students can join in the forum, providing resources that are generally not available in a traditional classroom setting.

Within the course management systems, there are seven major communication vehicles: announcements, email, bulletin boards, live chat, home pages, digital drop box, and online gradebook. All of these resources will be discussed below.

Announcements

The most immediate way to communicate with students is through the Announcements feature. All students see announcements from their instructor as soon as they log into the course website. Announcements can include text, images, and links. I usually post at least one announcement per week. A typical announcement will remind students about upcoming assignments, lab activities, study sessions, or quizzes/exams. They can also be more whimsical, such as mentioning important dates in the history of science as they occur, or displaying digital photos taken during recent class activities. It is important to check your particular course management system to find out if announcements disappear from the front page after a certain amount of time and are then only visible if the student clicks on a tab to show older messages. I have found it useful to include a permanent announcement reminding students to look for older announcements.

Email

Email is the most widely used form of electronic communication. It is effective because it is asynchronous, thereby allowing students to read your comments whenever they have time (often, it seems, late at night). Email also allows students and instructors to archive conversations and exchange documents. Personally, I prefer to receive electronic files from my students via email because it is easier to detect and avoid viruses; floppy disks from college students are notoriously prone to invisible viruses. Email makes for a good first technology assignment because most students are very comfortable with it. During the first week of the semester, have every student email you with a simple hello message, or perhaps answers to a questionnaire that you have sent them. The successful completion of this simple assignment ensures that every student has access to a working computer and an email account, and that every student knows how to contact the instructor via email. The instructor can then check the email addresses received against the email database maintained by the course management software to make sure they match. This step is important because some students maintain multiple accounts, and the course management software may use their school account or an internal email address as default. Within the course management system, it is easy to send email to an individual, the entire class, or any subset thereof. This feature is available to all users so that students can easily email each other. Informing students that they should expect regular email from you will ensure effective communication in most cases.

Bulletin Boards

While e-mail simulates a private office meeting, bulletin boards offer a reasonable simulation of classroom question-and-answer sessions. The bulletin board allows everyone in the class to "hear" the question and answer. I typically expect every student to participate verbally at least once during each in-class lecture. Similarly, I expect every student to participate at least once a week in the class bulletin board, either by posting a question/comment or by responding to a classmate's question/comment. Some instructors require students to post a number of questions and a number of answers in a given time period. In a typical bulletin board assignment, I will bring up an important biological issue (such as the use of DNA forensic evidence to examine old criminal cases or the ethics of reproductive technologies) and assign half the class to each side of that issue. I am often impressed with the enthusiasm and sophistication with which students participate in these discussions. The course management systems include a good threaded discussion system in their bulletin boards. Students can start new discussion topics and can include Internet links in their postings. The instructor can create new threads and has the option of allowing students to create them. I usually create a new thread for each week, so that the topmost level of the bulletin board has a link to each week and subject (such as "Week #3: The cell"). Within each week, I then create some standard subthreads that appear every week: questions/comments, homework assignments, and extra credit. Students are also free to create their own additional subthreads to raise issues of importance to them. The instructor can monitor the discussion and remove repeated, blank, erroneous, or inappropriate postings. I try to read the bulletin board every day during the school week so that I can answer questions, correct misconceptions, and keep the discussion focused on the subject. I find the bulletin board is used most heavily during the weeks before exams. This electronic forum can stimulate interesting questions, debates, and discussions among the students. The class bulletin board is particularly important when teaching distance learning courses because it can go a long way toward supplying interaction among the participants that might otherwise be absent. It also provides a good forum for working on group projects where progress can be monitored in real time.

Live Chat

In-class study sessions can be supplemented or replaced by a virtual discussion held in an online chat room. Such virtual chats have the additional benefit of being logged and archived for students who could not participate. The course management software includes an easy-to-use but sophisticated virtual chat room. The instructor can monitor who is present and everyone can read everyone else's comments. I have found that students often need to "warm up" and to be encouraged to participate, so I always have several practice questions prepared, just as I would for an in-person study session. The virtual chat forum is particularly handy before an exam and can also be used to facilitate virtual office hours. I always schedule two virtual chats during the week before an exam to accommodate a wide range of schedules. Classes comprised largely of traditional on-campus students probably fare better with live meetings. In classes with significant numbers of nontraditional, part-time, or off-campus students, however, the virtual meetings are often much more convenient for the students and may significantly increase participation levels.

Home Pages

Home pages offer a good way for members of the class to get to know each other. The course management systems provide an easy-to-use tool that guides even the most novice users to create a home page in a few minutes. For the more sophisticated, home pages can include images, links, or any other HTML code. Having every student create their own home page with answers to standard questions ("What is your major?" "What are your hobbies and interests?") is a good early technology assignment. Students always appreciate a detailed home page from the instructor and teaching assistants. I have found that students truly enjoy the chance to get to know me better, both personally and professionally, through my home page. I tend to add many personal details, such as photos of my children and pets, links to my favorite websites, etc.

Digital Drop Box

Much communication within a class, particularly a large class, centers on the receipt and acknowledgement of assignments. The course management systems offer a "Digital Drop Box" feature that allows students to submit assignments electronically. The students submit their assignments as electronic files into the drop box and receive a receipt. The instructor can remove assignments at any time, from any location with Internet access. This method is much more convenient for both parties than having a fixed location for students to turn in their assignments. Materials placed in the drop box have an attached link that allows an instructor to send an email to the student with one click. I usually send a quick email note to let the student know that his or her materials have been successfully received.

Online Gradebook

While an online gradebook may not seem like a form of communication, it is, and it can have a great impact. The course management systems offer an online gradebook with many organizational features. Only the instructor can view the entire set of results and modify them, but each student can see his or her own grades. Instructors can add, edit, or remove gradebook entries at will. Online grade posting allows for rapid communication of grades, and students can track their progress during the course. By viewing the gradebook as a spreadsheet, exporting the grade database to an external tool, or using various analysis tools included in the course management software, instructors can view trends, compare students, and search for weaknesses and strengths within the class.

Customization of the Curriculum

There is probably no introductory biology course that teaches the entire curriculum covered in *BIOLOGY,* Seventh Edition. Printed textbooks are, by necessity, designed to carry the superset of possible materials covered in any individual course. Different courses will cover only a subset of these materials based on the interests of the students, the instructor, and the program. One advantage of technology is that it can help focus the curriculum from the full range of possible subject matter to just the subset covered in any particular course.

Students appreciate it when their study materials are concise and focused. The recent popularity of custom printed texts that incorporate just a portion of the possible materials confirms this need. Some instructors prepare their own self-written materials in order to make them more focused, but this approach requires a large start-up cost and will usually not reach the quality of professionally prepared learning aids.

Course management software provides an opportunity to have the best of both worlds: to pick and choose appropriate high-quality pre-written materials for your course from a large set prepared by the publisher. The ability to customize curricular materials lies within the course management systems. When instructors copy the *BIOLOGY* CourseCompass™ course, building upon it to create their own course website, or when they download the *BIOLOGY* Blackboard or WebCT courses, they will find courses pre-loaded with the content of the Campbell/Reece *BIOLOGY* website, such as Internet links, quizzes, and interactive activities, as well as the entire computerized test bank. An optional e-book is available.

Instructors have the ability to customize these pre-loaded materials in several ways. First, any unwanted materials (e.g., those that cover chapters not included in the course) can be deleted from the course website. Students will thus be assured that all of the material on the course website is directly applicable to their particular course, as opposed to the CD-ROM or Campbell *BIOLOGY* website which contain the full set of materials. The instructor can also modify some of the default material; for example, the instructor can change quiz questions or answers. Finally, instructors always have the ability to create new materials to upload to the site, either from scratch or by using external utilities such as Word or the TestGen software to prepare new quizzes. Instructors can thus simply and effectively customize the instructional materials available to students in ways that are impossible with the standard printed medium.

Portability

Students appreciate the ability to access their study materials from multiple locations, and Internet-based materials offer this convenience. Students can view the summaries, practice tests, news articles, and so on, from their dorm, the library, work, or home during vacation. Several students have told me that they like to access the multimedia elements from work because of the higher available bandwidth. Students can leave their book in their primary study location and then use the Internet in several satellite locations. For students who travel, CD-ROMs are also considerably more portable and therefore more convenient than the book. Commuting students appreciate that the CD-ROM can turn travel time into productive study time. I have also heard stories from several students of sharing their class materials from home with family and friends, thereby connecting their academic interests to the larger world.

The ultimate portability is achieved through the use of an electronic version of the text. E-books free students from the physical book in the printed medium altogether, providing the full text in a lighter-weight format. The Campbell *BIOLOGY* website includes an e-book for students who buy a new book. The website plus e-book can also be purchased separately. The course management systems (CourseCompass™, Blackboard, and WebCT) are available with or without an e-book.

Conclusions

As technology plays an increasingly larger role in the modern biology classroom, two general types of features are emerging. The first are those that simply increase convenience for the student and/or the instructor. Examples include being able to access learning materials from multiple locations, the online gradebook, and the ability to customize a set of learning materials for a particular course. The second category of technology features includes those technologies that actually increase the potential for teaching and learning. Examples include the ability to provide access to very timely materials (i.e., News Links), multimedia explanations of important concepts, and access to outside resources via the Internet.

The instructional technologies included with *BIOLOGY,* Seventh Edition, address both categories described above. Through proper implementation of the CD-ROM, the Campbell *BIOLOGY* website, the Media Manager, and/or the course management systems, a lively and informative learning atmosphere can be created that benefits all students and the instructor.

Name _____ Course _____ Section _____

1. How comfortable are you with each of the following? (circle one)

   1 = not at all comfortable → 5 = extremely comfortable

A. Computers in general	1	2	3	4	5
B. Email	1	2	3	4	5
C. Word processing	1	2	3	4	5
D. Bulletin boards	1	2	3	4	5
E. CD-ROMs	1	2	3	4	5
F. Internet searches	1	2	3	4	5
G. Presentation software (e.g., PowerPoint)	1	2	3	4	5
H. Chat rooms	1	2	3	4	5

2. How comfortable are you using computers as an educational tool?

               1   2   3   4   5

3. How would you rate your computer literacy compared to your peers? (circle one)

   way below average   below average   average   above average   way above average

4. Are there any computer technologies that give you particular difficulties?

5. Do you think you need training in the use of any of the computer technologies listed above? If so, which ones?

Figure I-1 A sample questionnaire that can be distributed at the start of a course to determine the level of computer literacy among students. The results can be used to guide the pace of technology usage, determine necessary levels of training and supervision, and guide in the creation of teams of students.

Course _____ Section _____

1. Please rate your overall level of satisfaction with the instructional technologies used in this course.

   1 = not at all satisfied → 5 = extremely satisfied

   (circle one)   1   2   3   4   5

2. Please rate your level of satisfaction with each of the following specific technologies used in this course:

A. Email	1	2	3	4	5
B. Word processing	1	2	3	4	5
C. Bulletin boards	1	2	3	4	5
D. CD-ROMs	1	2	3	4	5
E. Internet	1	2	3	4	5
F. Presentation software (e.g., PowerPoint)	1	2	3	4	5
G. Chat rooms	1	2	3	4	5

3. What were the advantages of using technology in this course?

4. What were the disadvantages of using technology in this course?

5. Which technologies would you like to see emphasized more in this course? Less?

6. Please make specific suggestions for how technology usage in this course can be improved.

7. Did you feel unprepared for any of the technologies used?

Figure I-2 A sample questionnaire that can be distributed at the end of a semester or course to determine the level of satisfaction with instructional technologies.

CHAPTER 1

Exploring Life

Teaching Objectives

Exploring Life on Its Many Levels

1. Briefly describe the unifying themes that characterize the biological sciences.
2. Diagram the hierarchy of structural levels in biological organization.
3. Explain how the properties of life emerge from complex organization.
4. Describe the two major dynamic processes of any ecosystem.
5. Distinguish between prokaryotic and eukaryotic cells.
6. Describe the basic structure and function of DNA.
7. Describe the dilemma of reductionism.
8. Discuss the goals and activities of systems biology. List three research developments that have advanced systems biology.
9. Explain the importance of regulatory mechanisms in living things. Distinguish between positive and negative feedback.

Evolution, Unity, and Diversity

10. Distinguish among the three domains of life. List and distinguish among the three kingdoms of multicellular, eukaryotic life.
11. Explain the phrase "life's dual nature of unity and diversity."
12. Describe the observations and inferences that led Charles Darwin to his theory of evolution by natural selection.
13. Explain why diagrams of evolutionary relationships have a treelike form.

The Process of Science

14. Distinguish between discovery science and hypothesis-based science. Explain why both types of exploration contribute to our understanding of nature.
15. Distinguish between quantitative and qualitative data.
16. Distinguish between inductive and deductive reasoning.
17. Explain why hypotheses must be testable and falsifiable but are not provable.
18. Describe what is meant by a controlled experiment.
19. Distinguish between the everyday meaning of the term *theory* and its meaning to scientists.
20. Explain how science is influenced by social and cultural factors.
21. Distinguish between science and technology. Explain how science and technology are interdependent.

Student Misconceptions

1. Point out to your students that the universal genetic code provides the best evidence of a common ancestry for all life.

2. The concept of emergent properties is a difficult one for students to master. Provide examples of properties that emerge at each level in the hierarchy of biological organization in order to clarify this concept.

3. Many students do not recognize the extent to which life has shaped the Earth. Although students may acknowledge that living things interact with the abiotic components of their environment, they may not realize the extent to which the atmosphere, oceans, and land of our modern Earth have been changed by life.

4. Students tend to think that there is one universally applied scientific method, and that all "real science" is hypothesis-driven and experimental. As a result of this misunderstanding, students may discount theories about historical events. Impress upon your students that scientists use many different methods to investigate biological questions.

5. Students may have difficulty understanding that scientific hypotheses cannot be proven. An example that may help to illustrate this is the recent modification of the long-accepted five-kingdom theory of biological diversity, which has been replaced with a theory of three domains and additional kingdoms based on new evidence from DNA comparisons of living organisms.

Further Reading

Cooper, R. A. 2002. Scientific knowledge of the past is possible: Confronting myths about evolution and scientific methods. *The American Biology Teacher, 64(6), 427–432.*

Chapter Guide to Teaching Resources

Overview: Biology's most exciting era

Concept 1.1 Biologists explore life from the microscopic to the global scale

Transparencies

Figure 1.4   Basic scheme for energy flow through an ecosystem

Figure 1.6   Inherited DNA directs development of an organism

Figure 1.7   DNA: The genetic material

Instructor and Student Media Resources

Activity: The levels of life card game

Activity: Energy flow and chemical cycling

Activity: Comparing prokaryotic and eukaryotic cells
Activity: Heritable information: DNA
Video: Seahorse camouflage

Concept 1.2 Biological systems are much more than the sum of their parts

Transparencies
Figure 1.10   A systems map of interactions between proteins in a cell
Figure 1.11   Negative feedback
Figure 1.12   Positive feedback

Student Media Resource
Activity: Regulation: Negative and positive feedback

Concept 1.3 Biologists explore life across its great diversity of species

Transparencies
Figure 1.14   Classifying life
Figure 1.16   An example of unity underlying the diversity of life:
               The architecture of cilia in eukaryotes

Student Media Resource
Activity: Classification schemes

Concept 1.4 Evolution accounts for life's unity and diversity

Transparencies
Figure 1.20   Summary of natural selection
Figure 1.21   Natural selection
Figure 1.23   Descent with modification: Adaptive radiation of finches on the
               Galápagos Islands

Instructor and Student Media Resources
Investigation: How do environmental changes affect a population?
Activity: Form fits function: Cells
Video: Soaring hawk
Video: Albatross courtship ritual
Video: Blue-footed boobies courtship ritual
Video: Galápagos Islands overview
Video: Galápagos marine iguana
Video: Galápagos sea lion
Video: Galápagos tortoise

Concept 1.5 Biologists use various forms of inquiry to explore life

Transparencies

Figure 1.25   A campground example of hypothesis-based inquiry

Figure 1.27   Geographic ranges of Carolina coral snakes and king snakes

Figure 1.29   Does the presence of poisonous coral snakes affect predation rates on their mimics, king snakes?

Figure 1.30   Modeling the pattern of blood flow through the four chambers of a human heart

Student Media Resources

Graph It: An introduction to graphing

Investigation: How does acid precipitation affect trees?

Activity: Science, technology, and society: DDT

Concept 1.6 A set of themes connects the concepts of biology

Transparency

Table 1.1   Eleven themes that unify biology

For additional resources such as digital images and lecture outlines, go to the Campbell Media Manager or the Instructor Resources section of **www.campbellbiology.com.**

Key Terms

archaea	domain Bacteria	negative feedback
bacteria	domain Eukarya	organ
bioinformatics	ecosystem	organ system
biology	emergent properties	organelle
biosphere	eukaryotic cell	organism
cell	gene	population
community	genome	positive feedback
consumer	hypothesis	producer
controlled experiment	inductive reasoning	prokaryotic cell
data	inquiry	reductionism
deductive reasoning	kingdom Animalia	system
deoxyribonucleic acid (DNA)	kingdom Fungi	systems biology
	kingdom Plantae	technology
discovery science	model	theory
domain Archaea	molecule	tissue

Word Roots

bio- = life (*biology:* the scientific study of life; *biosphere:* all the environments on Earth that are inhabited by life; *bioinformatics:* using information technology to extract useful information from large sets of biological data)

eu- = true (*eukaryotic cell:* a cell that has a true nucleus)

-ell = small (*organelle:* a small, formed body with a specialized function found in the cytoplasm of eukaryotic cells)

pro- = before; **karyo-** = nucleus (*prokaryotic cell:* a cell that has no nucleus)

CHAPTER 2

The Chemical Context of Life

Teaching Objectives

Elements and Compounds

1. Distinguish between an element and a compound.

2. Identify the four elements that make up 96% of living matter.

3. Define the term **trace element** and give an example.

Atoms and Molecules

4. Draw and label a simplified model of an atom. Explain how this model simplifies our understanding of atomic structure.

5. Distinguish between each of the following pairs of terms:

   a. neutron and proton

   b. atomic number and mass number

   c. atomic weight and mass number

6. Explain how the atomic number and mass number of an atom can be used to determine the number of neutrons.

7. Explain how two isotopes of an element are similar. Explain how they are different.

8. Describe two biological applications that use radioactive isotopes.

9. Define the terms **energy** and **potential energy.** Explain why electrons in the first electron shell have less potential energy than electrons in higher electron shells.

10. Distinguish among nonpolar covalent, polar covalent and ionic bonds.

11. Explain why strong covalent bonds and weak bonds are both essential in living organisms.

12. Distinguish between hydrogen bonds and van der Waals interactions.

13. Give an example that illustrates how a molecule's shape can determine its biological function.

14. Explain what is meant by a chemical equilibrium.

Student Misconceptions

1. The simplified models of the atom (Figure 2.4), electron shells (Figure 2.8), and covalent bonding (Figure 2.11) can confuse students who take them too literally. It is important to make sure that students understand that:

   - Atoms do not have defined surfaces.
   - Electrons do not travel in planetary orbits around the nucleus of the atom.
   - Shared electron pairs are not paired spatially in covalent bonds.
   - Electron shells represent energy levels rather than the position of electrons.

2. Students have difficulty fully grasping the concept of energy, and especially the concept of potential energy. Potential energy can be misunderstood as a substance or fuel that is somehow stored in matter. Explain to students that potential energy is associated with an object's ability to move to a lower-energy state, thus releasing some of the potential energy. Return to the concept of potential energy in discussing electron shells, emphasizing that electrons in different electron shells differ in potential energy rather than in position.

3. Students should recognize that weak bonds play important roles in the chemistry of life, despite the transient nature of each individual bond. Page 42 gives the compelling example of the gecko, able to walk on ceilings because of the van der Waals interactions between the ceiling and the hairs on the gecko's toes. Emphasize that strong and weak bonds are both important in the chemistry of life, and ask students to provide examples illustrating this.

Chapter Guide to Teaching Resources

Overview: Chemical Foundations of Biology

Concept 2.1 Matter consists of chemical elements in pure form and in combinations called compounds

Transparency

Table 2.1   Naturally occurring elements in the human body

Student Media Resource

Investigation: How are space rocks analyzed for signs of life?

Concept 2.2 An element's properties depend on the structure of its atoms

Transparencies

Figure 2.4   Simplified models of a helium (He) atom

Figure 2.5   Radioactive tracers

Figure 2.7   Energy levels of an atom's electrons

Figure 2.8   Electron-shell diagrams of the first 18 elements in the periodic table

Figure 2.9   Electron orbitals

Student Media Resources

Activity: Structure of the atomic nucleus

Activity: Electron arrangement

Activity: Build an atom

Concept 2.3 The formation and function of molecules depend on chemical bonding between atoms

Transparencies

Figure 2.10   Formation of a covalent bond

Figure 2.11   Covalent bonding in four molecules

Figure 2.12   Polar covalent bonds in a water molecule

Figure 2.13   Electron transfer and ionic bonding

Figure 2.14   A sodium chloride crystal

Figure 2.15   A hydrogen bond

Figure 2.16   Molecular shapes due to hybrid orbitals

Figure 2.17   A molecular mimic

Student Media Resources

Activity: Covalent bonds

Activity: Nonpolar and polar molecules

Activity: Ionic bonds

Activity: Hydrogen bonds

Concept 2.4 Chemical reactions make and break chemical bonds

Transparency

Page 44   An example of a chemical reaction

For additional resources such as digital images and lecture outlines, go to the Campbell Media Manager or the Instructor Resources section of **www.campbellbiology.com.**

Key Terms

anion	energy	polar covalent bond
atom	energy level	potential energy
atomic mass	hydrogen bond	product
atomic nucleus	ion	proton
atomic number	ionic bond	radioactive isotope
cation	ionic compound	reactant
chemical bond	isotope	salt
chemical equilibrium	mass number	single bond
chemical reaction	matter	structural formula
compound	molecular formula	trace element
covalent bond	molecule	valence
dalton	neutron	valence electron
double bond	nonpolar covalent	valence shell
electron	bond	van der Waals
electron shell	orbital	interactions
electronegativity	periodic table of the	
element	elements	

Word Roots

an- = not (*anion:* a negatively charged ion)

co- = together; **-valent** = strength (*covalent bond:* an attraction between atoms that share one or more pairs of outer-shell electrons)

electro- = electricity (*electronegativity:* the tendency for an atom to pull electrons toward itself)

iso- = equal (*isotope:* an element having the same number of protons and electrons but a different number of neutrons)

neutr- = neither (*neutron:* a subatomic particle with a neutral electrical charge)

pro- = before (*proton:* a subatomic particle with a single positive electrical charge)

CHAPTER 3

Water and the Fitness of the Environment

Teaching Objectives

The Properties of Water

1. With the use of a diagram or diagrams, explain why water molecules are:
   a. polar
   b. capable of hydrogen bonding with four neighboring water molecules
2. List four characteristics of water that are emergent properties resulting from hydrogen bonding.
3. Define **cohesion** and **adhesion.** Explain how water's cohesion and adhesion contribute to the movement of water from the roots to the leaves of a tree.
4. Distinguish between heat and temperature, using examples to clarify your definitions.
5. Explain the following observations by referring to the properties of water:
   - Coastal areas have milder climates than adjacent inland areas.
   - Ocean temperatures fluctuate much less than air temperatures on land.
   - Insects like water striders can walk on the surface of a pond without breaking the surface.
   - If you slightly overfill a water glass, the water will form a convex surface above the top of the glass.
   - If you place a paper towel so that it touches spilled water, the towel will draw in the water.
   - Ice floats on water.
   - Humans sweat and dogs pant to cool themselves on hot days.
6. Distinguish among a solute, a solvent, and a solution.
7. Distinguish between hydrophobic and hydrophilic substances.
8. Explain how you would make up a one molar ($1M$) solution of ethyl alcohol.

The Dissociation of Water Molecules

9. Name the products of the dissociation of water and give their concentration in pure water.
10. Define **acid, base,** and **pH.**
11. Explain how acids and bases may directly or indirectly alter the hydrogen ion concentration of a solution.

12. Using the bicarbonate buffer system as an example, explain how buffers work.

13. Briefly explain the causes and effects of acid precipitation.

Student Misconceptions

1. For students to understand the emergent properties of water and the importance of these properties to living things, they must fully understand the structure of water and its ability to form hydrogen bonds with neighboring molecules.

2. Some students may think that water forms hydrogen bonds only in the liquid state. These students will find it difficult to understand the arrangement of water molecules in ice and will fail to recognize that frozen water molecules form a crystalline lattice, with each water molecule forming four hydrogen bonds.

3. Clarify for students the difference between physical and chemical changes. An ability to distinguish between these is important in understanding many of the key properties of water, such as its role as a solute and its dissociation to form hydroxide and hydronium ions.

4. Many students do not fully understand the exchange of protons between water molecules. An appreciation of water's dissociation to form hydroxide and hydronium ions is crucial to understanding acid-base relationships, the effects of excess OH^- and H_3O^+ ions in solution, and the role of buffers.

Chapter Guide to Teaching Resources

Overview: The Molecule That Supports All of Life

Concept 3.1 The polarity of water molecules results in hydrogen bonding

Transparency

Figure 3.2   Hydrogen bonds between water molecules

Student Media Resource

Activity: The polarity of water

Concept 3.2 Four emergent properties of water contribute to Earth's fitness for life

Transparencies

Figure 3.5   Ice: crystalline structure and floating barrier

Figure 3.6   A crystal of table salt dissolving in water

Figure 3.7   A water-soluble protein

Student Media Resource
Activity: Cohesion of water

Concept 3.3 Dissociation of water molecules leads to acidic and basic conditions that affect living organisms

Transparencies
Page 53   Reaction producing hydroxide and hydronium ions
Figure 3.8   The pH scale and pH values of some aqueous solutions

Student Media Resources
Activity: Dissociation of water molecules
Activity: Acids, bases, and pH
Investigation: How does acid precipitation affect trees?

For additional resources such as digital images and lecture outlines, go to the Campbell Media Manager or the Instructor Resources section of **www.campbellbiology.com.**

Key Terms

acid	heat	mole (mol)
acid precipitation	heat of vaporization	molecular mass
adhesion	hydration shell	pH
aqueous solution	hydrogen ion	polar molecule
base	hydrophilic	solute
buffer	hydrophobic	solution
calorie (cal)	hydroxide ion	solvent
Celsius scale	joule (J)	specific heat
cohesion	kilocalorie (kcal)	surface tension
colloid	kinetic energy	temperature
evaporative cooling	molarity	

Word Roots

hydro- = water; **-philos** = loving; **-phobos** = fearing (*hydrophilic:* having an affinity for water; *hydrophobic:* having an aversion to water)

kilo- = a thousand (*kilocalorie:* a thousand calories)

CHAPTER 4

Carbon and the Molecular Diversity of Life

Teaching Objectives

The Importance of Carbon

1. Explain how carbon's electron configuration accounts for its ability to form large, complex, and diverse organic molecules.
2. Describe how carbon skeletons may vary, and explain how this variation contributes to the diversity and complexity of organic molecules.
3. Describe the basic structure of a hydrocarbon and explain why these molecules are hydrophobic.
4. Distinguish among the three types of isomers: structural, geometric, and enantiomer.

Functional Groups

5. Name the major functional groups found in organic molecules. Describe the basic structure of each functional group and outline the chemical properties of the organic molecules in which they occur.

Student Misconceptions

1. Students often misunderstand the interaction of hydrophobic molecules and water. Many students think that individual oil and water molecules repel each other. Explain to students that individual hydrocarbon molecules are attracted to water molecules, but with a force much less than the attraction of water molecules to each other.
2. Students find it difficult to understand the differences among structural isomers, geometric isomers, and enantiomers. Three-dimensional models, or pictures of such models, are very useful tools in discussion of these terms.

Chapter Guide to Teaching Resources

Overview: Carbon—The Backbone of Biological Molecules

Concept 4.1 Organic chemistry is the study of carbon compounds

Concept 4.2 Carbon atoms can form diverse molecules by bonding to four other atoms

Transparencies

Figure 4.3	The shapes of three simple organic molecules
Figure 4.4	Electron-shell diagrams showing valences for the major elements of organic molecules
Figure 4.5	Variations in carbon skeletons
Figure 4.6	The role of hydrocarbons in fats
Figure 4.7	Three types of isomers
Figure 4.8	The pharmacological importance of enantiomers

Student Media Resources

Activity: Diversity of carbon-based molecules

Activity: Isomers

Investigation: What factors determine the effectiveness of drugs?

Concept 4.3 Functional groups are the parts of molecules involved in chemical reactions

Transparencies

Figure 4.9	A comparison of functional groups of female (estradiol) and male (testosterone) sex hormones
Figure 4.10	Exploring some important functional groups of organic compounds (part 1)
Figure 4.10	Exploring some important functional groups of organic compounds (part 2)

Student Media Resource

Activity: Functional groups

For additional resources such as digital images and lecture outlines, go to the Campbell Media Manager or the Instructor Resources section of **www.campbellbiology.com.**

Key Terms

adenosine
  triphosphate (ATP)
amino group
carbonyl group
carboxyl group

enantiomer
functional group
geometric isomer
hydrocarbon
hydroxyl group

isomer
organic chemistry
phosphate group
structural isomer
sulfhydryl group

Word Roots

carb- = coal (*carboxyl group:* a functional group present in organic acids, consisting of a carbon atom double-bonded to an oxygen atom and a hydroxyl group)

enanti- = opposite (*enantiomer:* molecules that are mirror images of each other)

hydro- = water (*hydrocarbon:* an organic molecule consisting only of carbon and hydrogen)

iso- = equal (*isomer:* one of several organic compounds with the same molecular formula but different structures and, therefore, different properties)

sulf- = sulfur (*sulfhydryl group:* a functional group that consists of a sulfur atom bonded to an atom of hydrogen)

thio- = sulfur (*thiol:* organic compounds containing sulfhydryl groups)

CHAPTER 5

The Structure and Function of Macromolecules

Teaching Objectives

The Principles of Polymers

1. List the four major classes of macromolecules.
2. Distinguish between monomers and polymers.
3. Draw diagrams to illustrate condensation and hydrolysis reactions.

Carbohydrates Serve as Fuel and Building Material

4. Distinguish among monosaccharides, disaccharides, and polysaccharides.
5. Describe the formation of a glycosidic linkage.
6. Distinguish between the glycosidic linkages found in starch and cellulose. Explain why the difference is biologically important.
7. Describe the role of symbiosis in cellulose digestion.

Lipids Are a Diverse Group of Hydrophobic Molecules

8. Describe the building-block molecules, structure, and biological importance of fats, phospholipids, and steroids.
9. Identify an ester linkage and describe how it is formed.
10. Distinguish between saturated and unsaturated fats.
11. Name the principal energy storage molecules of plants and animals.

Proteins Have Many Structures and Many Functions

12. Distinguish between a protein and a polypeptide.
13. Explain how a peptide bond forms between two amino acids.
14. List and describe the four major components of an amino acid. Explain how amino acids may be grouped according to the physical and chemical properties of the R group.
15. Explain what determines protein conformation and why it is important.
16. Explain how the primary structure of a protein is determined.
17. Name two types of secondary protein structure. Explain the role of hydrogen bonds in maintaining secondary structure.

18. Explain how weak interactions and disulfide bridges contribute to tertiary protein structure.

19. List four conditions under which proteins may be denatured.

Nucleic Acids Store and Transmit Hereditary Information

20. List the major components of a nucleotide, and describe how these monomers are linked to form a nucleic acid.

21. Distinguish between:

    a. pyrimidine and purine

    b. nucleotide and nucleoside

    c. ribose and deoxyribose

    d. 5′ end and 3′ end of a nucleotide

22. Briefly describe the three-dimensional structure of DNA.

Student Misconceptions

1. Students may think that two-dimensional representations of organic molecules are accurate. These molecules are less static than students imagine. Conveniently drawn as linear, monosaccharides usually form rings in aqueous solutions. There may be considerable rotation around single bonds within organic molecules, unless their conformation is stabilized by interactions between regions of the molecule. Emphasize to your students that 2D drawings of organic molecules are convenient but greatly oversimplified representations of molecular structure.

2. Students may not realize that every protein has primary, secondary, and tertiary structures and may think that any particular protein is characterized only by one level of structure. When lecturing on this material, introduce the four levels of protein structure and then spend time discussing how each level contributes to protein conformation.

3. The majority of students have difficulty visualizing the different levels of protein structure and the interaction of the regions of the protein molecule. To fully understand levels of protein structure, students must be able to mentally construct three-dimensional images of proteins. This can be very challenging. Assist your students by using 3D images to illustrate lectures. Encourage your students to develop their own mental images of protein conformation.

4. Students tend to define nucleic acids by the most familiar examples, DNA and RNA, rather than understanding the structure of nucleotide monomers. This causes confusion when students encounter important molecules such as ATP and cAMP and fail to recognize them as nucleotides.

Chapter Guide to Teaching Resources

Overview: The molecules of life

Concept 5.1 Most macromolecules are polymers, built from monomers

Transparency

Figure 5.2   The synthesis and breakdown of polymers

Student Media Resource
Activity: Making and breaking polymers

Concept 5.2 Carbohydrates serve as fuel and building material

Transparencies

Figure 5.3   The structure and classification of some monosaccharides
Figure 5.4   Linear and ring forms of glucose
Figure 5.5   Examples of disaccharide synthesis
Figure 5.6   Storage polysaccharides of plants and animals
Figure 5.7   Starch and cellulose structures
Figure 5.8   The arrangement of cellulose in plant cell walls
Figure 5.10   Chitin, a structural polysaccharide

Student Media Resources
Activity: Models of glucose
Activity: Carbohydrates

Concept 5.3 Lipids are a diverse group of hydrophobic molecules

Transparencies

Figure 5.11   The synthesis and structure of a fat, or triacylglycerol
Figure 5.12   Examples of saturated and unsaturated fats and fatty acids
Figure 5.13   The structure of a phospholipid
Figure 5.14   Bilayer structure formed by self-assembly of phospholipids in an aqueous environment
Figure 5.15   Cholesterol, a steroid

Student Media Resource
Activity: Lipids

Concept 5.4 Proteins have many structures, resulting in a wide range of functions

Transparencies

Table 5.1   An overview of protein functions

Page 78   An amino group and a carboxyl group

Figure 5.16   The catalytic cycle of an enzyme

Figure 5.17   The 20 amino acids of proteins: Nonpolar

Figure 5.17   The 20 amino acids of proteins: Polar and electrically charged

Figure 5.18   Making a polypeptide chain

Figure 5.19   Conformation of a protein, the enzyme lysozyme

Figure 5.20   Levels of protein structure

Figure 5.20   Levels of protein structure: Primary structure

Figure 5.20   Levels of protein structure: Secondary structure

Figure 5.20   Levels of protein structure: Tertiary structure

Figure 5.20   Levels of protein structure: Quaternary structure

Figure 5.21   A single amino acid substitution in a protein causes sickle-cell disease

Figure 5.22   Denaturation and renaturation of a protein

Figure 5.23   A chaperonin in action

Figure 5.24   X-ray crystallography

Student Media Resources

Activity: Protein functions

Activity: Protein structure

Biology Labs On-Line: HemoglobinLab

Concept 5.5 Nucleic acids store and transmit hereditary information

Transparencies

Figure 5.25   DNA → RNA → protein: A diagrammatic overview of information flow in a cell

Figure 5.26   The components of nucleic acids

Figure 5.27   The DNA double helix and its replication

Student Media Resources

Activity: Nucleic acid functions

Activity: Nucleic acid structure

For additional resources such as digital images and lecture outlines, go to the Campbell Media Manager or the Instructor Resources section of **www.campbellbiology.com.**

Key Terms

alpha (α) helix
amino acid
antiparallel
beta (β) pleated sheet
carbohydrate
catalyst
cellulose
chaperonin
chitin
cholesterol
condensation reaction
dehydration reaction
denaturation
deoxyribonucleic acid
  (DNA)
deoxyribose
disaccharide
disulfide bridge
double helix

enzyme
fat
fatty acid
gene
glycogen
glycosidic linkage
hydrolysis
hydrophobic
  interaction
lipid
macromolecule
monomer
monosaccharide
nucleic acid
nucleotide
peptide bond
phospholipid
polymer
polynucleotide

polypeptide
polysaccharide
primary structure
protein
purine
pyrimidine
quaternary structure
ribonucleic acid
  (RNA)
ribose
saturated fatty acid
secondary structure
starch
steroid
tertiary structure
triacylglycerol
unsaturated fatty acid
X-ray crystallography

Word Roots

con- = together (*condensation reaction:* a reaction in which two molecules become covalently bonded to each other through the loss of a small molecule, usually water)

di- = two (*disaccharide:* two monosaccharides joined together)

glyco- = sweet (*glycogen:* a polysaccharide sugar used to store energy in animals)

hydro- = water; **-lyse** = break (*hydrolysis:* breaking chemical bonds by adding water)

macro- = large (*macromolecule:* a large molecule)

meros- = part (*polymer:* a chain made from smaller organic molecules)

mono- = single; **-facchar** = sugar (*monosaccharide:* simplest type of sugar)

poly- = many (*polysaccharide:* many monosaccharides joined together)

tri- = three (*triacylglycerol:* three fatty acids linked to one glycerol molecule)

CHAPTER 6

A Tour of the Cell

Teaching Objectives

How We Study Cells
1. Distinguish between magnification and resolving power.
2. Describe the principles, advantages, and limitations of the light microscope, transmission electron microscope, and scanning electron microscope.
3. Describe the major steps of cell fractionation and explain why it is a useful technique.

A Panoramic View of the Cell
4. Distinguish between prokaryotic and eukaryotic cells.
5. Explain why there are both upper and lower limits to cell size.
6. Explain the advantages of compartmentalization in eukaryotic cells.

The Nucleus and Ribosomes
7. Describe the structure and function of the nuclear envelope, including the role of the pore complex.
8. Briefly explain how the nucleus controls protein synthesis in the cytoplasm.
9. Explain how the nucleolus contributes to protein synthesis.
10. Describe the structure and function of a eukaryotic ribosome.
11. Distinguish between free and bound ribosomes in terms of location and function.

The Endomembrane System
12. List the components of the endomembrane system, and describe the structure and functions of each component.
13. Compare the structure and functions of smooth and rough ER.
14. Explain the significance of the *cis* and *trans* sides of the Golgi apparatus.
15. Describe the cisternal maturation model of Golgi function.
16. Describe three examples of intracellular digestion by lysosomes.
17. Name three different kinds of vacuoles, giving the function of each kind.

Other Membranous Organelles
18. Briefly describe the energy conversions carried out by mitochondria and chloroplasts.

19. Describe the structure of a mitochondrion and explain the importance of compartmentalization in mitochondrial function.

20. Distinguish among amyloplasts, chromoplasts, and chloroplasts.

21. Identify the three functional compartments of a chloroplast. Explain the importance of compartmentalization in chloroplast function.

22. Describe the evidence that mitochondria and chloroplasts are semiautonomous organelles.

23. Explain the roles of peroxisomes in eukaryotic cells.

The Cytoskeleton

24. Describe the functions of the cytoskeleton.

25. Compare the structure, monomers, and functions of microtubules, microfilaments, and intermediate filaments.

26. Explain how the ultrastructure of cilia and flagella relates to their functions.

Cell Surfaces and Junctions

27. Describe the basic structure of a plant cell wall.

28. Describe the structure and list four functions of the extracellular matrix in animal cells.

29. Explain how the extracellular matrix may act to integrate changes inside and outside the cell.

30. Name the intercellular junctions found in plant and animal cells and list the function of each type of junction.

Student Misconceptions

1. Most students can assemble an accurate list of the differences between prokaryotic and eukaryotic cells. Despite this, many students have fundamental misconceptions about prokaryotic cells.

   - Comparisons of size for prokaryotic and eukaryotic cells usually give values for typical diameter or length of cells. Students who are unfamiliar with the relationship between length and volume will not appreciate the tremendous difference in volume between prokaryotic and eukaryotic cells.

   - Many students think that prokaryotic cells lack internal organization because they lack membrane-bound organelles. Clarify to students that prokaryotes are relatively simple but have considerable internal organization. Point out that the plasma membrane of prokaryotic cells plays important roles similar to those of the membranes of eukaryotic organelles.

   - Students often fail to appreciate the metabolic capabilities of prokaryotic cells. Virtually all known metabolic pathways arose in prokaryotes. Prokaryotes live in almost all known environments, and display a great variety of complex biochemical adaptations to these environments. Prokaryotes are far more biochemically diverse than eukaryotes.

2. It is important to emphasize that cells are not the static, rigid structures familiar to students from schematic drawings and electron micrographs. The

term *cytoskeleton* is taken by some students to imply permanent scaffolding within the cell. Emphasize the continuous assembly and disassembly of cytoskeletal components and the role of the cytoskeleton in movements of organelles. Discuss the flow of membranes and other materials between organelles when teaching about the endomembrane system. Remind students that mitochondria and chloroplasts vary in shape between cells and move and change shape within cells. The message about the dynamic nature of a living cell is best taught by use of time-lapse movies.

Chapter Guide to Teaching Resources

Overview: The Importance of Cells

Concept 6.1 To study cells, biologists use microscopes and the tools of biochemistry

Transparencies

Figure 6.2	The size range of cells
Figure 6.3	Light microscopy
Figure 6.4	Electron microscopy
Figure 6.5	Cell fractionation

Student Media Resources

Activity: Metric system review

Investigation: What is the size and scale of our world?

Concept 6.2 Eukaryotic cells have internal membranes that compartmentalize their functions

Transparencies

Figure 6.6	A prokaryotic cell
Figure 6.7	Geometric relationships between surface area and volume
Figure 6.8	The plasma membrane
Figure 6.9	Animal and plant cells: the animal cell
Figure 6.9	Animal and plant cells: the plant cell

Student Media Resources

Activity: Prokaryotic cell structure and function

Activity: Comparing prokaryotic and eukaryotic cells

Activity: Build an animal cell and a plant cell

Concept 6.3 The eukaryotic cell's genetic instructions are housed in the nucleus and carried out by the ribosomes

Transparencies

Figure 6.10   The nucleus and its envelope

Figure 6.11   Ribosomes

Student Media Resource

Activity: Role of the nucleus and ribosomes in protein synthesis

Concept 6.4 The endomembrane system regulates protein traffic and performs metabolic functions in the cell

Transparencies

Figure 6.12   Endoplasmic reticulum (ER)

Figure 6.13   The Golgi apparatus

Figure 6.14   Lysosomes

Figure 6.15   The plant cell vacuole

Figure 6.16   Review: Relationships among organelles of the endomembrane system (layer 1)

Figure 6.16   Review: Relationships among organelles of the endomembrane system (layer 2)

Figure 6.16   Review: Relationships among organelles of the endomembrane system (layer 3)

Student Media Resource

Activity: The endomembrane system

Concept 6.5 Mitochondria and chloroplasts change energy from one form to another

Transparencies

Figure 6.17   The mitochondrion, site of cellular respiration

Figure 6.18   The chloroplast, site of photosynthesis

Figure 6.19   Peroxisomes

Student Media Resource

Activity: Build a chloroplast and a mitochondrion

Concept 6.6 The cytoskeleton is a network of fibers that organizes structures and activities in the cell

Transparencies

Figure 6.20   The cytoskeleton

Figure 6.21   Motor proteins and the cytoskeleton

Table 6.1   The structure and function of the cytoskeleton

Figure 6.22   Centrosome containing a pair of centrioles

Instructor and Student Media Resources
Activity: Cilia and flagella
Video: *Chlamydomonas*
Video: *Paramecium* vacuole
Video: *Paramecium* cilia
Video: Cytoplasmic streaming

Concept 6.7 Extracellular components and connections between cells help integrate cells into higher levels

Transparencies

Student Media Resources
Activity: Cell junctions
Activity: Review: Animal cell structure and function
Activity: Review: Plant cell structure and function

For additional resources such as digital images and lecture outlines, go to the Campbell Media Manager or the Instructor Resources section of **www.campbellbiology.com.**

Key Terms

actin	collagen	endomembrane system
basal body	contractile vacuole	endoplasmic reticulum
cell fractionation	crista	(ER)
cell wall	cytoplasm	eukaryotic cell
central vacuole	cytoplasmic streaming	extracellular matrix
centriole	cytoskeleton	(ECM)
centrosome	cytosol	fibronectin
chloroplast	desmosome	flagellum
chromatin	dynein	food vacuole
chromosome	electron microscope	gap junction
cilium	(EM)	glycoprotein

Golgi apparatus
granum
integrin
intermediate filament
light microscope (LM)
lysosome
microfilament
microtubule
middle lamella
mitochondrial matrix
mitochondrion
myosin
nuclear envelope
nuclear lamina

nucleoid
nucleolus
nucleus
organelle
peroxisome
phagocytosis
plasma membrane
plasmodesma
plastid
primary cell wall
prokaryotic cell
proteoglycan
pseudopodium
ribosome

rough ER
scanning electron
  microscope (SEM)
secondary cell wall
smooth ER
stroma
thylakoid
tight junction
tonoplast
transmission electron
  microscope (TEM)
transport vesicle
ultracentrifuge
vesicle

Word Roots

centro- = the center; **-soma** = a body (*centrosome:* material present in the cytoplasm of all eukaryotic cells and important during cell division)

chloro- = green (*chloroplast:* the site of photosynthesis in plants and eukaryotic algae)

cili- = hair (*cilium:* a short, hairlike cellular appendage with a microtubule core)

cyto- = cell (*cytosol:* a semifluid medium in a cell in which organelles are located)

-ell = small (*organelle:* a small, formed body with a specialized function found in the cytoplasm of eukaryotic cells)

endo- = inner (*endomembrane system:* the system of membranes within a cell that includes the nuclear envelope, endoplasmic reticulum, Golgi apparatus, lysosomes, vacuoles, and the plasma membrane)

eu- = true (*eukaryotic cell:* a cell that has a true nucleus)

extra- = outside (*extracellular matrix:* the substance in which animal tissue cells are embedded)

flagell- = whip (*flagellum:* a long, whiplike cellular appendage that moves cells)

glyco- = sweet (*glycoprotein:* a protein covalently bonded to a carbohydrate)

lamin- = sheet/layer (*nuclear lamina:* a netlike array of protein filaments that maintains the shape of the nucleus)

lyso- = loosen (*lysosome:* a membrane-bounded sac of hydrolytic enzymes that a cell uses to digest macromolecules)

micro- = small; **-tubul** = a little pipe (*microtubule:* a hollow rod of tubulin protein in the cytoplasm of almost all eukaryotic cells)

nucle- = nucleus; **-oid** = like (*nucleoid:* the region where the genetic material is concentrated in prokaryotic cells)

phago- = to eat; **-kytos** = vessel (*phagocytosis:* a form of cell eating in which a cell engulfs a smaller organism or food particle)

plasm- = molded; **-desma** = a band or bond (*plasmodesmata:* an open channel in a plant cell wall)

pro- = before; **-karyo** = nucleus (*prokaryotic cell:* a cell that has no nucleus)

pseudo- = false; **-pod** = foot (*pseudopodium:* a cellular extension of amoeboid cells used in moving and feeding)

thylaco- = sac or pouch (*thylakoid:* a series of flattened sacs within chloroplasts)

tono- = stretched; **-plast** = molded (*tonoplast:* the membrane that encloses a large central vacuole in a mature plant cell)

trans- = across; **-port** = a harbor (*transport vesicle:* a membranous compartment used to enclose and transport materials from one part of a cell to another)

ultra- = beyond (*ultracentrifuge:* a machine that spins test tubes at the fastest speeds to separate liquids and particles of different densities)

vacu- = empty (*vacuole:* sac that buds from the ER, Golgi, or plasma membrane)

CHAPTER 7

Membrane Structure and Function

Teaching Objectives

Membrane Structure

1. Explain why phospholipids are amphipathic molecules.
2. Explain what freeze-fracture techniques reveal about the arrangement of proteins in membranes.
3. Describe the fluidity of the components of a cell membrane and explain how membrane fluidity is influenced by temperature and membrane composition.
4. Explain how cholesterol resists changes in membrane fluidity with temperature change.

Traffic Across Membranes

5. Distinguish between peripheral and integral membrane proteins.
6. List six major functions of membrane proteins.
7. Explain the role of membrane carbohydrates in cell-cell recognition.
8. Explain how hydrophobic molecules cross cell membranes.
9. Distinguish between channel proteins and carrier proteins.
10. Define **diffusion.** Explain why diffusion is a spontaneous process.
11. Explain why a concentration gradient of a substance across a membrane represents potential energy.
12. Distinguish among hypertonic, hypotonic, and isotonic solutions.
13. Define **osmosis** and predict the direction of water movement based on differences in solute concentrations.
14. Describe how living cells with and without cell walls regulate water balance.
15. Explain how transport proteins facilitate diffusion.
16. Distinguish among osmosis, facilitated diffusion, and active transport.
17. Describe the two forces that combine to produce an electrochemical gradient.
18. Explain how an electrogenic pump creates voltage across a membrane.
19. Describe the process of cotransport.
20. Explain how large molecules are transported across a cell membrane.
21. Distinguish between pinocytosis and receptor-mediated endocytosis.

Student Misconceptions

1. The majority of students do not appreciate or even understand that diffusion is a vitally important biological process only over very small distances. Diffusion plays a key role in the movement of molecules across plasma membranes, which are only 8 nm thick. However, many students imagine that diffusion explains the spread of molecules of dye in a beaker of water or the movement of molecules of scent in a room. Such demonstrations illustrate convection, not diffusion. It is important to keep this distinction in mind in selecting examples or planning classroom demonstrations of diffusion. It is also important to emphasize to students that diffusion is an effective and important process for transport of molecules over small distances but is completely irrelevant at macroscopic scales.

2. Some students are confused about the random movements of molecules that lead to diffusion and osmosis across biological membranes. Watch out for some of these common misconceptions:

   ■ Osmosis and diffusion are fundamentally different processes.

   ■ Osmotic equilibrium cannot be reached unless solute concentrations equalize across the membrane.

   ■ Water molecules cease movement at osmotic equilibrium.

   ■ Diffusion and osmosis will not occur across non-living membranes.

3. Insist that students use the terms hypertonic, hypotonic, and isotonic only in comparing two solutions. Referring to a lone solution by one of these terms reflects a fundamental misunderstanding of the important concept of tonicity.

Further Reading

Vogel, S. 1994. Dealing honestly with diffusion. *The American Biology Teacher, 56(7),* 405–407.

Chapter Guide to Teaching Resources

Overview: Life at the Edge

Transparency

Figure 7.1   The plasma membrane

Concept 7.1 Cellular membranes are fluid mosaics of lipids and proteins

Transparencies

Figure 7.2   Phospholipid bilayer (cross section)

Figure 7.3   The fluid mosaic model for membranes

Figure 7.4   Freeze-fracture

Student Media Resource

Activity: Membrane structure

Concept 7.2 Membrane structure results in selective permeability

Student Media Resource

Activity: Selective permeability of membranes

Concept 7.3 Passive transport is diffusion of a substance across a membrane with no energy expenditure

Transparencies

Instructor and Student Media Resources

Activity: Diffusion

Activity: Osmosis and water balance in cells

Video: *Paramecium* vacuole

Video: *Chlamydomonas*

Video: Turgid *Elodea*

Video: Plasmolysis

Investigation: How do salt concentrations affect cells?

Activity: Facilitated diffusion

Concept 7.4 Active transport uses energy to move solutes against their gradients

Transparencies

Student Media Resource
Activity: Active transport

Concept 7.5 Bulk transport across the plasma membrane occurs by exocytosis and endocytosis

Transparency
Figure 7.20   Endocytosis in animal cells

Student Media Resource
Activity: Exocytosis and Endocytosis

Review

Page 140   An artificial cell immersed in a solution

For additional resources such as digital images and lecture outlines, go to the Campbell Media Manager or the Instructor Resources section of **www.campbellbiology.com.**

Key Terms

active transport	gated channel	phagocytosis
amphipathic molecule	glycolipid	pinocytosis
aquaporin	glycoprotein	plasmolysis
concentration gradient	hypertonic	proton pump
cotransport	hypotonic	receptor-mediated
diffusion	integral protein	endocytosis
electrochemical	ion channel	selective permeability
gradient	isotonic	sodium-potassium
electrogenic pump	ligand	pump
endocytosis	membrane potential	tonicity
exocytosis	osmoregulation	transport protein
facilitated diffusion	osmosis	turgid
flaccid	passive transport	
fluid mosaic model	peripheral protein	

Word Roots

amphi- = dual (*amphipathic molecule:* a molecule that has both a hydrophobic and a hydrophilic region)

aqua- = water; **-pori** = a small opening (*aquaporin:* a transport protein in the plasma membrane of a plant or animal cell that specifically facilitates the diffusion of water across the membrane)

co- = together; **trans-** = across (*cotransport:* the coupling of the "downhill" diffusion of one substance to the "uphill" transport of another against its own concentration gradient)

electro- = electricity; **-genic** = producing (*electrogenic pump:* an ion transport protein generating voltage across a membrane)

endo- = inner; **cyto-** = cell (*endocytosis:* the movement of materials into a cell; cell-eating)

exo- = outer (*exocytosis:* the movement of materials out of a cell)

hyper- = exceeding; **-tonus** = tension (*hypertonic:* a solution with a higher concentration of solutes)

hypo- = lower (*hypotonic:* a solution with a lower concentration of solutes)

iso- = same (*isotonic:* solutions with equal concentrations of solutes)

phago- = eat (*phagocytosis:* cell-eating)

pino- = drink (*pinocytosis:* cell-drinking)

plasm- = molded; **-lyso** = loosen (*plasmolysis:* a phenomenon in walled cells in which the cytoplasm shrivels and the plasma membrane pulls away from the cell wall when the cell loses water to a hypertonic environment)

CHAPTER 8

An Introduction to Metabolism

Teaching Objectives

Metabolism, Energy, and Life

1. Explain the role of catabolic and anabolic pathways in cellular metabolism.
2. Distinguish between kinetic and potential energy.
3. Explain why an organism is considered an open system.
4. Explain the first and second laws of thermodynamics in your own words.
5. Explain why highly ordered living organisms do not violate the second law of thermodynamics.
6. Write and define each component of the equation for free-energy change.
7. Distinguish between exergonic and endergonic reactions in terms of free energy change.
8. Explain why metabolic disequilibrium is one of the defining features of life.
9. List the three main kinds of cellular work. Explain in general terms how cells obtain the energy to do cellular work.
10. Describe the structure of ATP and identify the major class of macromolecules to which ATP belongs.
11. Explain how ATP performs cellular work.

Enzymes Are Catalytic Proteins

12. Describe the function of enzymes in biological systems.
13. Explain why an investment of activation energy is necessary to initiate a spontaneous reaction.
14. Explain how enzyme structure determines enzyme specificity.
15. Explain the induced-fit model of enzyme function.
16. Describe the mechanisms by which enzymes lower activation energy.
17. Explain how substrate concentration affects the rate of an enzyme-catalyzed reaction.
18. Explain how temperature, pH, cofactors, and enzyme inhibitors can affect enzyme activity.

The Control of Metabolism

19. Explain how metabolic pathways are regulated.
20. Explain how the location of enzymes in a cell may help order metabolism.

Student Misconceptions

1. Metabolism and energy transformations are inherently complex and challenging topics. One problem is that energy has a familiar connotation of strength and power that is very different from its definition in thermodynamics. Many students have difficulty distinguishing between the colloquial and the scientific uses of terms such as energy, work, and fuel. Clarify to students that work is not energy, but that the free energy change associated with chemical reactions can do work in living cells. Clarify to them that fuel or food are not energy, and emphasize that fuel may be used up while energy is always conserved.

2. Students tend to think of free energy as something that is stored within a cell or held in the bonds of a molecule. Avoid talking about the amount of energy that is stored in or possessed by an object or molecule. The amount of energy in a food molecule, in a cell, or in a living thing has little meaning, while energy transfer and free energy change are meaningful and quantifiable concepts.

3. Emphasize to students that both reactants and products are possible substrates for an enzyme. Of course, many reactions in a cell, especially those that are coupled to ATP hydrolysis, have equilibria that are far to the right. However, it is important that students realize that chemical reactions—including those catalyzed by enzymes—can proceed in either direction.

4. Students tend to visualize enzyme-substrate interaction as a lock and key, even when taught the induced-fit model. When teaching the induced-fit model, explain to students why the lock-and-key analogy is flawed.

5. Students may not realize that free energy changes are not fixed for a particular reaction, but vary considerably with alterations of pH and other conditions in various regions of the cell.

6. The "high-energy bond" that joins the terminal phosphate groups of ATP may be a useful concept, but it feeds several sources of student confusion.

   a. Students tend to imagine that a high level of free energy is stored in ATP's high-energy bonds, that this energy is released when the bond is broken, and that the terminal phosphate somehow takes ATP's high energy with it when it is removed. Students may discuss the hydrolysis of ATP, while not appreciating that bonds are both broken and created in this process. The net free energy change for ATP hydrolysis depends on the sum of all free energy changes for all parts of the reaction. Free energy is not, as students may visualize, stored in one "high-energy" covalent bond.

   b. Students imagine that the hydrolysis of the terminal phosphate group of ATP is associated with an exceptionally high release of free energy. In fact, the free energy released by ATP hydrolysis is near the midrange of $-\Delta G$ values for hydrolysis of phosphate groups from phosphorylated molecules. This allows ATP to accept phosphate groups from some compounds and donate them to other compounds.

Further Reading

Jennison, B. M., and M. J. Reiss. 1991. Does anyone know what energy is? *Journal of Biological Education, 25(3),* 173–177.

Chapter Guide to Teaching Resources

Overview: The energy of life

Concept 8.1 An organism's metabolism transforms matter and energy, subject to the laws of thermodynamics

Transparencies

Page 141   A metabolic pathway

Figure 8.3   The two laws of thermodynamics

Student Media Resource

Activity: Energy transformations

Concept 8.2 The free-energy change of a reaction tells us whether the reaction occurs spontaneously

Transparencies

Figure 8.5   The relationship of free energy to stability, work capacity, and
              spontaneous change

Figure 8.6   Free energy changes (ΔG) in exergonic and endergonic reactions

Figure 8.7   Equilibrium and work in closed and open systems

Concept 8.3 ATP powers cellular work by coupling exergonic reactions to endergonic reactions

Transparencies

Figure 8.8   The structure of adenosine triphosphate (ATP)

Figure 8.9   The hydrolysis of ATP

Figure 8.10   Energy coupling using ATP hydrolysis

Figure 8.11   How ATP drives cellular work

Figure 8.12   The ATP cycle

Student Media Resources

Activity: The structure of ATP

Activity: Chemical reactions and ATP

Concept 8.4 Enzymes speed up metabolic reactions by lowering energy barriers

Transparencies

Figure 8.13   Example of an enzyme-catalyzed reaction: hydrolysis of sucrose by sucrase

Figure 8.14   Energy profile of an exergonic reaction

Figure 8.15   The effect of enzymes on reaction rate

Figure 8.16   Induced fit between an enzyme and its substrate

Figure 8.17   The active site and catalytic cycle of an enzyme

Figure 8.18   Environmental factors affecting enzyme activity

Figure 8.19   Inhibition of enzyme activity

Student Media Resources

Activity: How enzymes work

Investigation: How is the rate of enzyme catalysis measured?

Biology Labs On-Line: EnzymeLab

Concept 8.5 Regulation of enzyme activity helps control metabolism

Transparencies

Figure 8.20   Allosteric regulation of enzyme activity

Figure 8.21   Feedback inhibition in isoleucine synthesis

Figure 8.22   Organelles and structural order in metabolism

For additional resources such as digital images and lecture outlines, go to the Campbell Media Manager or the Instructor Resources section of **www.campbellbiology.com.**

Key Terms

activation energy	endergonic reaction	heat
active site	energy	induced fit
allosteric regulation	energy coupling	kinetic energy
anabolic pathway	entropy	metabolic pathway
ATP (adenosine triphosphate)	enzyme	metabolism
bioenergetics	enzyme-substrate complex	noncompetitive inhibitor
catabolic pathway	exergonic reaction	phosphorylated
catalyst	feedback inhibition	potential energy
chemical energy	first law of thermodynamics	second law of thermodynamics
coenzyme	free energy	substrate
cofactor	free energy of activation	thermal energy
competitive inhibitor		thermodynamics
cooperativity		

Word Roots

allo- = different (*allosteric site:* a specific receptor site on some part of an enzyme molecule remote from the active site)

ana- = up (*anabolic pathway:* a metabolic pathway that consumes energy to build complex molecules from simpler ones)

bio- = life (*bioenergetics:* the study of how organisms manage their energy resources)

cata- = down (*catabolic pathway:* a metabolic pathway that releases energy by breaking down complex molecules into simpler ones)

endo- = within (*endergonic reaction:* a reaction that absorbs free energy from its surroundings)

ex- = out (*exergonic reaction:* a reaction that proceeds with a net release of free energy)

kinet- = movement (*kinetic energy:* the energy of motion)

therm- = heat (*thermodynamics:* the study of the energy transformations that occur in a collection of matter)

CHAPTER 9

Cellular Respiration: Harvesting Chemical Energy

Teaching Objectives

The Principles of Energy Harvest

1. In general terms, distinguish between fermentation and cellular respiration.
2. Write the summary equation for cellular respiration. Write the specific chemical equation for the degradation of glucose.
3. Define *oxidation* and *reduction.*
4. Explain in general terms how redox reactions are involved in energy exchanges.
5. Describe the role of NAD^+ in cellular respiration.
6. In general terms, explain the role of the electron transport chain in cellular respiration.

The Process of Cellular Respiration

7. Name the three stages of cellular respiration and state the region of the eukaryotic cell where each stage occurs.
8. Describe how the carbon skeleton of glucose changes as it proceeds through glycolysis.
9. Explain why ATP is required for the preparatory steps of glycolysis.
10. Identify where substrate-level phosphorylation and the reduction of NAD^+ occur in glycolysis.
11. Describe where pyruvate is oxidized to acetyl CoA, what molecules are produced, and how this process links glycolysis to the citric acid cycle.
12. List the products of the citric acid cycle. Explain why it is called a cycle.
13. Describe the point at which glucose is completely oxidized during cellular respiration.
14. Distinguish between substrate-level phosphorylation and oxidative phosphorylation.
15. In general terms, explain how the exergonic "slide" of electrons down the electron transport chain is coupled to the endergonic production of ATP by chemiosmosis.
16. Explain where and how the respiratory electron transport chain creates a proton gradient.

17. Describe the structure and function of the four subunits of ATP synthase.

18. Summarize the net ATP yield from the oxidation of a glucose molecule by constructing an ATP ledger.

19. Explain why it is not possible to state an exact number of ATP molecules generated by the oxidation of glucose.

Related Metabolic Processes

20. State the basic function of fermentation.

21. Compare the fate of pyruvate in alcohol fermentation and in lactic acid fermentation.

22. Compare the processes of fermentation and cellular respiration.

23. Describe the evidence that suggests that glycolysis is an ancient metabolic pathway.

24. Describe how food molecules other than glucose can be oxidized to make ATP.

25. Explain how glycolysis and the citric acid cycle can contribute to anabolic pathways.

26. Explain how ATP production is controlled by the cell, and describe the role that the allosteric enzyme phosphofructokinase plays in the process.

Student Misconceptions

1. Cellular respiration is one of the most difficult and poorly understood topics dealt with in general biology courses. Many students merely memorize the steps of glycolysis, the citric acid cycle, and the electron transfer chain. Such rote learning leads to fragmentation of student knowledge. Students may not understand how the processes of cellular metabolism relate to one another and may falter when asked to explain the significance of these stages. They may not appreciate how cellular metabolism is relevant to higher levels of biological organization, such as organismal physiology or energy flow in communities. Students may have considerable difficulty explaining the relationship of breathing and digestion to cellular respiration.

   As much as possible, avoid exam questions about cellular respiration that reward memorization and rote learning. Mention the significance of cellular metabolism when covering community ecology, gas exchange, digestion, and circulation.

2. Students may be confused by terms that have familiar, everyday meanings distinct from their biological definitions. The term *respiration* is particularly confusing, because it is an everyday term with two biological definitions, both in cellular respiration and in breathing.

3. Although most students recognize that plants respire, they may not fully understand that cellular respiration plays the same role in all aerobically respiring organisms. Many students do not appreciate the relationship between photosynthesis and respiration in plants. Watch out for some of these common misconceptions:

   a. Photosynthesis is the plant's form of cellular respiration.

   b. Plants respire only when they don't photosynthesize.

   c. Cellular respiration takes place only in plant roots, not throughout the plant.

4. Fermentation is misunderstood by many students. Many students do not recognize that it functions to regenerate NAD^+ and think that it yields additional ATP. You may be surprised to know that many students do not realize that yeast is a living organism. Many have the mistaken view that baking yeast is dead or think of yeast as a set of enzymes rather than living cells.

Chapter Guide to Teaching Resources

Overview: Life is work

Transparency
Figure 9.2   Energy flow and chemical recycling in ecosystems

Student Media Resource
Activity: Build a chemical cycling system

Concept 9.1 Catabolic pathways yield energy by oxidizing organic fuels

Transparencies
Figure 9.3   Methane combustion as an energy-yielding redox reaction
Figure 9.4 NAD^+ as an electron shuttle
Figure 9.5   An introduction to electron transport chains
Figure 9.6   An overview of cellular respiration (layer 1)
Figure 9.6   An overview of cellular respiration (layer 2)
Figure 9.6   An overview of cellular respiration (layer 3)
Figure 9.7   Substrate-level phosphorylation

Student Media Resource
Activity: Overview of cellular respiration

Concept 9.2 Glycolysis harvests chemical energy by oxidizing glucose to pyruvate

Transparencies
Figure 9.8   The energy input and output of glycolysis
Figure 9.9   A closer look at glycolysis: Energy investment phase (layer 1)
Figure 9.9   A closer look at glycolysis: Energy investment phase (layer 2)
Figure 9.9   A closer look at glycolysis: Energy payoff phase (layer 1)
Figure 9.9   A closer look at glycolysis: Energy payoff phase (layer 2)

Student Media Resource
Activity: Glycolysis

Concept 9.3 The citric acid cycle completes the energy-yielding oxidation of organic molecules

Transparencies

Figure 9.10   Conversion of pyruvate to acetyl CoA, the junction between glycolysis and the citric acid cycle

Figure 9.11   An overview of the citric acid cycle

Figure 9.12   A closer look at the citric acid cycle (layer 1)

Figure 9.12   A closer look at the citric acid cycle (layer 2)

Figure 9.12   A closer look at the citric acid cycle (layer 3)

Figure 9.12   A closer look at the citric acid cycle (layer 4)

Student Media Resource
Activity: The citric acid cycle

Concept 9.4 During oxidative phosphorylation, chemiosmosis couples electron transport to ATP synthesis

Transparencies

Figure 9.13   Free-energy change during electron transport

Figure 9.14   ATP synthase, a molecular mill

Figure 9.15   Chemiosmosis couples the electron transport chain to ATP synthesis

Figure 9.16   ATP yield per molecule of glucose at each stage of cellular respiration

Student Media Resources
Activity: Electron transport cycle
Biology Labs On-Line: MitochondriaLab
Investigation: How is the rate of cellular respiration measured?

Concept 9.5 Fermentation enables some cells to produce ATP without the use of oxygen

Transparencies

Figure 9.17   Fermentation

Figure 9.18   Pyruvate as a key juncture in catabolism

Student Media Resource
Activity: Fermentation

Concept 9.6 Glycolysis and the citric acid cycle connect to many other metabolic pathways

Transparencies

Figure 9.19   The catabolism of various food molecules

Figure 9.20   The control of cellular respiration

For additional resources such as digital images and lecture outlines, go to the Campbell Media Manager or the Instructor Resources section of **www.campbellbiology.com.**

Key Terms

acetyl CoA
aerobic
alcohol fermentation
anaerobic
ATP synthase
beta oxidation
cellular respiration
chemiosmosis
citric acid cycle
cytochrome

electron transport
   chain
facultative anaerobe
fermentation
glycolysis
lactic acid
   fermentation
NAD^+
oxidation

oxidative
   phosphorylation
oxidizing agent
proton-motive force
redox reaction
reducing agent
reduction
substrate-level
   phosphorylation

Word Roots

aero- = air (*aerobic:* chemical reaction using oxygen)

an- = not (*anaerobic:* chemical reaction not using oxygen)

chemi- = chemical (*chemiosmosis:* the production of ATP using the energy of hydrogen ion gradients across membranes to phosphorylate ADP)

glyco- = sweet; **-lysis** = split (*glycolysis:* the splitting of glucose into pyruvate)

CHAPTER 10

Photosynthesis

Teaching Objectives

The Process That Feeds the Biosphere

1. Distinguish between autotrophic and heterotrophic nutrition.
2. Distinguish between photoautotrophs and chemoautotrophs.
3. Describe the structure of a chloroplast, listing all membranes and compartments.

The Pathways of Photosynthesis

4. Write a summary equation for photosynthesis.
5. Explain van Niel's hypothesis and describe how it contributed to our current understanding of photosynthesis. Explain the evidence that supported his hypothesis.
6. In general terms, explain the role of redox reactions in photosynthesis.
7. Describe the two main stages of photosynthesis in general terms.
8. Describe the relationship between an action spectrum and an absorption spectrum. Explain why the action spectrum for photosynthesis differs from the absorption spectrum for chlorophyll *a*.
9. Explain how carotenoids protect the cell from damage by light.
10. List the wavelengths of light that are most effective for photosynthesis.
11. Explain what happens when a solution of chlorophyll *a* absorbs photons. Explain what happens when chlorophyll *a* in an intact chloroplast absorbs photons.
12. List the components of a photosystem and explain the function of each component.
13. Trace the movement of electrons in noncyclic electron flow. Trace the movement of electrons in cyclic electron flow.
14. Explain the functions of cyclic and noncyclic electron flow.
15. Describe the similarities and differences in chemiosmosis between oxidative phosphorylation in mitochondria and photophosphorylation in chloroplasts.
16. State the function of each of the three phases of the Calvin cycle.
17. Describe the role of ATP and NADPH in the Calvin cycle.
18. Describe what happens to rubisco when O_2 concentration is much higher than CO_2 concentration.
19. Describe the major consequences of photorespiration. Explain why it is thought to be an evolutionary relict.

20. Describe two important photosynthetic adaptations that minimize photorespiration.
21. List the possible fates of photosynthetic products.

Student Misconceptions

1. Students may have a number of misconceptions about photosynthesis. Some of the misunderstandings about the relationship between photosynthesis and respiration may be quite entrenched and thus difficult to correct.

   a. Some students hold a persistent notion of photosynthesis as a form of inverse respiration. These students think of photosynthesis primarily in term of gas exchange in which plants absorb carbon dioxide and expel oxygen, and do not fully appreciate the role of carbon dioxide in the production of organic molecules.

   b. Students may think that respiration only occurs in green plants when there is no light energy for photosynthesis.

2. Many students have memorized the details of the light reactions and the Calvin cycle, but do not understand the significance of these reactions. These students do not link their rote knowledge of photosynthesis to other aspects of plant functioning.

3. A small but significant percentage of first-year students think that plants are producers because they produce oxygen.

4. Many students show some confusion about the role of carbon dioxide. These students can provide explanations about the fixation of carbon during the Calvin cycle. However, when asked to identify the source of increased mass during plant growth, fully half do not mention carbon dioxide. Some students appear to be reluctant to fully accept that a gas can be a significant source of atoms for plant growth.

5. Avoid the terms "light-independent reactions" or "dark reactions" in discussing the Calvin cycle. The reactions of the Calvin cycle do not function in the dark. Short-lived products from the light reactions are required by the Calvin cycle, and several of the enzymes of the cycle are inactive or greatly reduced in activity in the dark. Students have likely heard these terms in earlier biology courses, so it is wise to explain why they are inaccurate.

6. Students unhesitatingly identify glucose as the product of photosynthesis. In fact, the intermediate produced by the Calvin cycle is G3P (glyceraldehyde-3-phosphate). Starch and sucrose are the primary carbohydrates synthesized from G3P. Very little free glucose is produced by or transported from photosynthetic cells. It is important to emphasize this point, and to clarify that we discuss glucose as the product of photosynthesis primarily for convenience.

7. Students will state that plants and other photosynthetic organisms are important producers of carbohydrates in ecosystems. A number of students do not realize that photosynthetic organisms also provide consumers with essential amino acids and fatty acids and that they are a major source of protein and lipids for consumers.

8. Students may not fully understand the role of water in photosynthesis. They may not appreciate the crucial need for a source of electrons to reduce oxidized chlorophyll *a* molecules, and may not realize that water acts as an electron donor.

Further Reading

Cañal, P. 1999. Photosynthesis and "inverse respiration" in plants: An inevitable misconception? *International Journal of Science Education, 21(4),* 363–371.

Longergan, T. A. 2000. The photosynthetic dark reactions do not operate in the dark. *The American Biology Teacher, 62(3),* 166–170.

Chapter Guide to Teaching Resources

Overview: The process that feeds the biosphere

Concept 10.1 Photosynthesis converts light energy to the chemical energy of food

Transparencies

Figure 10.3   Focusing in on the location of photosynthesis in a plant

Figure 10.4   Tracking atoms through photosynthesis

Figure 10.5   An overview of photosynthesis: Cooperation of the light reactions and the Calvin cycle (layer 1)

Figure 10.5   An overview of photosynthesis: Cooperation of the light reactions and the Calvin cycle (layer 2)

Figure 10.5   An overview of photosynthesis: Cooperation of the light reactions and the Calvin cycle (layer 3)

Student Media Resources

Activity: The sites of photosynthesis

Activity: Overview of photosynthesis

Concept 10.2 The light reactions convert solar energy to the chemical energy of ATP and NADPH

Transparencies

Figure 10.6   The electromagnetic spectrum

Figure 10.7   Why leaves are green: Interaction of light with chloroplasts

Figure 10.8   Determining an absorption spectrum

Figure 10.9   Which wavelengths of light are most effective in driving photosynthesis?

Figure 10.10   Structure of chlorophyll molecules in chloroplasts of plants

Figure 10.11   Excitation of isolated chlorophyll by light

Figure 10.12   How a photosystem harvests light

Figure 10.13   How noncyclic electron flow during the light reactions generates ATP and NADPH (layer 1)

Figure 10.13   How noncyclic electron flow during the light reactions generates ATP and NADPH (layer 2)

Figure 10.13   How noncyclic electron flow during the light reactions generates ATP and NADPH (layer 3)

Figure 10.13   How noncyclic electron flow during the light reactions generates ATP and NADPH (layer 4)

Figure 10.13   How noncyclic electron flow during the light reactions generates ATP and NADPH (layer 5)

Figure 10.14   A mechanical analogy for the light reactions

Figure 10.15   Cyclic electron flow

Figure 10.16   Comparison of chemiosmosis in mitochondria and chloroplasts

Figure 10.17   The light reactions and chemiosmosis: The organization of the thylakoid membrane

Student Media Resources

Activity: Light energy and pigments

Investigation: How does paper chromatography separate plant pigments?

Activity: The light reactions

Concept 10.3 The Calvin cycle uses ATP and NADPH to convert CO_2 to sugar

Transparencies

Figure 10.18   The Calvin cycle (layer 1)

Figure 10.18   The Calvin cycle (layer 2)

Figure 10.18   The Calvin cycle (layer 3)

Student Media Resources

Activity: The Calvin cycle

Investigation: How is the rate of photosynthesis measured?

Biology Labs On-Line: LeafLab

Concept 10.4 Alternative mechanisms of carbon fixation have evolved in hot, arid climates

Transparencies

Figure 10.19 C_4 leaf anatomy and the C_4 pathway

Figure 10.20 C_4 and CAM photosynthesis compared

Student Media Resource

Activity: Photosynthesis in dry climates

The Importance of Photosynthesis: *A Review*

Transparencies

Figure 10.21   A review of photosynthesis

Page 200   An experiment with isolated chloroplasts

For additional resources such as digital images and lecture outlines, go to the Campbell Media Manager or the Instructor Resources section of **www.campbellbiology.com.**

Key Terms

absorption spectrum
action spectrum
autotroph
bundle-sheath cell
C₃ plant
C₄ plant
Calvin cycle
CAM plant
carbon fixation
carotenoid
chlorophyll
chlorophyll *a*
chlorophyll *b*
crassulacean acid
  metabolism (CAM)
cyclic electron flow

electromagnetic
  spectrum
glyceraldehyde-3-
  phosphate (G3P)
heterotroph
light reactions
light-harvesting
  complex
mesophyll
mesophyll cell
NADP⁺
noncyclic electron
  flow
PEP carboxylase
photon
photophosphorylation

photorespiration
photosynthesis
photosystem
photosystem I (PS I)
photosystem II (PS II)
primary electron
  acceptor
reaction center
rubisco
spectrophotometer
stoma
stroma
thylakoid
visible light
wavelength

Word Roots

auto- = self; **-troph** = food (*autotroph:* an organism that obtains organic food molecules without eating other organisms)

chloro- = green; **-phyll** = leaf (*chlorophyll:* photosynthetic pigment in chloroplasts)

electro- = electricity; **magnet-** = magnetic (*electromagnetic spectrum:* the entire spectrum of radiation)

hetero- = other (*heterotroph:* an organism that obtains organic food molecules by eating other organisms or their by-products)

meso- = middle (*mesophyll:* the green tissue in the middle, inside of a leaf)

photo- = light (*photosystem:* cluster of pigment molecules)

CHAPTER 11

Cell Communication

Teaching Objectives

An Overview of Cell Signaling

1. Describe the basic signal-transduction pathway used for mating in yeast. Explain why we believe these pathways evolved before the first multicellular organisms appeared on Earth.
2. Define *paracrine signaling* and give an example.
3. Define *local regulation* and explain why hormones are not local regulators.
4. Explain how plant and animal hormones travel to target cells.
5. List and briefly define the three stages of cell signaling.

Signal Reception and the Initiation of Transduction

6. Describe the nature of a ligand-receptor interaction and state how such interactions initiate a signal-transduction system.
7. State where signal receptors may be located in target cells.
8. Compare and contrast G-protein-linked receptors, tyrosine-kinase receptors, and ligand-gated ion channels.

Signal-Transduction Pathways

9. Describe two advantages of using a multistep pathway in the transduction stage of cell signaling.
10. Explain how the original signal molecule can produce a cellular response when it may not even enter the target cell.
11. Describe how phosphorylation propagates signal information.
12. Explain why a single cell may require hundreds of different protein kinases.
13. Explain how protein phosphatases turn off signal-transduction pathways.
14. Define the term *second messenger*. Briefly describe the role of these molecules in signaling pathways.
15. Describe how cyclic AMP is formed and how it propagates signal information in target cells.
16. Explain how the cholera bacterium causes the symptoms of cholera by disrupting G-protein-signaling pathways.
17. Describe how the cytosolic concentration of Ca^{2+} can be altered and how the increased pool of Ca^{2+} is involved with signal transduction.

Cellular Responses to Signals

18. Describe how signal information is transduced into cellular responses in the cytoplasm and in the nucleus.

19. Describe how signal amplification is accomplished in target cells.

20. Explain why different types of cells may respond differently to the same signal molecule.

21. Explain how scaffolding proteins help to coordinate a cell's response to incoming signals.

Student Misconceptions

1. The topic of cell signaling is difficult for students to master. Students must learn the details of the complex interactions of several large sets of unfamiliar molecules, and also grasp the important general principles that cell-signaling pathways illustrate. Faced with this challenge, many students focus on memorization of details and miss the broad picture. Remind students of the significance of the steps of cell signaling: the amplification of the signal, the recycling of relay molecules between activated and inactivated forms to regulate the cellular response, and the multiple roles of the same simple players to provide specificity.

2. When teaching cell communication, judicious use of interesting examples can capture student interest and help to clarify difficult concepts. Students' curiosity will be piqued when the instructor describes how the principles of cell signaling explain how a familiar drug works or how the symptoms of a deadly disease arise.

Chapter Guide to Teaching Resources

Overview: The cellular Internet

Concept 11.1 External signals are converted into responses within the cell

Transparencies

Figure 11.2   Communication between mating yeast cells

Figure 11.3   Communication by direct contact between cells

Figure 11.4   Local and long-distance cell communication in animals

Figure 11.5   Overview of cell signaling (layer 1)

Figure 11.5   Overview of cell signaling (layer 2)

Figure 11.5   Overview of cell signaling (layer 3)

Student Media Resources
Investigation: How do cells communicate with each other?
Activity: Overview of cell signaling

Concept 11.2 Reception: A signal molecule binds to a receptor protein, causing it to change shape

Transparencies
Figure 11.6   Steroid hormone interacting with an intracellular receptor
Figure 11.7   Membrane receptors: G-protein-linked receptors
Figure 11.7   Membrane receptors: Receptor tyrosine kinases
Figure 11.7   Membrane receptors: Ion channel receptors

Student Media Resource
Activity: Reception

Concept 11.3 Transduction: Cascades of molecular interactions relay signals from receptors to target molecules in the cell

Transparencies
Figure 11.8   A phosphorylation cascade
Figure 11.9   Cyclic AMP
Figure 11.10   cAMP as a second messenger in a G-protein-signaling pathway
Figure 11.11   The maintenance of calcium ion concentrations in an animal cell
Figure 11.12   Calcium and IP_3 in signaling pathways (layer 1)
Figure 11.12   Calcium and IP_3 in signaling pathways (layer 2)
Figure 11.12   Calcium and IP_3 in signaling pathways (layer 3)

Student Media Resource
Activity: Signal transduction pathways

Concept 11.4 Response: Cell signaling leads to regulation of cytoplasmic activities or transcription

Transparencies
Figure 11.13   Cytoplasmic response to a signal: The stimulation of glycogen breakdown by epinephrine
Figure 11.14   Nuclear responses to a signal: The activation of a specific gene by a growth factor
Figure 11.15   The specificity of cell signaling
Figure 11.16   A scaffolding protein

Student Media Resources
Activity: Cellular responses
Activity: Build a signaling pathway

For additional resources such as digital images and lecture outlines, go to the Campbell Media Manager or the Instructor Resources section of **www.campbellbiology.com.**

Key Terms

adenylyl cyclase	ligand	response
cyclic AMP (cAMP)	ligand-gated ion	scaffolding protein
diacylglycerol (DAG)	channel	second messenger
G protein	local regulator	signal transduction
G-protein-linked	protein kinase	pathway
receptor	protein phosphatase	transduction
hormone	reception	
inositol trisphosphate	receptor tyrosine	
(IP₃)	kinase	

Word Roots

liga- = bound or tied (*ligand:* a small molecule that specifically binds to a larger one)

trans- = across (*signal-transduction pathway:* the process by which a signal on a cell's surface is converted into a specific cellular response inside the cell)

-yl = substance or matter (*adenylyl cyclase:* an enzyme built into the plasma membrane that converts ATP to cAMP)

CHAPTER 12

The Cell Cycle

Teaching Objectives

The Key Roles of Cell Division

1. Explain how cell division functions in reproduction, growth, and repair.
2. Describe the structural organization of a prokaryotic and a eukaryotic genome.
3. Describe the major events of cell division that enable the genome of one cell to be passed on to two daughter cells.
4. Describe how chromosome number changes throughout the human life cycle.

The Mitotic Cell Cycle

5. List the phases of the cell cycle and describe the sequence of events that occurs during each phase.
6. List the phases of mitosis and describe the events characteristic of each phase.
7. Recognize the phases of mitosis from diagrams and micrographs.
8. Draw or describe the spindle apparatus, including centrosomes, kinetochore microtubules, nonkinetochore microtubules, asters, and centrioles (in animal cells).
9. Describe what characteristic changes occur in the spindle apparatus during each phase of mitosis.
10. Explain the current models for poleward chromosomal movement and elongation of the cell's polar axis.
11. Compare cytokinesis in animals and in plants.
12. Describe the process of binary fission in bacteria and explain how eukaryotic mitosis may have evolved from binary fission.

Regulation of the Cell Cycle

13. Describe the roles of checkpoints, cyclin, Cdk, and MPF in the cell cycle control system.
14. Describe the internal and external factors that influence the cell cycle control system.
15. Explain how the abnormal cell division of cancerous cells escapes normal cell cycle controls.
16. Distinguish among benign, malignant, and metastatic tumors.

Student Misconceptions

1. There are several common misunderstandings about the structure and organization of chromosomes in dividing cells. These misunderstandings can be reduced if you clarify to students the importance of DNA duplication as a precursor to mitotic cell division.

    a. Students may not realize that both haploid and diploid cells can divide by mitosis to produce two daughter cells with the same chromosome component as the parent cell.

    b. Students may not appreciate the significance of the structure of the chromosome following the S phase of interphase. Some students think that a replicated chromosome with two chromatids joined at the centromere is characteristic of diploid cells. Other students may think that the two chromatids making up a single replicated chromosome are joined at fertilization, and that they represent maternal and paternal genetic information.

2. The unfortunate terminology of interphase with its G_1 and G_2 phases may lead students to think of this portion of the cell cycle as a "resting" stage in which the cell is inactive and does little. It is important to remind students that many events critical to the cell cycle take place during interphase, and to clarify that the cell is metabolically active during this phase.

3. Remind students that the events of mitosis and cytokinesis are continuous, and that cell division is organized into discrete stages largely for convenience. The use of time-lapse films of cell division may help to make this point.

4. Students may be motivated to understand the complex components of the cell cycle control system by discussion of the loss of cell cycle controls in cancer cells.

Chapter Guide to Teaching Resources

Overview: The key roles of cell division

Concept 12.1 Cell division results in genetically identical daughter cells

Transparency

Figure 12.4   Chromosome duplication and distribution during cell division

Student Media Resource

Activity: Roles of cell division

Concept 12.2 The mitotic phase alternates with interphase in the cell cycle

Transparencies

Figure 12.5   The cell cycle

Figure 12.6   The mitotic division of an animal cell: G_2 of interphase; prophase; prometaphase

Figure 12.6   The mitotic division of an animal cell: Metaphase; anaphase; telophase and cytokinesis

Figure 12.7   The mitotic spindle at metaphase

Figure 12.8   During anaphase, do kinetochore microtubules shorten at their spindle pole ends or their kinetochore ends?

Figure 12.9   Cytokinesis in animal and plant cells

Figure 12.11   Bacterial cell division (binary fission) (layer 1)

Figure 12.11   Bacterial cell division (binary fission) (layer 2)

Figure 12.11   Bacterial cell division (binary fission) (layer 3)

Figure 12.12   A hypothetical sequence for the evolution of mitosis

Instructor and Student Media Resources

Activity: The cell cycle

Activity: Mitosis and cytokinesis animation

Activity: Mitosis and cytokinesis video

Investigation: How much time do cells spend in each phase of mitosis?

Video: Animal mitosis (time-lapse)

Video: Sea urchin embryonic development (time-lapse)

Concept 12.3 The cell cycle is regulated by a molecular control system

Transparencies

Figure 12.13   Are there molecular signals in the cytoplasm that regulate the cell cycle?

Figure 12.14   Mechanical analogy for the cell cycle control system

Figure 12.15   The G_1 checkpoint

Figure 12.16   Molecular control of the cell cycle at the G_2 checkpoint

Figure 12.17   Does platelet-derived growth factor (PDGF) stimulate the division of human fibroblast cells in culture?

Figure 12.18   Density-dependent inhibition and anchorage dependence of cell division

Figure 12.19   The growth and metastasis of a malignant breast tumor

Student Media Resource
Activity: Causes of cancer

For additional resources such as digital images and lecture outlines, go to the Campbell Media Manager or the Instructor Resources section of **www.campbellbiology.com.**

Key Terms

anaphase	cyclin	metaphase
anchorage dependence	cyclin-dependent	metaphase plate
aster	kinase (Cdk)	metastasis
benign tumor	cytokinesis	mitosis
binary fission	density-dependent	mitotic (M) phase
cell cycle	inhibition	mitotic spindle
cell cycle control	G_0 phase	MPF
system	G_1 phase	origin of replication
cell division	G_2 phase	prometaphase
cell plate	gamete	prophase
centromere	genome	S phase
centrosome	growth factor	sister chromatids
checkpoint	interphase	somatic cell
chromatin	kinetochore	telophase
chromosome	M phase	transformation
cleavage	malignant tumor	
cleavage furrow	meiosis	

Word Roots

ana- = up, throughout, again (*anaphase:* the mitotic stage in which the chromatids of each chromosome have separated and the daughter chromosomes are moving to the poles of the cell)

bi- = two (*binary fission:* a type of cell division in which a cell divides in half)

centro- = the center; **-mere** = a part (*centromere:* the narrow "waist" of a condensed chromosome)

chroma- = colored (*chromatin:* DNA and the various associated proteins that form eukaryotic chromosomes)

cyclo- = a circle (*cyclin:* a regulatory protein whose concentration fluctuates cyclically)

cyto- = cell; **-kinet** = move (*cytokinesis:* division of the cytoplasm)

gamet- = a wife or husband (*gamete:* a haploid egg or sperm cell)

gen- = produce (*genome:* a cell's endowment of DNA)

inter- = between (*interphase:* time when a cell metabolizes and performs its various functions)

mal- = bad or evil (*malignant tumor:* a cancerous tumor that is invasive enough to impair functions of one or more organs)

meio- = less (*meiosis:* a variation of cell division that yields daughter cells with half as many chromosomes as the parent cell)

meta- = between (*metaphase:* the mitotic stage in which the chromosomes are aligned in the middle of the cell, at the metaphase plate)

mito- = a thread (*mitosis:* the division of the nucleus)

pro- = before (*prophase:* the first mitotic stage in which the chromatin is condensing)

-soma = body (*centrosome:* a nonmembranous organelle that functions throughout the cell cycle to organize the cell's microtubules)

telos = an end (*telophase:* the final stage of mitosis in which daughter nuclei are forming and cytokinesis has typically begun)

trans- = across; **-form** = shape (*transformation:* the process that converts a normal cell into a cancer cell)

CHAPTER 13

Meiosis and Sexual Life Cycles

Teaching Objectives

The Basis of Heredity

1. Explain in general terms how traits are transmitted from parents to offspring.
2. Distinguish between asexual and sexual reproduction.

The Role of Meiosis in Sexual Life Cycles

3. Distinguish between the following pairs of terms:
   a. somatic cell and gamete
   b. autosome and sex chromosome
4. Explain how haploid and diploid cells differ from each other. State which cells in the human body are diploid and which are haploid.
5. Explain why fertilization and meiosis must alternate in all sexual life cycles.
6. Distinguish among the three life-cycle patterns characteristic of eukaryotes, and name one organism that displays each pattern.
7. List the phases of meiosis I and meiosis II and describe the events characteristic of each phase.
8. Recognize the phases of meiosis from diagrams or micrographs.
9. Describe the process of synapsis during prophase I and explain how genetic recombination occurs.
10. Describe three events that occur during meiosis I but not during mitosis.

Origins of Genetic Variation

11. Explain how independent assortment, crossing over, and random fertilization contribute to genetic variation in sexually reproducing organisms.
12. Explain why heritable variation is crucial to Darwin's theory of evolution by natural selection.

Student Misconceptions

1. The majority of your students will have some level of confusion about the structures and processes of meiosis. And, of course, students who misunderstand meiosis often have difficulty with genetics as well.

Most students have studied meiosis in high school. As a result, students are not fully attentive when they encounter the topic again in a first-year class. However, it is likely that they didn't "get it" the first time and that unresolved misunderstandings will continue.

Think carefully about how to engage students in this important topic. Rather than asking students the questions they expect—*compare and contrast meiosis and mitosis; describe the events of prophase I*—give them problems that require them to reason about the process of meiosis. State specific combinations of alleles in daughter cells and ask students to explain the steps that would produce each combination. Such questions will be more likely to reveal misunderstandings, both to students themselves and to their instructors.

2. Many students have fundamental misunderstandings about chromosomes and their structure and behavior during meiosis. It is very common for students to be confused about ploidy and chromosome structure. Some students are uncertain about the significance of the centromere.

   a. Many students think that chromosomes with a single unreplicated chromatid are characteristic of haploid cells and that replicated chromosomes with two chromatids are characteristic of diploid cells.

   b. Some students think that chromosomes consisting of two chromatids are formed not by replication, but when a maternal chromatid and a paternal chromatid come together during fertilization and join at the centromere.

   c. Some students do not realize that sister chromatids are joined at the centromere. These students will draw sister chromatids as independent entities throughout meiosis I.

   d. Other students think that all four chromatids of a tetrad are joined by a single centromere during prophase I.

   How can an instructor address these fundamental misunderstandings? Clearly distinguish between the concepts of chromosome structure and chromosome number (ploidy) in all discussions of life cycles or the cell cycle. Explain explicitly how the replicated chromosome (with two chromatids joined by a centromere) arises and address possible misunderstandings at the same time.

   If students are asked to model the events of meiosis in lab, look carefully at student models for evidence of these common misunderstandings in order to address and resolve them.

3. Of necessity, instructors mention replication while teaching meiosis. Early prophase I chromosomes appear unreplicated in drawings and micrographs. These features of instruction may foster student confusion about the timing of the processes of replication and meiosis. Many students think that replication occurs during early meiosis. This is not a trivial mistake. It is hard for students to fully understand the processes of condensation and DNA replication if they imagine that a condensing chromosome can replicate. It is best to address this potential misunderstanding explicitly, by pointing it out as a common source of error.

4. Students often fail to draw the connections between Mendelian genetics and the process of meiosis. Emphasize segregation and the independent assortment of chromosomes when teaching meiosis, and ask students to explain how Mendel's laws of segregation and independent assortment can be explained by the behavior of chromosomes during meiosis.

Further Reading

Kindfield, A.C.H. 1994. Understanding a basic biological process: Expert and novice models of meiosis. *Science Education, 78(3)*, 255–283.

Chapter Guide to Teaching Resources

Overview: Hereditary similarity and variation

Concept 13.1 Offspring acquire genes from parents by inheriting chromosomes

Instructor and Student Media Resources
Activity: Asexual and sexual life cycles
Video: Hydra budding

Concept 13.2 Fertilization and meiosis alternate in sexual life cycles

Transparencies
Figure 13.3   Preparing a karyotype
Figure 13.4   Describing chromosomes
Figure 13.5   The human life cycle
Figure 13.6   Three types of sexual life cycles

Concept 13.3 Meiosis reduces the number of chromosome sets from diploid to haploid

Transparencies
Figure 13.7   Overview of meiosis: How meiosis reduces chromosome number
Figure 13.8   The meiotic division of an animal cell (part 1)
Figure 13.8   The meiotic division of an animal cell (part 2)
Figure 13.9   A comparison of mitosis and meiosis

Student Media Resource
Activity: Meiosis animation

Concept 13.4 Genetic variation produced in sexual life cycles contributes to evolution

Transparencies

Figure 13.10   The independent assortment of homologous chromosomes in meiosis

Figure 13.11   The results of crossing over during meiosis

Student Media Resources

Activity: Origins of genetic variation

Investigation: How can the frequency of crossing over be estimated?

For additional resources such as digital images and lecture outlines, go to the Campbell Media Manager or the Instructor Resources section of **www.campbellbiology.com.**

Key Terms

alternation of generations	genetics	recombinant chromosome
asexual reproduction	haploid cell	sex chromosome
autosome	heredity	sexual reproduction
chiasma	homologous chromosomes	somatic cell
clone	karyotype	spore
crossing over	life cycle	sporophyte
diploid cell	locus	synapsis
fertilization	meiosis	tetrad
gamete	meiosis I	variation
gametophyte	meiosis II	zygote
gene		

Word Roots

a- = not or without (*asexual:* type of reproduction not involving fertilization)

-apsis = juncture (*synapsis:* the pairing of replicated homologous chromosomes during prophase I of meiosis)

auto- = self (*autosome:* the chromosomes that do not determine gender)

chiasm- = marked crosswise (*chiasma:* the X-shaped, microscopically visible region representing homologous chromosomes that have exchanged genetic material through crossing over during meiosis)

di- = two (*diploid:* cells that contain two homologous sets of chromosomes)

fertil- = fruitful (*fertilization:* process of fusion of a haploid sperm and a haploid egg cell)

haplo- = single (*haploid:* cells that contain only one chromosome of each homologous pair)

homo- = like (*homologous:* like chromosomes that form a pair)

karyo- = nucleus (*karyotype:* a display of the chromosomes of a cell)

meio- = less (*meiosis:* a variation of cell division which yields daughter cells with half as many chromosomes as the parent cell)

soma- = body (*somatic:* body cells with 46 chromosomes in humans)

sporo- = a seed; **-phyt** = a plant (*sporophyte:* the multicellular diploid form in organisms undergoing alternation of generations that results from a union of gametes and that meiotically produces haploid spores that grow into the gametophyte generation)

syn- = together; **gam-** = marriage (*syngamy:* the process of cellular union during fertilization)

tetra- = four (*tetrad:* the four closely associated chromatids of a homologous pair of chromosomes)

CHAPTER 14

Mendel and the Gene Idea

Teaching Objectives

Gregor Mendel's Discoveries

1. Explain how Mendel's particulate mechanism differed from the blending theory of inheritance.

2. Define the following terms: *true-breeding, hybridization, monohybrid cross, P generation, F₁ generation,* and *F₂ generation*.

3. List and explain the four components of Mendel's hypothesis that led him to deduce the law of segregation.

4. Use a Punnett square to predict the results of a monohybrid cross, stating the phenotypic and genotypic ratios of the F_2 generation.

5. Distinguish between the following pairs of terms: *dominant* and *recessive; heterozygous* and *homozygous; genotype* and *phenotype*.

6. Explain how a testcross can be used to determine if an individual with the dominant phenotype is homozygous or heterozygous.

7. Use a Punnett square to predict the results of a dihybrid cross and state the phenotypic and genotypic ratios of the F_2 generation.

8. State Mendel's law of independent assortment and describe how this law can be explained by the behavior of chromosomes during meiosis.

9. Use the rule of multiplication to calculate the probability that a particular F_2 individual will be homozygous recessive or dominant.

10. Given a Mendelian cross, use the rule of addition to calculate the probability that a particular F_2 individual will be heterozygous.

11. Use the laws of probability to predict, from a trihybrid cross between two individuals that are heterozygous for all three traits, what expected proportion of the offspring would be:

    a. homozygous dominant for the three traits

    b. heterozygous for all three traits

    c. homozygous recessive for two specific traits and heterozygous for the third

12. Explain why it is important that Mendel used large sample sizes in his studies.

Extending Mendelian Genetics

13. Give an example of incomplete dominance and explain why it does not support the blending theory of inheritance.

14. Explain how phenotypic expression of the heterozygote differs with complete dominance, incomplete dominance, and codominance.

15. Explain why Tay-Sachs disease is considered recessive at the organismal level but codominant at the molecular level.

16. Explain why genetic dominance does not mean that a dominant allele subdues a recessive allele. Illustrate your explanation with the use of round versus wrinkled pea seed shape.

17. Explain why dominant alleles are not necessarily more common in a population. Illustrate your explanation with an example.

18. Describe the inheritance of the ABO blood system and explain why the I^A and I^B alleles are said to be codominant.

19. Define and give examples of *pleiotropy* and *epistasis.*

20. Describe a simple model for polygenic inheritance and explain why most polygenic characters are described in quantitative terms.

21. Describe how environmental conditions can influence the phenotypic expression of a character. Explain what is meant by "a norm of reaction."

22. Distinguish between the specific and broad interpretations of the terms *phenotype* and *genotype.*

Mendelian Inheritance in Humans

23. Explain why studies of human inheritance are not as easily conducted as Mendel's work with his peas.

24. Given a simple family pedigree, deduce the genotypes for some of the family members.

25. Explain how a lethal recessive allele can be maintained in a population.

26. Describe the inheritance and expression of cystic fibrosis, Tay-Sachs disease, and sickle-cell disease.

27. Explain why lethal dominant genes are much rarer than lethal recessive genes.

28. Give an example of a late-acting lethal dominant gene in humans and explain how it can escape elimination by natural selection.

29. Define and give examples of multifactorial disorders in humans.

30. Explain how carrier recognition, fetal testing, and newborn screening can be used in genetic screening and counseling.

Student Misconceptions

1. Students (and some instructors) tend to use the terms *gene* and *allele* interchangeably. This leads to confusion for students, who may have difficulty understanding the distinction between these terms. Clearly define these terms for your students and be consistent and accurate when you use them.

2. Punnett squares are useful devices for predicting the genetic ratios of offspring when parent genotypes are known. However, use of Punnett squares may lead students to think of genetic ratios as fixed and deterministic, rather than probabilistic. Many students memorize familiar ratios, and fail to appreciate the role of probability in the segregation and independent assortment of alleles. These students think that the offspring

shown in a Punnett square are individuals and do not recognize them as probabilities of offspring having a given genotype. When using Punnett squares in classroom instruction, take care to refer to probability rather than number of each type of offspring.

3. Look out for these common misunderstandings:

   a. Chromosomes with a single unreplicated chromatid are found in haploid cells; replicated chromosomes with two chromatids are found in diploid cells.

   b. Chromosomes consisting of two chromatids are formed when a maternal chromatid and a paternal chromatid come together during fertilization and join at the centromere.

4. The everyday meaning of *dominance* implies strength and power in a contest with a weaker opponent. Many students think of the relationship between dominant and recessive alleles in this context. As a result, your students may have some or all of these common misconceptions:

   a. Dominant alleles are more likely to be inherited than recessive alleles.

   b. Dominant alleles are found at greater frequency than recessive alleles in populations.

   c. Adaptive traits will become dominant over time through the action of natural selection.

   d. Mutations are recessive.

   e. Recessive alleles are deleterious.

   f. Dominant alleles regulate the expression of recessive alleles.

5. Students have great difficulty understanding the mechanism of dominance. They tend to think that the dominant allele masks or overrides the recessive allele in some way. They do not recognize that recessive alleles are expressed through transcription and translation, and that they may have functional gene products. Work through a couple of examples with students to illustrate how both alleles may affect phenotype and how these effects manifest themselves when the phenotype is considered at the molecular, biochemical, and organismal levels.

6. Students might be able to understand the nature of inheritance and gene expression more easily if the first examples they encounter show incomplete dominance. When you first introduce the monohybrid cross to your students, use red and white flowered snapdragons rather than purple and white flowered peas. Use superscript notation as used in blood types, rather than capital and small letters. These teaching strategies will address several areas of potential student confusion. Students will find it easier to recognize that offspring inherit alleles from each parent and that these alleles are expressed and may affect phenotype. They will be less likely to think that traits "skip a generation" or to imagine that offspring inherit an active gene for each trait from only one parent. This will help students to focus on alleles and how they segregate and recombine.

7. Students tend to think that every trait is represented by a gene and that each gene has two and only two alleles. This oversimplification causes problems later, when students try to understand the evolution of quantitative and multifactorial characters.

Further Reading

Allchin, D. 2000. Mending Mendelism. *The American Biology Teacher, 62(9)*, 633–639.

Kindfield, A.C.H. 1991. Confusing chromosome number and structure: A common student error. *Journal of Biological Education, 25(3)*, 193–201.

Chapter Guide to Teaching Resources

Overview: Drawing from the deck of genes

Concept 14.1 Mendel used the scientific approach to identify two laws of inheritance

Transparencies

Figure 14.2	Crossing pea plants
Figure 14.3	When F_1 pea plants with purple flowers are allowed to self-pollinate, what flower color appears in the F_2 generation?
Table 14.1	The results of Mendel's F_1 crosses for seven characters in pea plants
Figure 14.4	Alleles, alternative versions of a gene
Figure 14.5	Mendel's law of segregation (layer 1)
Figure 14.5	Mendel's law of segregation (layer 2)
Figure 14.6	Phenotype versus genotype
Figure 14.7	The testcross
Figure 14.8	Do the alleles for seed color and seed shape sort into gametes dependently (together) or independently?

Student Media Resources

Activity: Monohybrid cross

Activity: Dihybrid cross

Concept 14.2 The laws of probability govern Mendelian inheritance

Transparency

Figure 14.9	Segregation of alleles and fertilization as chance events

Student Media Resource

Activity: Gregor's garden

Concept 14.3 Inheritance patterns are often more complex than predicted by simple Mendelian genetics

Transparencies

Figure 14.10   Incomplete dominance in snapdragon color

Table 14.2   Determination of ABO blood group by multiple alleles

Figure 14.11   An example of epistasis

Figure 14.12   A simplified model for polygenic inheritance of skin color

Student Media Resource

Activity: Incomplete dominance

Concept 14.4 Many human traits follow Mendelian patterns of inheritance

Transparencies

Figure 14.14   Pedigree analysis

Figure 14.17   Testing a fetus for genetic disorders

Student Media Resource

Investigation: How do you diagnose a genetic disorder?

Review

Transparency

Page 273   A pedigree tracing the inheritance of alkaptonuria

For additional resources such as digital images and lecture outlines, go to the Campbell Media Manager or the Instructor Resources section of **www.campbellbiology.com.**

Key Terms

allele	F_2 generation	P generation
amniocentesis	genotype	pedigree
carrier	heterozygous	phenotype
character	homozygous	pleiotropy
chorionic villus sampling (CVS)	Huntington's disease	polygenic inheritance
codominance	hybridization	Punnett square
complete dominance	incomplete dominance	quantitative character
cystic fibrosis	law of independent assortment	recessive allele
dihybrid		sickle-cell disease
dominant allele	law of segregation	Tay-Sachs disease
epistasis	monohybrid	testcross
F_1 generation	multifactorial	trait
	norm of reaction	true-breeding

Word Roots

-centesis = a puncture (*amniocentesis:* a technique for determining genetic abnormalities in a fetus by the presence of certain chemicals or defective fetal cells in the amniotic fluid, obtained by aspiration from a needle inserted into the uterus)

co- = together (*codominance:* phenotype in which both dominant alleles are expressed in the heterozygote)

di- = two (*dihybrid cross:* a breeding experiment in which parental varieties differing in two traits are mated)

epi- = beside; **-stasis** = standing (*epistasis:* a phenomenon in which one gene alters the expression of another gene that is independently inherited)

geno- = offspring (*genotype:* the genetic makeup of an organism)

hetero- = different (*heterozygous:* having two different alleles for a trait)

homo- = alike (*homozygous:* having two identical alleles for a trait)

mono- = one (*monohybrid cross:* a breeding experiment that uses parental varieties differing in a single character)

pedi- = a child (*pedigree:* a family tree describing the occurrence of heritable characters in parents and offspring across as many generations as possible)

pheno- = appear (*phenotype:* the physical and physiological traits of an organism)

pleio- = more (*pleiotropy:* when a single gene impacts more than one characteristic)

poly- = many; **gen-** = produce (*polygenic:* an additive effect of two or more gene loci on a single phenotypic character)

CHAPTER 15

The Chromosomal Basis of Inheritance

Teaching Objectives

Relating Mendelian Inheritance to the Behavior of Chromosomes

1. Explain how the observations of cytologists and geneticists provided the basis for the chromosome theory of inheritance.
2. Explain why *Drosophila melanogaster* is a good experimental organism for genetic studies.
3. Explain why linked genes do not assort independently.
4. Distinguish between parental and recombinant phenotypes.
5. Explain how crossing over can unlink genes.
6. Explain how Sturtevant created linkage maps.
7. Define a map unit.
8. Explain why Mendel did not find linkage between seed color and flower color, despite the fact that these genes are on the same chromosome.
9. Explain how genetic maps are constructed for genes located far apart on a chromosome.
10. Explain the effect of multiple crossovers between loci.
11. Explain what additional information cytogenetic maps provide.

Sex Chromosomes

12. Describe how sex is genetically determined in humans and explain the significance of the *SRY* gene.
13. Distinguish between linked genes and sex-linked genes.
14. Explain why sex-linked diseases are more common in human males.
15. Describe the inheritance patterns and symptoms of color blindness, Duchenne muscular dystrophy, and hemophilia.
16. Describe the process of X inactivation in female mammals. Explain how this phenomenon produces the tortoiseshell coloration in cats.

Errors and Exceptions in Chromosomal Inheritance

17. Explain how nondisjunction can lead to aneuploidy.
18. Define *trisomy, triploidy,* and *polyploidy.* Explain how these major chromosomal changes occur and describe possible consequences.

19. Distinguish among deletions, duplications, inversions, and translocations.

20. Describe the type of chromosomal alterations responsible for the following human disorders: Down syndrome, Klinefelter syndrome, extra Y, triple-X syndrome, Turner syndrome, *cri du chat* syndrome, and chronic myelogenous leukemia.

21. Define *genomic imprinting.* Describe the evidence that suggests that the *Igf2* gene is maternally imprinted.

22. Explain why extranuclear genes are not inherited in a Mendelian fashion.

Student Misconceptions

1. Many students have great difficulty understanding how the laws of Mendelian inheritance can be explained by the behavior of chromosomes during meiosis. Many cannot correctly describe the relationship between a pair of alleles and a homologous pair of chromosomes during meiosis, and do not recognize that meiosis is the mechanism for segregation of alleles.

2. To help students recognize the relationship between alleles of a gene and genes on a chromosome, expect your students to talk about and draw chromosomes wherever possible. Incorporate drawings of chromosomes into your instruction, and use such drawings to illustrate lectures on cell division, cell cycle, fertilization, and life cycles. Include diagrammatic representations of chromosomes carrying alleles in Punnett squares, and expect your students to do the same.

3. Students are taught about dominant and recessive alleles when they learn about Mendel's laws of inheritance. As a result, they may think that dominance is the norm and that incomplete dominance and codominance are rare exceptions. In fact, complete dominance is exceptional and incomplete dominance is the norm. Less than one-third of clinical human genetic conditions are explained by a model of one gene and two alleles, with complete dominance. The conventional examples of human traits that display complete dominance are rather trivial: tongue curling, PTC tasting, attached earlobes.

Further Reading

Donovan, M. P. 1997. The vocabulary of biology and the problem of semantics: "Dominant," "recessive" and the puzzling role of alleles. *Journal of College Science Teaching, 26,* 381–382.

Chapter Guide to Teaching Resources

Overview: Locating genes on chromosomes

Concept 15.1 Mendelian inheritance has its physical basis in the behavior of chromosomes

Transparencies

Figure 15.2   The chromosomal basis of Mendel's laws

Figure 15.4   In a cross between a wild-type female fruit fly and a mutant white-eyed male, what color eyes will the F_1 and F_2 offspring have?

Concept 15.2 Linked genes tend to be inherited together because they are located near each other on the same chromosome

Transparencies

Page 278   *Drosophila* testcross

Page 278   Punnett square showing recombination of unlinked genes

Figure 15.5   Are the genes for body color and wing size in fruit flies located on the same chromosome or different chromosomes?

Figure 15.6   Chromosomal basis for recombination of linked genes

Figure 15.7   Constructing a linkage map

Figure 15.8   A partial genetic (linkage) map of a *Drosophila* chromosome

Student Media Resource

Activity: Linked genes and crossing over

Concept 15.3 Sex-linked genes exhibit unique patterns of inheritance

Transparencies

Figure 15.9   Some chromosomal systems of sex determination

Figure 15.10   The transmission of sex-linked recessive traits

Figure 15.11   X inactivation and the tortoiseshell cat

Student Media Resources
Activity: Sex-linked genes
Investigation: What can fruit flies reveal about inheritance?
Biology Labs On-Line: FlyLab
Biology Labs On-Line: Pedigree lab

Concept 15.4 Alterations of chromosome number or structure cause some genetic disorders

Transparencies

Figure 15.12   Meiotic nondisjunction

Figure 15.14   Alterations of chromosome structure

Figure 15.16   Translocation associated with chronic myelogenous leukemia (CML)

Student Media Resource
Activity: Polyploid plants

Concept 15.5 Some inheritance patterns are exceptions to the standard chromosome theory

Transparency

Figure 15.17   Genomic imprinting of the mouse *Igf2* gene

For additional resources such as digital images and lecture outlines, go to the Campbell Media Manager or the Instructor Resources section of **www.campbellbiology.com.**

Key Terms

aneuploidy	duplication	nondisjunction
Barr body	genetic map	parental type
chromosome theory	genetic recombination	polyploidy
of inheritance	genomic imprinting	recombinant
crossing over	hemophilia	sex-linked gene
cytogenetic map	inversion	translocation
deletion	linkage map	trisomic
Down syndrome	linked genes	wild type
Duchenne muscular	map unit	
dystrophy	monosomic	

Word Roots

aneu- = without (*aneuploidy:* a chromosomal aberration in which certain chromosomes are present in extra copies or are deficient in number)

cyto- = cell (*cytological maps:* charts of chromosomes that locate genes with respect to chromosomal features)

hemo- = blood (*hemophilia:* a human genetic disease caused by a sex-linked recessive allele, characterized by excessive bleeding following injury)

mono- = one (*monosomic:* a chromosomal condition in which a particular cell has only one copy of a chromosome, instead of the normal two; the cell is said to be monosomic for that chromosome)

non- = not; **dis-** = separate (*nondisjunction:* an accident of meiosis or mitosis, in which both members of a pair of homologous chromosomes or both sister chromatids fail to move apart properly)

poly- = many (*polyploidy:* a chromosomal alteration in which the organism possesses more than two complete chromosome sets)

re- = again; **com-** = together; **-bin** = two at a time (*recombinant:* an offspring whose phenotype differs from that of the parents)

trans- = across (*translocation:* attachment of a chromosomal fragment to a nonhomologous chromosome)

tri- = three; **soma-** = body (*trisomic:* a chromosomal condition in which a particular cell has an extra copy of one chromosome, instead of the normal two; the cell is said to be trisomic for that chromosome)

CHAPTER 16

The Molecular Basis of Inheritance

Teaching Objectives

DNA as the Genetic Material

1. Explain why researchers originally thought protein was the genetic material.
2. Summarize the experiments performed by the following scientists that provided evidence that DNA is the genetic material:
   a. Frederick Griffith
   b. Oswald Avery, Maclyn McCarty, and Colin MacLeod
   c. Alfred Hershey and Martha Chase
   d. Erwin Chargaff
3. Explain how Watson and Crick deduced the structure of DNA and describe the evidence they used. Explain the significance of the research of Rosalind Franklin.
4. Describe the structure of DNA. Explain the base-pairing rule and describe its significance.

DNA Replication and Repair

5. Describe the semiconservative model of replication and the significance of the experiments of Matthew Meselson and Franklin Stahl.
6. Describe the process of DNA replication, including the role of the origins of replication and replication forks.
7. Explain the role of DNA polymerases in replication.
8. Explain what energy source drives the polymerization of DNA.
9. Define *antiparallel* and explain why continuous synthesis of both DNA strands is not possible.
10. Distinguish between the leading strand and the lagging strand.
11. Explain how the lagging strand is synthesized even though DNA polymerase can add nucleotides only to the 3′ end. Describe the significance of Okazaki fragments.
12. Explain the roles of DNA ligase, primer, primase, helicase, topoisomerase, and single-strand binding proteins.
13. Explain why an analogy can be made comparing DNA replication to a locomotive made of DNA polymerase moving along a railroad track of DNA.
14. Explain the roles of DNA polymerase, mismatch repair enzymes, and nuclease in DNA proofreading and repair.

15. Describe the structure and function of telomeres.

16. Explain the possible significance of telomerase in germ cells and cancerous cells.

Student Misconceptions

1. The process of DNA replication is complex and difficult for students to master. Students must learn the details and understand the significance of many important processes: They must distinguish between $5' \rightarrow 3'$ and $3' \rightarrow 5'$ strands, understand the different mechanisms of replication for leading and lagging strands, learn the functions of a great variety of enzymes, and understand the energetics of the whole process. Students may master the many details of DNA replication but fail to understand their significance. It is important to emphasize *why* as well as *how* in teaching students about this fascinating and important topic.

2. Students may imagine separate DNA polymerase molecules moving along a stationary DNA molecule during the process of replication. It is important to point out that the polymerase enzymes involved in replication form a large protein complex, and that interactions between proteins in this complex greatly facilitate the efficiency of the replication process.

Chapter Guide to Teaching Resources

Overview: Life's operating instructions

Concept 16.1 DNA is the genetic material

Transparencies

Figure 16.2   Can the genetic trait of pathogenicity be transferred between bacteria?

Figure 16.3   Viruses infecting a bacterial cell

Figure 16.4   Is DNA or protein the genetic material of phage T2?

Figure 16.5   The structure of a DNA strand

Figure 16.7   The double helix

Page 298   Purine and pyrimidine

Figure 16.8   Base pairing in DNA

Student Media Resources

Activity: The Hershey-Chase experiment

Activity: DNA and RNA structure

Activity: DNA double helix

Concept 16.2 Many proteins work together in DNA replication and repair

Transparencies

Student Media Resources

Activity: DNA replication: An overview

Investigation: What is the correct model for DNA replication?

Activity: DNA replication: A closer look

Activity: DNA replication: A review

For additional resources such as digital images and lecture outlines, go to the Campbell Media Manager or the Instructor Resources section of **www.campbellbiology.com.**

Key Terms

bacteriophage	helicase	nuclease
DNA ligase	lagging strand	nucleotide excision
DNA polymerase	leading strand	repair
double helix	mismatch repair	Okazaki fragment

origin of replication   semiconservative   telomere
phage   model   topoisomerase
primase   single-strand binding   transformation
primer   protein
replication fork   telomerase

Word Roots

helic- = a spiral (*helicase:* an enzyme that untwists the double helix of DNA at the replication forks)

liga- = bound or tied (*DNA ligase:* a linking enzyme for DNA replication)

-phage = to eat (*bacteriophages:* viruses that infect bacteria)

semi- = half (*semiconservative model:* type of DNA replication in which the replicated double helix consists of one old strand, derived from the old molecule, and one newly made strand)

telos- = an end (*telomere:* the protective structure at each end of a eukaryotic chromosome)

trans- = across (*transformation:* a phenomenon in which external DNA is assimilated by a cell)

CHAPTER 17

From Gene to Protein

Teaching Objectives

The Connection Between Genes and Proteins

1. Explain why dwarf peas have shorter stems than tall varieties.
2. Explain the reasoning that led Archibald Garrod to first suggest that genes dictate phenotypes through enzymes.
3. Describe Beadle and Tatum's experiments with *Neurospora* and explain the contribution they made to our understanding of how genes control metabolism.
4. Distinguish between the "one gene–one enzyme" hypothesis and the "one gene–one polypeptide" hypothesis and explain why the original hypothesis was changed.
5. Explain how RNA differs from DNA.
6. Briefly explain how information flows from gene to protein.
7. Distinguish between transcription and translation.
8. Compare where transcription and translation occur in prokaryotes and in eukaryotes.
9. Define *codon* and explain the relationship between the linear sequence of codons on mRNA and the linear sequence of amino acids in a polypeptide.
10. Explain the early techniques used to identify what amino acids are specified by the triplets UUU, AAA, GGG, and CCC.
11. Explain why polypeptides begin with methionine when they are synthesized.
12. Explain what it means to say that the genetic code is redundant and unambiguous.
13. Explain the significance of the reading frame during translation.
14. Explain the evolutionary significance of a nearly universal genetic code.

The Synthesis and Processing of RNA

15. Explain how RNA polymerase recognizes where transcription should begin. Describe the promoter, the terminator, and the transcription unit.
16. Explain the general process of transcription, including the three major steps of initiation, elongation, and termination.
17. Explain how RNA is modified after transcription in eukaryotic cells.
18. Define and explain the role of *ribozymes*.
19. Describe the functional and evolutionary significance of introns.

The Synthesis of Protein

20. Describe the structure and functions of tRNA.

21. Explain the significance of wobble.

22. Explain how tRNA is joined to the appropriate amino acid.

23. Describe the structure and functions of ribosomes.

24. Describe the process of translation (including initiation, elongation, and termination) and explain which enzymes, protein factors, and energy sources are needed for each stage.

25. Describe the significance of polyribosomes.

26. Explain what determines the primary structure of a protein and describe how a polypeptide must be modified before it becomes fully functional.

27. Describe what determines whether a ribosome will be free in the cytosol or attached to the rough endoplasmic reticulum.

28. Describe two properties of RNA that allow it to perform so many different functions.

29. Compare protein synthesis in prokaryotes and in eukaryotes.

30. Define *point mutations.* Distinguish between base-pair substitutions and base-pair insertions. Give examples of each and note the significance of such changes.

31. Describe several examples of mutagens and explain how they cause mutations.

32. Describe the historical evolution of the concept of a gene.

Student Misconceptions

1. A significant number of students have the mistaken notion that amino acids are produced by translation. As students study protein synthesis, they learn that each codon specifies an amino acid and that amino acids are involved in translation. They also learn that various enzymes—such as aminoacyl-tRNA synthetase—play roles in protein synthesis. Some students have difficulty understanding which of the molecules involved in translation are also the products of protein synthesis. These students may think that amino acids— but not enzymes involved in protein synthesis—are produced by translation.

   You might wish to address some of these sources of confusion in your lectures on protein synthesis. Clarify for your students that enzymes catalyze steps in protein synthesis, but that they are also the products of protein synthesis. Recognize that students may not understand the source of amino acids that are used in translation, and address this topic directly.

2. Emphasize to your students that proteins are not the only catalysts in living cells. The discovery of ribozymes and the increasing recognition of the important role they play in translation have changed our understanding of protein synthesis and provided new insights into the origin of life on Earth. Use this example to point out to your students that our understanding of the processes of life continues to change and grow, and that each new discovery can lead to new and exciting questions.

3. It may be difficult for your students to keep track of the plethora of RNA molecules and the roles they play. Emphasize the reasons for the versatility of this molecule and clarify for your students the significance of the multiple roles of RNA.

Further Reading

Fisher, K. M. 1985. A misconception in biology: Amino acids and translation. *Journal of Research in Science Teaching, 22(1)*, 53–62.

Chapter Guide to Teaching Resources

Overview: The flow of genetic information

Concept 17.1 Genes specify proteins via transcription and translation

Transparencies

Figure 17.2	Do individual genes specify different enzymes in arginine biosynthesis?
Figure 17.3	Overview: The roles of transcription and translation in the flow of genetic information (layer 1)
Figure 17.3	Overview: The roles of transcription and translation in the flow of genetic information (layer 2)
Figure 17.3	Overview: The roles of transcription and translation in the flow of genetic information (layer 3)
Figure 17.3	Overview: The roles of transcription and translation in the flow of genetic information (layer 4)
Figure 17.3	Overview: The roles of transcription and translation in the flow of genetic information (layer 5)
Figure 17.4	The triplet code
Figure 17.5	The dictionary of the genetic code

Student Media Resources

Investigation: How is a metabolic pathway analyzed?

Activity: Overview of protein synthesis

Concept 17.2 Transcription is the DNA-directed synthesis of RNA: *A closer look*

Transparencies

Figure 17.7	The stages of transcription: Initiation, elongation, and termination (layer 1)
Figure 17.7	The stages of transcription: Initiation, elongation, and termination (layer 2)

Figure 17.7   The stages of transcription: Initiation, elongation, and termination (layer 3)

Figure 17.7   The stages of transcription: Initiation, elongation, and termination (layer 4)

Figure 17.7   The stages of transcription: Elongation

Figure 17.8   The initiation of transcription at a eukaryotic promoter

Student Media Resource
Activity: Transcription

Concept 17.3 Eukaryotic cells modify RNA after transcription

Transparencies
Figure 17.9   RNA processing: Addition of the 5′ cap and poly-A tail
Figure 17.10   RNA processing: RNA splicing
Figure 17.11   The roles of snRNPs and spliceosomes in pre-mRNA splicing
Figure 17.12   Correspondence between exons and protein domains

Student Media Resource
Activity: RNA Processing

Concept 17.4 Translation is the RNA-directed synthesis of a polypeptide: *A closer look*

Transparencies
Figure 17.13   Translation: The basic concept
Figure 17.14   The structure of transfer RNA (tRNA): Two-dimensional structure
Figure 17.14   The structure of transfer RNA (tRNA): Three-dimensional structure
Figure 17.15   An aminoacyl-tRNA synthetase joins a specific amino acid to a tRNA
Figure 17.16   The anatomy of a functioning ribosome
Figure 17.17   The initiation of translation
Figure 17.18   The elongation cycle of translation
Figure 17.19   The termination of translation
Figure 17.20   Polyribosomes
Figure 17.21   The signal mechanism for targeting proteins to the ER

Student Media Resources
Activity: Translation
Biology Labs On-Line: TranslationLab

Concept 17.5 RNA plays multiple roles in the cell: *A review*

Transparency
Table 17.1   Types of RNA in a eukaryotic cell

Concept 17.6 Comparing gene expression in prokaryotes and eukaryotes reveals key differences

Transparency

Figure 17.22   Coupled transcription and translation in bacteria

Concept 17.7 Point mutations can affect protein structure and function

Transparencies

Figure 17.23   The molecular basis of sickle-cell disease: A point mutation

Figure 17.24   Base-pair substitution

Figure 17.25   Base-pair insertion or deletion

Figure 17.26   A summary of transcription and translation in a eukaryotic cell

For additional resources such as digital images and lecture outlines, go to the Campbell Media Manager or the Instructor Resources section of **www.campbellbiology.com.**

Key Terms

5′ cap	mutagen	RNA processing
A site	mutation	RNA splicing
alternative RNA splicing	nonsense mutation	signal peptide
aminoacyl-tRNA synthetase	one gene–one polypeptide hypothesis	signal-recognition particle (SRP)
anticodon	P site	spliceosome
base-pair substitution	point mutation	TATA box
codon	poly-A tail	template strand
deletion	polyribosome (polysome)	terminator
domain	primary transcript	transcription
E site	promoter	transcription factor
exon	reading frame	transcription initiation complex
frameshift mutation	ribosomal RNA (rRNA)	transcription unit
insertion	ribosome	transfer RNA (tRNA)
intron	ribozyme	translation
messenger RNA (mRNA)	RNA polymerase	triplet code
missense mutation		wobble

Word Roots

anti- = opposite (*anticodon:* a specialized base triplet on one end of a tRNA molecule that recognizes a particular complementary codon on an mRNA molecule)

exo- = out, outside, without (*exon:* a coding region of a eukaryotic gene that is expressed)

intro- = within (*intron:* a noncoding, intervening sequence within a eukaryotic gene)

muta- = change; **-gen** = producing (*mutagen:* a physical or chemical agent that causes mutations)

poly- = many (*polyA tail:* the modified end of the 3′ end of an mRNA molecule consisting of the addition of some 50 to 250 adenine nucleotides)

trans- = across; **-script** = write (*transcription:* the synthesis of RNA on a DNA template)

CHAPTER 18

The Genetics of Viruses and Bacteria

Teaching Objectives

The Genetics of Viruses

1. Recount the history leading up to the discovery of viruses. Include the contributions of Adolf Mayer, Dimitri Ivanowsky, Martinus Beijerinck, and Wendell Stanley.
2. List and describe the structural components of viruses.
3. Explain why viruses are obligate intracellular parasites.
4. Explain how a virus identifies its host cell.
5. Describe bacterial defenses against phages.
6. Distinguish between the lytic and lysogenic reproductive cycles, using phage lambda as an example.
7. Describe the reproductive cycle of an enveloped virus. Explain the reproductive cycle of the herpesvirus.
8. Describe the reproductive cycle of retroviruses.
9. List some characteristics that viruses share with living organisms and explain why viruses do not fit our usual definition of life.
10. Describe the evidence that viruses probably evolved from fragments of cellular nucleic acids.
11. Define and describe mobile genetic elements.
12. Explain how viral infections in animals cause disease.
13. Describe the best current medical defenses against viruses. Explain how AZT helps to fight HIV infections.
14. Describe the mechanisms by which new viral diseases emerge.
15. Distinguish between the horizontal and vertical routes of viral transmission in plants.
16. Describe viroids and prions.
17. Explain how a non-replicating protein can act as a transmissible pathogen.

The Genetics of Bacteria

18. Describe the structure of a bacterial chromosome.
19. Compare the sources of genetic variation in bacteria and humans.
20. Compare the processes of transformation, transduction, and conjugation.
21. Distinguish between generalized and specialized transduction.
22. Define an *episome*. Explain why a plasmid can be an episome.

23. Explain how the F plasmid controls conjugation in bacteria.

24. Describe the significance of R plasmids. Explain how the widespread use of antibiotics contributes to R plasmid-related disease.

25. Explain how transposable elements may cause recombination of bacterial DNA.

26. Distinguish between an insertion sequence and a transposon.

27. Describe the role of transposase in the process of transposition.

28. Briefly describe two main strategies that cells use to control metabolism.

29. Explain the adaptive advantage of genes grouped into an operon.

30. Using the *trp* operon as an example, explain the concept of an operon and the function of the operator, repressor, and corepressor.

31. Distinguish between structural and regulatory genes.

32. Describe how the *lac* operon functions and explain the role of the inducer, allolactose.

33. Explain how repressible and inducible enzymes differ and how those differences reflect differences in the pathways they control.

34. Distinguish between positive and negative control and give examples of each from the *lac* operon.

35. Explain how cyclic AMP and catabolite activator protein are affected by glucose concentration.

Student Misconceptions

1. Students may find it difficult to understand how viroids and prions can act as infectious agents to spread disease. Clearly explain the mechanisms by which these molecules cause infection and disease, and discuss the possible implications of these pathogens to our understanding of life.

2. Teaching about the genetics of viruses and bacteria provides an opportunity to familiarize students with some important health treatment issues. Explain to your class the futility—and the danger—of prescribing antibiotics to treat viral disease. Discuss with them the science of vaccines, and ask them to assess the legitimacy of the concerns of some parents about vaccination.

3. Students may find it difficult to understand how conjugation can be considered "bacterial sex." Explain that, in biological terms, sex is a process that produces a genetically novel individual with genetic contributions from two "parents."

4. Many students have difficulty mastering the distinction between repressible and inducible operons. When teaching this material, remind students of the role of each type of operon in cell metabolism. This will help students to understand the significance of these forms of negative gene regulation, rather than focusing on memorization of detail.

Chapter Guide to Teaching Resources

Overview: Microbial model systems

Concept 18.1 A virus has a genome but can reproduce only within a host cell

Transparencies

Figure 18.2	Comparing the size of a virus, a bacterium, and an animal cell
Figure 18.4	Viral structure
Figure 18.5	A simplified viral reproductive cycle
Figure 18.6	The lytic cycle of phage T4, a virulent phage
Figure 18.7	The lytic and lysogenic cycles of phage λ, a temperate phage
Table 18.1	Classes of animal viruses
Figure 18.8	The reproductive cycle of an enveloped RNA virus
Figure 18.9	The structure of HIV, the retrovirus that causes AIDS
Figure 18.10	The reproductive cycle of HIV, a retrovirus

Student Media Resources

Activity: Simplified viral reproductive cycle
Activity: Phage lytic cycle
Activity: Phage lysogenic and lytic cycles
Activity: Retrovirus (HIV) reproductive cycle

Concept 18.2 Viruses, viroids, and prions are formidable pathogens in animals and plants

Transparency

Figure 18.13   Model for how prions propagate

Student Media Resources

Investigation: What causes infections in AIDS patients?
Investigation: Why do AIDS rates differ across the U.S.?

Concept 18.3 Rapid reproduction, mutation, and genetic recombination contribute to the genetic diversity of bacteria

Transparencies

Figure 18.14	Replication of a bacterial chromosome
Figure 18.15	Can a bacterial cell acquire genes from another bacterial cell?
Figure 18.16	Generalized transduction (layer 1)
Figure 18.16	Generalized transduction (layer 2)
Figure 18.18	Conjugation and recombination in *E. coli* (layer 1)
Figure 18.18	Conjugation and recombination in *E. coli* (layer 2)

Figure 18.18   Conjugation and recombination in *E. coli* (layer 3)

Figure 18.18   Conjugation and recombination in *E. coli* (layer 4)

Figure 18.19   Transposable genetic elements in bacteria

Instructor and Student Media Resources

Video: Prokaryotic flagella

Investigation: What are the patterns of antibiotic resistance?

Concept 18.4 Individual bacteria respond to environmental change by regulating their gene expression

Transparencies

Figure 18.20   Regulation of a metabolic pathway

Figure 18.21a The *trp* operon: Regulated synthesis of repressible enzymes

Figure 18.21b The *trp* operon: Regulated synthesis of repressible enzymes (layer 1)

Figure 18.21b The *trp* operon: Regulated synthesis of repressible enzymes (layer 2)

Figure 18.22a The *lac* operon: Regulated synthesis of inducible enzymes

Figure 18.22b The *lac* operon: Regulated synthesis of inducible enzymes

Figure 18.23   Positive control of the *lac* operon by catabolite activator protein (CAP)

Student Media Resource

Activity: The *lac* operon in *E. coli*

Review

Transparency

Page 358   Bacterial and viral growth curves

For additional resources such as digital images and lecture outlines, go to the Campbell Media Manager or the Instructor Resources section of **www.campbellbiology.com.**

Key Terms

activator	F factor	nucleoid
AIDS (acquired immunodeficiency syndrome)	F plasmid	operator
	HIV (human immunodeficiency virus)	operon
		phage
bacteriophage		plasmid
capsid	host range	prion
conjugation	inducer	prophage
corepressor	insertion sequence	provirus
cyclic AMP (cAMP)	lysogenic cycle	R plasmid
episome	lytic cycle	regulatory gene

repressor	transduction	viral envelope
restriction enzyme	transformation	viroid
retrovirus	transposable element	virulent phage
reverse transcriptase	transposon	
temperate phage	vaccine	

Word Roots

capsa- = a box (*capsid:* the protein shell that encloses the viral genome)

conjug- = together (*conjugation:* in bacteria, the transfer of DNA between two cells that are temporarily joined)

lyto- = loosen (*lytic cycle:* a type of viral replication cycle resulting in the release of new phages by death or lysis of the host cell)

-oid = like, form (*nucleoid:* a dense region of DNA in a prokaryotic cell)

-phage = to eat (*bacteriophages:* viruses that infect bacteria)

pro- = before (*provirus:* viral DNA that inserts into a host genome)

retro- = backward (*retrovirus:* an RNA virus that reproduces by transcribing its RNA into DNA and then inserting the DNA into a cellular chromosome)

trans- = across (*transformation:* a phenomenon in which external DNA is assimilated by a cell)

virul- = poisonous (*virulent virus:* a virus that reproduces only by a lytic cycle)

CHAPTER 19

Eukaryotic Genomes: Organization, Regulation, and Evolution

Teaching Objectives

The Structure of Eukaryotic Chromatin

1. Compare the structure and organization of prokaryotic and eukaryotic genomes.
2. Describe the current model for progressive levels of DNA packing in eukaryotes.
3. Explain how histones influence folding in eukaryotic DNA.
4. Distinguish between heterochromatin and euchromatin.

The Control of Gene Expression

5. Explain the relationship between differentiation and differential gene expression.
6. Describe at what level gene expression is generally controlled.
7. Explain how DNA methylation and histone acetylation affect chromatin structure and the regulation of transcription.
8. Define *epigenetic inheritance*.
9. Describe the processing of pre-mRNA in eukaryotes.
10. Define *control elements* and explain how they influence transcription.
11. Distinguish between general and specific transcription factors.
12. Explain the role that promoters, enhancers, activators, and repressors may play in transcriptional control.
13. Explain how eukaryotic genes can be coordinately expressed and give some examples of coordinate gene expression in eukaryotes.
14. Describe the process and significance of alternative RNA splicing.
15. Describe factors that influence the life span of mRNA in the cytoplasm. Compare the longevity of mRNA in prokaryotes and in eukaryotes.
16. Explain how gene expression may be controlled at the translational and post-translational level.

The Molecular Biology of Cancer

17. Distinguish between proto-oncogenes and oncogenes. Describe three genetic changes that can convert proto-oncogenes into oncogenes.

18. Explain how mutations in tumor-suppressor genes can contribute to cancer.

19. Explain how excessive cell division can result from mutations in the *ras* proto-oncogenes.

20. Explain why a mutation knocking out the *p53* gene can lead to excessive cell growth and cancer. Describe three ways that *p53* prevents a cell from passing on mutations caused by DNA damage.

21. Describe the set of genetic factors typically associated with the development of cancer.

22. Explain how viruses can cause cancer. Describe several examples.

23. Explain how inherited cancer alleles can lead to a predisposition to certain cancers.

Genome Organization at the DNA Level

24. Describe the structure and functions of the portions of eukaryotic DNA that do not encode protein or RNA.

25. Distinguish between transposons and retrotransposons.

26. Describe the structure and location of *Alu* elements in primate genomes.

27. Describe the structure and possible function of simple sequence DNA.

28. Using the genes for rRNA as an example, explain how multigene families of identical genes can be advantageous for a cell.

29. Using α-globin and β-globin genes as examples, describe how multigene families of nonidentical genes may have evolved.

30. Define *pseudogenes.* Explain how such genes may have evolved.

31. Describe the hypothesis for the evolution of α-lactalbumin from an ancestral lysozyme gene.

32. Explain how exon shuffling could lead to the formation of new proteins with novel functions.

33. Describe how transposition of an *Alu* element may allow the formation of new genetic combinations while retaining gene function.

Student Misconceptions

1. Students may have difficulty visualizing the different levels of DNA packing in eukaryotic cells. Use visual aids—models or a series of images with 3D representations of DNA—to assist students in understanding how the different levels of packing relate to one another.

2. Students may find it hard to grasp the idea of epigenetic inheritance. They may not understand how modifications to the chromosome that do not alter the sequence of bases can still be passed on to subsequent generations of offspring. Explaining some of the fascinating examples of epigenetic inheritance—including the effects of imprinting in human development—may motivate students to gain a clearer understanding of this concept.

3. Students may find the large number of control points regulating eukaryotic gene expression bewildering. It is important to remind them of the significance of these mechanisms in allowing exquisite control of gene expression during development and in changing environments.

4. The significance of the large number of transposable elements in eukaryotic genomes and the contribution of these elements to the evolution of eukaryotic genomes are difficult concepts for students to master.

Chapter Guide to Teaching Resources

Overview: How eukaryotic genomes work and evolve

Concept 19.1 Chromatin structure is based on successive levels of DNA packing

Transparency
Figure 19.2   Levels of chromatin packing

Student Media Resource
Activity: DNA packing

Concept 19.2 Gene expression can be regulated at any stage, but the key step is transcription

Transparencies
Figure 19.3   Stages in gene expression that can be regulated in eukaryotic cells
Figure 19.4   A simple model of histone tails and the effect of histone acetylation
Figure 19.5   A eukaryotic gene and its transcript
Figure 19.6   A model for the action of enhancers and transcription activators
Figure 19.7   Cell type–specific transcription
Figure 19.8   Alternative RNA splicing
Figure 19.9   Regulation of gene expression by microRNAs (miRNAs)
Figure 19.10   Degradaton of a protein by a proteasome

Student Media Resources
Activity: Overview: Control of gene expression
Activity: Control of transcription
Investigation: How do you design a gene expression system?
Activity: Post-transcriptional control mechanisms
Activity: Review: Control of gene expression

Concept 19.3 Cancer results from genetic changes that affect cell cycle control

Transparencies
Figure 19.11   Genetic changes that can turn proto-oncogenes into oncogenes
Figure 19.12   Signaling pathways that regulate cell division
Figure 19.13   A multistep model for the development of colorectal cancer

Student Media Resource

Activity: Causes of cancer

Concept 19.4 Eukaryotic genomes can have many noncoding DNA sequences in addition to genes

Transparencies

Figure 19.14   Types of DNA sequences in the human genome

Figure 19.16   Movement of eukaryotic transposable elements

Figure 19.17   Gene families

Concept 19.5 Duplications, rearrangements, and mutations of DNA contribute to genome evolution

Transparencies

Figure 19.18   Gene duplication due to unequal crossing over

Figure 19.19   Evolution of the human α-globin and β-globin gene families

Table 19.1   Percentage of similarity in amino acid sequence between human globin proteins

Figure 19.20   Evolution of a new gene by exon shuffling

For additional resources such as digital images and lecture outlines, go to the Campbell Media Manager or the Instructor Resources section of **www.campbellbiology.com.**

Key Terms

activator

alternative RNA
  splicing

cell differentiation

chromatin

control element

differential gene
  expression

enhancer

epigenetic inheritance

euchromatin

genomic imprinting

heterochromatin

histone

histone acetylation

microRNA (miRNA)

multigene family

nucleosome

oncogene

p53 gene

proteasome

proto-oncogene

pseudogene

ras gene

repetitive DNA

repressor

retrotransposon

RNA interference RNA
  (RNAi)

small interfering RNA
  (siRNA)

transcription factor

transposon

tumor-suppressor gene

Word Roots

eu- = true (*euchromatin:* the more open, unraveled form of eukaryotic chromatin)

hetero- = different (*heterochromatin:* nontranscribed eukaryotic chromatin that is so highly compacted that it is visible with a light microscope during interphase)

nucleo- = the nucleus; **-soma** = body (*nucleosome:* the basic beadlike unit of DNA packaging in eukaryotes)

proto- = first, original; **onco-** = tumor (*proto-oncogene:* a normal cellular gene corresponding to an oncogene)

pseudo- = false (*pseudogenes:* DNA segments that are very similar to real genes but do not yield functional products)

retro- = backward (*retrotransposons:* transposable elements that move within a genome by means of an RNA intermediate, a transcript of the retrotransposon DNA)

CHAPTER 20

DNA Technology and Genomics

Teaching Objectives

DNA Cloning

1. Explain how advances in recombinant DNA technology have helped scientists study the eukaryotic genome.
2. Describe the natural function of restriction enzymes and explain how they are used in recombinant DNA technology.
3. Explain how the creation of sticky ends by restriction enzymes is useful in producing a recombinant DNA molecule.
4. Outline the procedures for cloning a eukaryotic gene in a bacterial plasmid.
5. Describe techniques that allow identification of recombinant cells that have taken up a gene of interest.
6. Define and distinguish between genomic libraries using plasmids, phages, and cDNA.
7. Describe the role of an expression vector.
8. Describe two advantages of using yeast cells instead of bacteria as hosts for cloning or expressing eukaryotic genes.
9. Describe two techniques to introduce recombinant DNA into eukaryotic cells.
10. Describe the polymerase chain reaction (PCR) and explain the advantages and limitations of this procedure.
11. Explain how gel electrophoresis is used to analyze nucleic acids and to distinguish between two alleles of a gene.
12. Describe the process of nucleic acid hybridization.
13. Describe the Southern blotting procedure and explain how it can be used to detect and analyze instances of restriction fragment length polymorphism (RFLP).
14. Explain how RFLP analysis facilitated the process of genomic mapping.

DNA Analysis and Genomics

15. Explain the goals of the Human Genome Project.
16. Explain how linkage mapping, physical mapping, and DNA sequencing each contributed to the genome mapping project.
17. Describe the alternate approach to whole-genome sequencing pursued by J. Craig Venter and the Celera Genomics company.
18. Explain how researchers recognize protein-coding genes within DNA sequences.
19. Describe the surprising results of the Human Genome Project.

20. Explain how the vertebrate genome, including that of humans, generates greater diversity than the genomes of invertebrate organisms.

21. Explain how *in vitro* mutagenesis and RNA interference help researchers to discover the functions of some genes.

22. Explain the purposes of gene expression studies. Describe the use of DNA microarray assays and explain how they facilitate such studies.

23. Define and compare the fields of *proteomics* and *genomics*.

24. Explain the significance of single nucleotide polymorphisms in the study of the human evolution.

Practical Applications of DNA Technology

25. Describe how DNA technology can have medical applications in such areas as the diagnosis of genetic disease, the development of gene therapy, vaccine production, and the development of pharmaceutical products.

26. Explain how DNA technology is used in the forensic sciences.

27. Describe how gene manipulation has practical applications for environmental and agricultural work.

28. Describe how plant genes can be manipulated using the Ti plasmid carried by *Agrobacterium* as a vector.

29. Explain how DNA technology can be used to improve the nutritional value of crops and to develop plants that can produce pharmaceutical products.

30. Discuss the safety and ethical questions related to recombinant DNA studies and the biotechnology industry.

Student Misconceptions

1. Students may have difficulty understanding the significance of the genes for antibiotic resistance and sugar metabolism in the bacterial plasmid used in gene cloning. Take students through the procedure step-by-step, pointing out the phenotypic differences between bacteria with and without the plasmid and between bacteria with recombinant and nonrecombinant plasmids.

2. The Human Genome Project has changed our understanding of the evolutionary relationships between living organisms and has provided surprising insights into the nature of the human genome. First-year students may think of biology as a body of well-established facts to be learned, not recognizing the extent to which our knowledge is incomplete. Teaching students about the recent findings that have emerged from the Human Genome Project provides an excellent opportunity to point out how our understanding of life has changed and continues to change.

3. The ongoing debate over the risks and benefits of GM organisms can be used to engage and educate students. Students can explore websites and read primary articles to obtain information about public views and scientific evidence on this controversial topic.

Chapter Guide to Teaching Resources

Overview: Understanding and manipulating genomes

Concept 20.1 DNA cloning permits production of multiple copies of a specific gene or other DNA segment

Transparencies

Figure 20.2   Overview of gene cloning with a bacterial plasmid, showing various uses of cloned genes

Figure 20.3   Using a restriction enzyme and DNA ligase to make recombinant DNA

Figure 20.4   Cloning a human gene in a bacterial plasmid (layer 1)

Figure 20.4   Cloning a human gene in a bacterial plasmid (layer 2)

Figure 20.4   Cloning a human gene in a bacterial plasmid (layer 3)

Figure 20.5   Nucleic acid probe hybridization

Figure 20.6   Genomic libraries

Figure 20.7   The polymerase chain reaction (PCR)

Student Media Resources

Activity: Applications of DNA technology

Activity: Restriction enzymes

Activity: Cloning a gene in bacteria

Investigation: How can antibiotic-resistant plasmids transform *E. coli*?

Concept 20.2 Restriction fragment analysis detects DNA differences that affect restriction sites

Transparencies

Figure 20.8   Gel electrophoresis

Figure 20.9   Using restriction fragment analysis to distinguish the normal and sickle-cell alleles of the β-globin gene

Student Media Resources

Activity: Gel electrophoresis of DNA

Activity: Analyzing DNA fragments using gel electrophoresis

Investigation: How can gel electrophoresis be used to analyze DNA?

Concept 20.3 Entire genomes can be mapped at the DNA level

Transparencies

Figure 20.10   Southern blotting of DNA fragments

Figure 20.11   Three-stage approach to mapping an entire genome

Figure 20.12   Dideoxy chain-termination method for sequencing DNA

Figure 20.13   Whole-genome shotgun approach to sequencing

Student Media Resource

Activity: The Human Genome Project: Genes on human chromosome 17

Concept 20.4 Genome sequences provide clues to important biological questions

Transparencies

Table 20.1   Genome sizes and estimated numbers of genes

Figure 20.14   DNA microarray assay of gene expression levels

Concept 20.5 The practical applications of DNA technology affect our lives in many ways

Transparencies

Figure 20.15   RFLPs as markers for disease-causing alleles

Figure 20.16   Gene therapy using a retroviral vector

Figure 20.17   DNA fingerprints from a murder case

Figure 20.19   Using the Ti plasmid to produce transgenic plants

Instructor and Student Media Resources

Activity: DNA fingerprinting

Activity: Making decisions about DNA technology: Golden rice

Video: Biotechnology lab

For additional resources such as digital images and lecture outlines, go to the Campbell Media Manager or the Instructor Resources section of **www.campbellbiology.com.**

Key Terms

bacterial artificial
  chromosome (BAC)
biotechnology
cDNA library
clone
cloning vector
complementary DNA
  (cDNA)
denaturation
DNA fingerprint
DNA ligase
DNA microarray assay
electroporation
expression vector
gel electrophoresis
gene cloning
gene therapy

genetic engineering
genetically modified
  (GM) organism
genomic library
genomics
Human Genome
  Project
in vitro mutagenesis
linkage map
nucleic acid
  hybridization
nucleic acid probe
physical map
polymerase chain
  reaction (PCR)
proteomics
recombinant DNA

restriction enzyme
restriction fragment
restriction fragment
  length polymorphism
  (RFLP)
restriction site
RNA interference
  (RNAi)
single nucleotide
  polymorphism (SNP)
Southern blotting
sticky end
Ti plasmid
transgenic
yeast artificial
  chromosome (YAC)

Word Roots

liga- = bound, tied (*DNA ligase:* a linking enzyme essential for DNA replication)

electro- = electricity (*electroporation:* a technique to introduce recombinant DNA into cells by applying a brief electrical pulse to a solution containing cells)

muta- = change; **-genesis** = origin, birth (*in vitro mutagenesis:* a technique to discover the function of a gene by introducing specific changes into the sequence of a cloned gene, reinserting the mutated gene into a cell, and studying the phenotype of the mutant)

poly- = many; **morph-** = form (*single nucleotide polymorphism:* one base-pair variation in the genome sequence)

CHAPTER 21

The Genetic Basis of Development

Teaching Objectives

From Single Cell to Multicellular Organism

1. List the animals used as models for developmental biology research and provide a rationale for their choice.
2. Distinguish between the patterns of morphogenesis in plants and in animals.

Differential Gene Expression

3. Describe how genomic equivalence was determined for plants and animals.
4. Describe what kinds of changes occur to the genome during differentiation.
5. Describe the general process by which the ewe Dolly and the first mice were cloned.
6. Describe the characteristics of stem cells. Explain their significance to medicine.
7. Distinguish between determination and differentiation. Explain why determination precedes differentiation.
8. Describe the molecular basis of determination.
9. Describe the two sources of information that instruct a cell to express genes at the appropriate time.

Genetic and Cellular Mechanisms of Pattern Formation

10. Describe how *Drosophila* was used to investigate the basic aspects of pattern formation (axis formation and segmentation).
11. Explain how maternal genes affect polarity and development in *Drosophila* embryos.
12. Describe how gradients of morphogens may specify the axes of developing *Drosophila* embryos.
13. Describe how homeotic genes define the anatomical identity of the segments of a developing organism.
14. Describe how the study of nematodes contributed to an understanding of the role of induction in development.
15. Describe how apoptosis functions in normal and abnormal development.
16. Describe how the study of tomatoes has contributed to the understanding of flower development.
17. Describe how the study of *Arabidopsis* has contributed to the understanding of organ identity in plants.
18. Provide evidence of the conservation of homeobox patterns.

Student Misconceptions

1. Students must recognize the important distinction between determination and differentiation. A clear understanding of this distinction is key to an appreciation of how development proceeds, with progressive regulation of gene expression leading to the appearance of tissue-specific proteins.

2. Many students do not appreciate the fundamental differences in organization and development between plants and animals. Plants are modular in construction, with highly variable form and a program of development that depends strongly on interaction with the environment. The fundamental unit of development in plants is a permanently embryonic meristem. Most animals are unitary organisms: highly determinant in form with clearly identifiable life stages, including a restricted period of embryonic development.

3. Students may find it difficult to understand how maternal effect genes affect the development of offspring. This concept can be clarified by presenting examples of some of the best-understood maternal effect genes.

Chapter Guide to Teaching Resources

Overview: From single cell to multicellular organism

Concept 21.1 Embryonic development involves cell division, cell differentiation, and morphogenesis

Transparency
Figure 21.4   Some key stages of development in animals and plants

Instructor and Student Media Resources
Video: *C. elegans* crawling
Video: *C. elegans* embryo development (time-lapse)

Concept 21.2 Different cell types result from differential gene expression in cells with the same DNA

Transparencies
Figure 21.5   Can a differentiated plant cell develop into a whole plant?
Figure 21.6   Can the nucleus from a differentiated animal cell direct development of an organism?
Figure 21.7   Reproductive cloning of a mammal by nuclear transplantation
Figure 21.9   Working with stem cells
Figure 21.10   Determination and differentiation of muscle cells (layer 1)
Figure 21.10   Determination and differentiation of muscle cells (layer 2)
Figure 21.10   Determination and differentiation of muscle cells (layer 3)
Figure 21.11   Sources of developmental information for the early embryo

Student Media Resource

Activity: Signal transduction pathways

Concept 21.3 Pattern formation in animals and plants results from similar genetic and cellular mechanisms

Transparencies

Figure 21.12   Key developmental events in the life cycle of *Drosophila*

Figure 21.14   The effect of the *bicoid* gene, a maternal effect (egg-polarity) gene in *Drosophila*

Figure 21.15   Cell lineage in *C. elegans*

Figure 21.16   Cell signaling and induction during development of the nematode

Figure 21.18   Molecular basis of apoptosis in *C. elegans*

Figure 21.20   Flower development

Figure 21.21   Which cell layers in the floral meristem determine the number of floral organs?

Student Media Resources

Activity: Role of *bicoid* gene in *Drosophila* development

Investigation: How do *bicoid* mutations alter development?

Concept 21.4 Comparative studies help explain how the evolution of development leads to morphological diversity

Transparencies

Figure 21.23   Conservation of homeotic genes in a fruit fly and a mouse

Figure 21.24   Effect of differences in *Hox* gene expression during development in crustaceans and insects

For additional resources such as digital images and lecture outlines, go to the Campbell Media Manager or the Instructor Resources section of **www.campbellbiology.com.**

Key Terms

apical meristem	determination	morphogenesis
apoptosis	egg-polarity gene	organ identity gene
cell differentiation	embryonic lethal	pattern formation
cell lineage	homeobox	pluripotent
chimera	homeotic gene	positional information
clone	induction	segmentation gene
cloning	maternal effect gene	stem cell
cytoplasmic	model organism	totipotent
determinants	morphogen	

Word Roots

apic- = tip (*apical meristem:* embryonic plant tissue in the tips of roots and in the buds of shoots that supplies cells for the plant to grow in length)

morph- = form; **-gen** = produce (*morphogen:* a substance that provides positional information in the form of a concentration gradient along an embryonic axis)

toti- = all; **-potent** = powerful (*totipotent:* the ability of a cell to form all parts of the mature organism)

CHAPTER 22

Descent with Modification: A Darwinian View of Life

Teaching Objectives

The Historical Context for Evolutionary Theory

1. Explain the mechanism for evolutionary change proposed by Charles Darwin in *On the Origin of Species*.
2. Define *evolution* and *adaptation*.
3. Compare and contrast Aristotle's *scala naturae* to Carolus Linnaeus' classification scheme.
4. Describe the theories of catastrophism, gradualism, and uniformitarianism.
5. Explain the mechanism for evolutionary change proposed by Jean-Baptiste de Lamarck. Explain why modern biology has rejected Lamarck's theories.

The Darwinian Revolution

6. Describe how Darwin's observations on the voyage of the HMS *Beagle* led him to formulate and support his theory of evolution.
7. Explain how the principle of gradualism and Charles Lyell's theory of uniformitarianism influenced Darwin's ideas about evolution.
8. Explain what Darwin meant by "descent with modification."
9. Explain what evidence convinced Darwin that species change over time.
10. Explain how Linnaeus' classification scheme fit Darwin's theory of evolution by natural selection.
11. Describe the three inferences Darwin made from his observations that led him to propose natural selection as a mechanism for evolutionary change.
12. Explain how an essay by the Rev. Thomas Malthus influenced Charles Darwin.
13. Distinguish between artificial selection and natural selection.
14. Explain why an individual organism cannot evolve.
15. Describe the experiments that supported Reznick and Endler's hypothesis that differences in life-history traits between guppy populations are due to selective pressure based on predation.
16. Explain how the existence of homologous and vestigial structures can be explained by Darwin's theory of natural selection.
17. Explain how evidence from biogeography supports the theory of evolution by natural selection.

18. Explain the problem with the statement that Darwinism is "just a theory." Distinguish between the scientific and colloquial use of the word *theory.*

Student Misconceptions

1. Many first-year students misunderstand the vitally important theory of evolution by natural selection. One problem is that many of the biological terms associated with evolution have familiar, everyday meanings that are different from their strict biological definitions. The following terms may be problematic:

   - *Fitness.* When students think of fitness, they usually think of an organism's general health, vigor, strength, or intelligence. As a result, they may find it hard to appreciate that any trait that increases an organism's relative reproductive success increases its fitness.

   - *Adaptation.* In everyday use, adaptation refers to an individual changing over its lifetime in response to the environment. Students may confuse the colloquial and scientific meanings of this term and arrive at the mistaken notion that changes ("adaptations") over individual lifetimes accumulate to bring about evolutionary change in populations.

   - *Theory.* Students may tell you, "Evolution is only a theory, not a fact." In common usage, the term *theory* means a tentative explanation. In a scientific context, a theory is a useful, comprehensive, and well-supported explanation for a wide range of observations.

   - *Evolution.* In its strict biological meaning, evolution is defined as a change in allele frequencies in a population over time. By this definition, no one can challenge the "fact" of evolution. Of course, evolution is also used in its broader sense of macroevolutionary change. Students may confuse these two meanings.

2. Many students think that evolution results from a purposeful striving for progress and complexity that results in the appearance of more advanced, "higher" life forms. Adaptive processes are misunderstood as purposive and goal-driven.

3. Many students do not appreciate that two separate and distinct processes are necessary for new traits to arise and flourish in populations. New traits appear because of random mutation and sexual recombination. A novel trait that increases the fitness of individuals in their environment will persist in the population and increase in frequency over time. Many students think that a single process leads to the appearance and survival of new adaptive traits. These students think of this process in Lamarckian rather than Darwinian terms. If carefully questioned, they will express Lamarckian ideas of need, use and disuse, and inheritance of acquired characteristics. Such students think that individual organisms develop traits that allow them to survive and reproduce in their environment, change over their lifetimes in response to environmental pressure, and pass on acquired changes to their offspring.

4. Although students will state that mutations are rare and random events, careful questioning will show that some students think of mutations as adaptive

responses to environmental conditions. In discussion, such students will provide explanations that suggest that mutations are in some sense intentional: that an organism mutates in order to adapt to its environment.

5. Few students are able to generalize their understanding of homology beyond familiar examples such as vertebrate forelimbs. To test this, ask students to give plant examples of homologous structures. For a student who understands the concept of homology, this is very easy. Students who have learned the text examples, but not the concept, will be unable to come up with suitable answers.

6. Heritable variation in a population is an essential condition for evolutionary change. Many students do not fully understand this and do not realize that variation is important to evolution. They discount variation within populations and think of populations as consisting of equivalent or identical individuals.

7. Many students do not appreciate that natural selection acts on populations consisting of variant individuals. They think of natural selection as a process that acts on and gradually changes species as a whole. Such students do not realize that evolutionary change comes about as the proportion of individuals in the population displaying a particular trait increases from generation to generation. Instead, they think that the trait changes gradually in all members of the population. For example, if directional selection favors increased antibiotic resistance in a population of bacteria, these students will think that bacteria become more resistant, rather than recognizing that more bacteria become resistant.

8. How can instructors address the many misconceptions that students may have about evolution by natural selection?

    ■ Historical review can be very fruitful. Many of your students' mistaken notions match early evolutionary theories that are now discredited. Provide examples of Lamarckian explanations that may seem superficially reasonable to your students and discuss why these explanations are in error.

    ■ Provide opportunities for your students to discuss their ideas about evolution. Foster these discussions by asking challenging questions that require students to reason and to apply evolutionary principles. As students elaborate and explain their ideas, challenge and correct incorrect views.

    ■ Be careful in your use of language. Avoid figurative language that inappropriately attributes agency to individuals or the environment, recognizing that these explanations mislead students.

    ■ Require your students to read and discuss Jonathan Weiner's *The Beak of the Finch*. Students who read this excellent book will gain a much deeper understanding of evolution by natural selection.

Further Reading

Lord, T., and S. Marino. 1993. How university students view the theory of evolution. *Journal of College Science Teaching, 22(6)*, 353–357.

Moore, R. 1997. The persuasive Mr. Darwin. *Bioscience, 47(2)*, 107–115.

Weiner, J. 1994. *The Beak of the Finch: A Story of Evolution in Our Time.* New York: Random House.

Chapter Guide to Teaching Resources

Overview: Darwin introduces a revolutionary theory

Concept 22.1 The Darwinian revolution challenged traditional views of a young Earth inhabited by unchanging species

Transparency
Figure 22.2   The historical context of Darwin's life and ideas

Instructor and Student Media Resource
Video: Grand Canyon

Concept 22.2 In *The Origin of Species*, Darwin proposed that species change through natural selection

Transparencies
Figure 22.5   The voyage of HMS *Beagle*
Figure 22.7   Descent with modification
Figure 22.10   Artificial selection

Instructor and Student Media Resources
Activity: Darwin and the Galápagos Islands
Video: Galápagos Islands overview
Video: Galápagos marine iguana
Video: Galápagos sea lion
Video: Galápagos tortoise
Video: Soaring hawk
Activity: The voyage of the *Beagle:* Darwin's trip around the world
Biology Labs On-Line: EvolutionLab
Video: Snake ritual wrestling
Video: Albatross courtship ritual
Video: Blue-footed boobies' courtship ritual
Video: Sea horses

Concept 22.3 Darwin's theory explains a wide range of observations

Transparencies
Figure 22.12   Can predation pressure select for size and age at maturity in guppies?
Figure 22.13   Evolution of drug resistance in HIV
Figure 22.14   Mammalian forelimbs: homologous structures

Figure 22.15   Anatomical similarities in vertebrate embryos
Figure 22.16   Comparison of a protein found in diverse vertebrates
Figure 22.17   Different geographic regions, different mammalian "brands"
Figure 22.18   A transitional fossil linking past and present

Student Media Resources

Investigation: How do environmental changes affect a population?

Investigation: What are the patterns of antibiotic resistance?

Activity: Reconstructing forelimbs

For additional resources such as digital images and lecture outlines, go to the Campbell Media Manager or the Instructor Resources section of **www.campbellbiology.com.**

Key Terms

artificial selection
biogeography
catastrophism
descent with
  modification
endemic

evolution
evolutionary adaptation
fossil
gradualism
homologous structures
homology

natural selection
paleontology
sedimentary rock
taxonomy
uniformitarianism
vestigial organ

Word Roots

bio- = life; **geo-** the Earth (*biogeography:* the study of the past and present distribution of species)

end- = within (*endemic:* a type of species that is found only in one region and nowhere else in the world.)

homo- = like, resembling (*homology:* similarity in characteristics resulting from a shared ancestry)

paleo- = ancient (*paleontology:* the scientific study of fossils)

taxo- = arrange (*taxonomy:* the branch of biology concerned with naming and classifying the diverse forms of life)

vestigi- = trace (*vestigial organs:* structures of marginal, if any, importance to an organism; they are historical remnants of structures that had important functions in ancestors)

CHAPTER 23

The Evolution of Populations

Teaching Objectives

Population Genetics

1. Explain the statement "It is the population, not the individual, that evolves."
2. Explain how Mendel's particulate hypothesis of inheritance provided much-needed support for Darwin's theory of evolution by natural selection.
3. Distinguish between discrete and quantitative traits. Explain how Mendel's laws of inheritance apply to quantitative traits.
4. Explain what is meant by "the modern synthesis."
5. Define the terms *population, species,* and *gene pool.*
6. Explain why meiosis and random fertilization alone will not alter the frequency of alleles or genotypes in a population.
7. List the five conditions that must be met for a population to remain in Hardy-Weinberg equilibrium.
8. Write the Hardy-Weinberg equation. Use the equation to calculate allele frequencies when the frequency of homozygous recessive individuals in a population is 25%.

Mutation and Sexual Recombination

9. Explain why the majority of point mutations are harmless.
10. Explain why mutation has little quantitative effect on allele frequencies in a large population.
11. Describe the significance of transposons in the generation of genetic variability.
12. Explain how sexual recombination generates genetic variability.

Natural Selection, Genetic Drift, and Gene Flow

13. Explain the following statement: "Only natural selection leads to the adaptation of organisms to their environment."
14. Explain the role of population size in genetic drift.
15. Distinguish between the bottleneck effect and the founder effect.
16. Describe how gene flow can act to reduce genetic differences between adjacent populations.

Genetic Variation, the Substrate for Natural Selection

17. Explain how quantitative and discrete characters contribute to variation within a population.

18. Distinguish between average heterozygosity and nucleotide variability. Explain why average heterozygosity tends to be greater than nucleotide variability.

19. Define a *cline.*

20. Define *relative fitness.*

    a. Explain why relative fitness is zero for a healthy, long-lived, sterile organism.

    b. Explain why relative fitness could be high for a short-lived organism.

21. Distinguish among directional, disruptive, and stabilizing selection. Give an example of each mode of selection.

22. Explain how diploidy can protect a rare recessive allele from elimination by natural selection.

23. Describe how heterozygote advantage and frequency-dependent selection promote balanced polymorphism.

24. Define *neutral variations.* Explain why natural selection does not act on these alleles.

25. Distinguish between intrasexual selection and intersexual selection.

26. Explain how female preferences for showy male traits may benefit the female.

27. Describe the disadvantages of sexual reproduction.

28. Explain how the genetic variation promoted by sex may be advantageous to individuals on a generational time scale.

29. List four reasons why natural selection cannot produce perfect organisms.

Student Misconceptions

1. Students often misunderstand the significance of individuals and individual variation to the theory of evolution by natural selection.

   a. In everyday language, *adaptation* refers to changes in an individual over its lifetime. Students may think that such changes are or lead to evolutionary change.

   b. Students may mistakenly think that evolutionary change comes about as traits gradually change in all members of a population, rather than realizing that individuals with favorable heritable traits come to make up an increasing proportion of the population.

2. Many students find it hard to understand the Hardy-Weinberg theorem and do not know *how* and *when* to use the Hardy-Weinberg equations. They do not realize that the Hardy-Weinberg theorem clarifies the factors that alter allele frequency, and that it does not imply that allele frequencies are static. These students do not appreciate that the Hardy-Weinberg equations are used with respect to a particular gene.

3. Students can be confused about the role of chance in evolution and natural selection. New alleles arise by chance mutations, new combinations of alleles arise by the shuffling of genes in sexual recombination, and chance events may alter allele frequencies in small populations. Certainly chance is important in

evolutionary change. However, students may think that evolution itself proceeds by an accumulation of changes occurring by chance. Such students completely misunderstand the role of natural selection as the mechanism of adaptive evolution. Genetic variation arises by chance. However, the action of natural selection to favor variants that survive and reproduce with relatively high success in their environment is not based on chance.

4. Students may think that most selection is directional and not realize that stabilizing selection is the norm. Organisms are generally well adapted to their environments. Selection primarily acts to remove deleterious mutations that alter the phenotype in ways that reduce fitness.

5. Students may have great difficulty in understanding the subtle arguments about the costs and benefits of sex. Ensure that your students realize that the issue is not whether sex promotes genetic variation—of course it does—but rather what short-term advantage this variation confers on individuals.

Further Reading

Anderson, D. L., K. M. Fisher, and G. J. Norman. 2002. Development and evaluation of the conceptual inventory of natural selection. *Journal of Research in Science Teaching, 39(10)*, 952–978.

Bishop, B. A., and C. W. Anderson. 1990. Student conceptions of natural selection and its role in evolution. *Journal of Research in Science Teaching, 27(5)*, 415–427.

Chapter Guide to Teaching Resources

Overview: The smallest unit of evolution

Concept 23.1 Population genetics provides a foundation for studying evolution

Transparencies

Figure 23.3   One species, two populations

Figure 23.4   Mendelian inheritance preserves genetic variation from one generation to the next

Figure 23.5   The Hardy-Weinberg theorem

Student Media Resources

Investigation: How can frequency of alleles be calculated?

Biology Labs On-Line: PopulationGeneticsLab

Activity: Causes of microevolution

Concept 23.2 Mutation and sexual recombination produce the variation that makes evolution possible

Concept 23.3 Natural selection, genetic drift, and gene flow can alter a population's genetic composition

Transparencies

Figure 23.7   Genetic drift

Figure 23.8   The bottleneck effect

Student Media Resources

Biology Labs On-Line: EvolutionLab

Activity: Genetic variation from sexual recombination

Concept 23.4 Natural selection is the primary mechanism of adaptive evolution

Transparencies

Figure 23.11   Does geographic variation in yarrow plants have a genetic component?

Figure 23.12   Modes of selection

Figure 23.13   Mapping malaria and the sickle-cell allele

Figure 23.14   Using a virtual population to study the effects of selection

Figure 23.16   The "reproductive handicap" of sex

For additional resources such as digital images and lecture outlines, go to the Campbell Media Manager or the Instructor Resources section of **www.campbellbiology.com.**

Key Terms

average heterozygosity	gene flow	modern synthesis
balanced polymorphism	gene pool	mutation
balancing selection	genetic drift	neutral variation
bottleneck effect	genetic polymorphism	phenotypic polymorphism
cline	geographic variation	population
directional selection	Hardy-Weinberg equilibrium	population genetics
disruptive selection	Hardy-Weinberg theorem	pseudogene
duplication	heterozygote advantage	relative fitness
fitness	intersexual selection	sexual dimorphism
founder effect	intrasexual selection	sexual selection
frequency-dependent selection	microevolution	stabilizing selection

Word Roots

inter- = between (*intersexual selection:* individuals of one sex are choosy in selecting their mates from individuals of the other sex; also called mate choice)

intra- = within (*intrasexual selection:* a direct competition among individuals of one sex for mates of the opposite sex)

micro- = small (*microevolution:* a change in the gene pool of a population over a succession of generations)

muta- = change (*mutation:* a change in the DNA of genes that ultimately creates genetic diversity)

poly- = many; **morph-** = form (*polymorphism:* the coexistence of two or more distinct forms of individuals in the same population)

CHAPTER 24

The Origin of Species

Teaching Objectives

What Is a Species?

1. Distinguish between anagenesis and cladogenesis.
2. Define Ernst Mayr's biological species concept.
3. Distinguish between prezygotic and postzygotic isolating mechanisms.
4. Describe five prezygotic isolating mechanisms and give an example of each.
5. Explain a possible cause for reduced hybrid viability.
6. Explain how hybrid breakdown maintains separate species even if fertilization occurs.
7. Describe some limitations of the biological species concept.
8. Define and distinguish among the following: ecological species concept, paleontological species concept, phylogenetic species concept, and morphological species concept.

Modes of Speciation

9. Distinguish between allopatric and sympatric speciation.
10. Explain the allopatric speciation model and describe the mechanisms that may lead to divergence of isolated gene pools.
11. Describe examples of adaptive radiation in the Galápagos and Hawaiian archipelagoes.
12. Explain how reproductive barriers evolve. Describe an example of the evolution of a prezygotic barrier and the evolution of a postzygotic barrier.
13. Define *sympatric speciation* and explain how polyploidy can cause reproductive isolation.
14. Distinguish between an autopolyploid and an allopolyploid species and describe examples of each.
15. Describe how cichlid fishes may have speciated in sympatry in Lake Victoria.

Adaptive Radiation

16. Define *adaptive radiation* and describe the circumstances under which adaptive radiation may occur.
17. Describe the two gene loci implicated in speciation in *Mimulus*.

From Speciation to Macroevolution

18. Explain in general terms how a complex structure can evolve by natural selection.

19. Define *exaptation* and illustrate this concept with an example.

20. Explain how slight genetic divergences may lead to major morphological differences between species.

21. Explain how the evolution of changes in temporal and spatial developmental dynamics can result in evolutionary novelties.

22. Define *evo-devo, heterochrony, allometric growth,* and *paedomorphosis.*

23. Explain why extracting a single evolutionary progression from a fossil record can be misleading.

24. Define and illustrate the concept of species selection.

25. Explain why evolutionary change is not goal-directed.

Student Misconceptions

1. Students may think that although many species are going extinct, no new species are forming. Speciation is viewed as a process from the distant past that can only be inferred from the fossil record and molecular data. Few students realize that there are many well-studied cases of recent or ongoing speciation events. Classroom discussion of these cases can be an excellent tool for engaging students and teaching them about speciation and its mechanisms. If possible, use examples of speciation involving species that are familiar and local.

2. Students may think that evolutionary change in a genetically isolated population results from a purposeful striving for adaptation to a new environment. Such students mistakenly think that evolutionary change results from a gradual increase in favorable traits in all members of a population, and fail to realize that individuals with heritable traits that are adaptive in the new environment come to make up an increasing proportion of the population. These students think that the evolution of reproductive isolating mechanisms after two isolated populations come into renewed contact results from the purposeful striving of individuals or the population to reduce hybridization. They do not realize that the evolution of these mechanisms results from increased representation in the population of descendents of individuals who had heritable traits that led them to mate assortatively with "their own kind."

3. Students find it difficult to understand that complex features can evolve by natural selection. It is important to emphasize that complex biochemical pathways, morphological features, physiological traits, or behaviors can evolve by natural selection, but must evolve step by step, with each step conferring a fitness benefit.

Further Reading

Boxton, J. 1995. Observed instances of speciation. *The Talk.Origins Archive,* http://www.talkorigins.org/faqs/faq-speciation.html.

Sharp, J. 2004. Something's fishy in Paxton Lake: A case on speciation in sticklebacks. *Journal of College Science Teaching, 32(1),* 42–47.

Chapter Guide to Teaching Resources

Overview: That "mystery of mysteries"

Transparency
Figure 24.2   Two patterns of evolutionary change

Concept 24.1 The biological species concept emphasizes reproductive isolation

Transparency
Figure 24.4   Reproductive barriers

Instructor and Student Media Resources
Activity: Overview of macroevolution
Video: Galápagos
Video: Albatross courtship ritual
Video: Blue-footed boobies courtship ritual
Video: Giraffe courtship ritual

Concept 24.2 Speciation can take place with or without geographic separation

Transparencies
Figure 24.5   Two main modes of speciation
Figure 24.7   Can adaptive divergence of allopatric fruit fly populations lead to reproductive isolation?
Figure 24.8   Sympatric speciation by autopolyploidy in plants
Figure 24.9   One mechanism for allopolyploid speciation in plants
Figure 24.12   Adaptive radiation
Figure 24.13   Two models for the tempo of speciation

Student Media Resource
Investigation: How do new species arise by genetic isolation?

Concept 24.3 Macroevolutionary changes can accumulate through many speciation events

Transparencies
Figure 24.14   A range of eye complexity among molluscs
Figure 24.15   Allometric growth

Figure 24.16   Heterochrony and the evolution of salamander feet in closely related species

Figure 24.18   *Hox* genes and the evolution of tetrapod limbs

Figure 24.19   *Hox* mutations and the origin of vertebrates

Figure 24.20   The branched evolution of horses

Student Media Resource

Activity: Allometric growth

For additional resources such as digital images and lecture outlines, go to the Campbell Media Manager or the Instructor Resources section of **www.campbellbiology.com.**

Key Terms

adaptive radiation	homeotic gene	polyploidy
allometric growth	macroevolution	postzygotic barrier
allopatric speciation	microevolution	prezygotic barrier
allopolyploid	morphological species	punctuated
autopolyploid	concept	equilibrium
biological species	paedomorphosis	reproductive isolation
concept	paleontological species	speciation
ecological species	concept	species
concept	phylogenetic species	species selection
heterochrony	concept	sympatric speciation

Word Roots

allo- = other; **-metron** = measure (*allometric growth:* the variation in the relative rates of growth of various parts of the body, which helps shape the organism)

ana- = up; **-genesis** = origin, birth (*anagenesis:* a pattern of evolutionary change involving the transformation of an entire population, sometimes to a state different enough from the ancestral population to justify renaming it as a separate species)

auto- = self; **poly-** = many (*autopolyploid:* a type of polyploid species resulting from one species doubling its chromosome number to become tetraploid)

clado- = branch (*cladogenesis:* a pattern of evolutionary change that produces biological diversity by budding one or more new species from a parent species that continues to exist)

hetero- = different (*heterochrony:* evolutionary changes in the timing or rate of development)

macro- = large (*macroevolution:* evolutionary change beginning with speciation, encompassing the origin of novel designs, evolutionary trends, adaptive radiation, and mass extinction)

paedo- = child (*paedomorphosis:* the retention in the adult organism of the juvenile features of its evolutionary ancestors)

post- = after (*postzygotic barrier:* any of several species-isolating mechanisms that prevent hybrids produced by two different species from developing into viable, fertile adults)

sym- = together; **-patri** = father (*sympatric speciation:* a mode of speciation occurring as a result of a radical change in the genome that produces a reproductively isolated subpopulation in the midst of its parent population)

CHAPTER 25

Phylogeny and Systematics

Teaching Objectives

Phylogenies are Based on Common Ancestries

1. Distinguish between phylogeny and systematics.

2. Describe the process of sedimentation and the formation of fossils. Explain which portions of organisms are most likely to fossilize.

3. Explain why it is crucial to distinguish between homology and analogy before selecting characters to use in the reconstruction of phylogeny.

4. Explain why bird and bat wings are homologous as vertebrate forelimbs but analogous as wings.

5. Define *molecular systematics*. Explain some of the problems that systematists may face in carrying out molecular comparisons of nucleic acids.

Phylogenetic Systematics: Connecting Classification with Evolutionary History

6. Explain the following characteristics of the Linnaean system of classification:

    a. binomial nomenclature

    b. hierarchical classification

7. List the major taxonomic categories from most to least inclusive.

8. Define a *clade*. Distinguish between a monophyletic clade and paraphyletic and polyphyletic groupings of species.

9. Distinguish between shared primitive characters and shared derived characters.

10. Explain how shared derived characters can be used to construct a phylogenetic diagram.

11. Explain how outgroup comparison can be used to distinguish between shared primitive characters and shared derived characters.

12. Define an *ingroup*.

13. Distinguish between a phylogram and an ultrameric tree.

14. Discuss how systematists use the principles of maximum parsimony and maximum likelihood in reconstructing phylogenies.

15. Explain why any phylogenetic diagram represents a hypothesis about evolutionary relationships among organisms.

16. Distinguish between orthologous and paralogous genes. Explain how gene duplication has led to families of paralogous genes.

17. Explain how molecular clocks are used to determine the approximate time of key evolutionary events. Explain how molecular clocks are calibrated in actual time.

18. Describe some of the limitations of molecular clocks.

19. Explain the neutral theory of evolutionary change.

20. Explain how scientists determined the approximate time when HIV-1 M first infected humans.

21. Describe the evidence that suggests there is a universal tree of life.

Student Misconceptions

1. Many students find it difficult to generalize their understanding of homology and analogy beyond the familiar textbook examples. A good test for this important distinction is to ask students to explain why bird and bat wings are homologous as vertebrate forelimbs and analogous as wings.

2. Students may have difficulty in understanding the relationship among taxonomy, classification, systematics, and phylogeny. Clarify for students that hierarchical *classification* is the ordered division of organisms into increasingly broad *taxonomic* categories based on their similarities and differences with respect to a set of characteristics. *Systematics* is an analytical approach to understanding the diversity and relationships of living and extinct organisms based on similarities and differences and using this understanding to reconstruct *phylogeny,* the evolutionary history of a group of organisms.

3. The term *primitive character* can lead students to think of such characters as inferior or defective. Emphasize that primitive characters are ancestral traits that were present in the common ancestor of a particular clade, and that the biological meaning of this term is very different from its everyday meaning.

Chapter Guide to Teaching Resources

Overview: Investigating the tree of life

Transparency

Figure 25.2   An unexpected family tree

Concept 25.1 Phylogenies are based on common ancestries inferred from fossil, morphological, and molecular evidence

Transparencies

Figure 25.3   Formation of sedimentary strata containing fossils

Figure 25.6   Aligning segments of DNA

Figure 25.7   A molecular homoplasy

Instructor and Student Media Resources
Activity: A scrolling geologic time scale
Video: Grand Canyon

Concept 25.2 Phylogenetic systematics connects classification with evolutionary history

Transparencies

Figure 25.8   Hierarchical classification

Figure 25.9   The connection between classification and phylogeny

Page 497   Phylogenetic trees

Student Media Resource
Activity: Classification schemes

Concept 25.3 Phylogenetic systematics informs the construction of phylogenetic trees based on shared characters

Transparencies

Figure 25.10   Monophyletic, paraphyletic, and polyphyletic groupings

Figure 25.11   Constructing a cladogram

Figure 25.12   Phylograms

Figure 25.13   Ultrametric trees

Figure 25.14   Applying the principle of maximum likelihood

Figure 25.15   Applying parsimony to a problem in molecular systematics (part 1)

Figure 25.15   Applying parsimony to a problem in molecular systematics (part 2)

Figure 25.16   Parsimony and the analogy-versus-homology pitfall

Student Media Resource
Investigation: How is phylogeny determined by comparing proteins?

Concept 25.4 Much of an organism's evolutionary history is documented in its genome

Transparency

Figure 25.17   Two types of homologous genes

Concept 25.5 Molecular clocks help track evolutionary time

Transparency

Figure 25.18   The universal tree of life

For additional resources such as digital images and lecture outlines, go
to the Campbell Media Manager or the Instructor Resources section of
www.campbellbiology.com.

Key Terms

analogy	maximum likelihood	phylogram
binomial	maximum parsimony	phylum
clade	molecular clock	polyphyletic
cladistics	molecular systematics	shared derived
cladogram	monophyletic	character
class	neutral theory	shared primitive
domain	order	character
family	orthologous genes	specific epithet
fossil record	outgroup	systematics
genus	paralogous genes	taxon
homoplasy	paraphyletic	taxonomy
ingroup	phylogenetic tree	ultrametric tree
kingdom	phylogeny	

Word Roots

analog- = proportion (*analogy:* similarity due to convergence)

bi- = two; **-nom** = name (*binomial:* a two-part latinized name of a species)

clado- = branch (*cladogram:* a dichotomous phylogenetic tree that branches repeatedly)

homo- = like, resembling (*homology:* similarity in characteristics resulting from a shared ancestry)

mono- = one (*monophyletic:* pertaining to a taxon derived from a single ancestral species that gave rise to no species in any other taxa)

parsi- = few (*principle of parsimony:* the premise that a theory about nature should be the simplest explanation that is consistent with the facts)

phylo- = tribe; **-geny** = origin (*phylogeny:* the evolutionary history of a taxon)

CHAPTER 26

The Tree of Life: An Introduction to Biological Diversity

Teaching Objectives

The Origin of Life

1. Describe the four stages of the hypothesis for the origin of life on Earth by chemical evolution.

2. Describe the contributions that A. I. Oparin, J.B.S. Haldane, and Stanley Miller made toward developing a model for the abiotic synthesis of organic molecules. Describe the conditions and locations where most of these chemical reactions probably occurred on Earth.

3. Describe the evidence that suggests that RNA was the first genetic material. Explain the significance of the discovery of ribozymes.

4. Describe how natural selection may have worked in an early RNA world.

5. Describe how natural selection may have favored the proliferation of stable protobionts with self-replicating, catalytic RNA.

Introduction to the History of Life

6. Explain how the histories of Earth and life are inseparable.

7. Explain how index fossils can be used to determine the relative age of fossil-bearing rock strata. Explain how radiometric dating can be used to determine the absolute age of rock strata. Explain how magnetism can be used to date rock strata.

8. Describe the major events in Earth's history from its origin until 2 billion years ago. In particular, note when Earth first formed, when life first evolved, and what forms of life existed in each eon.

9. Describe the mass extinctions of the Permian and Cretaceous periods. Discuss a hypothesis that accounts for each of these mass extinctions.

The Major Lineages of Life

10. Describe how chemiosmotic ATP production may have arisen.

11. Describe the timing and significance of the evolution of oxygenic photosynthesis.

12. Explain the endosymbiotic theory for the evolution of the eukaryotic cell. Describe the evidence that supports this theory.

13. Explain how genetic annealing may have led to modern eukaryotic genomes.

14. Describe the timing of key events in the evolution of the first eukaryotes and later multicellular eukaryotes.

15. Explain how the snowball Earth hypothesis explains why multicellular eukaryotes were so limited in size, diversity, and distribution until the late Proterozoic.

16. Describe the key evolutionary adaptations that arose as life colonized land.

17. Explain how continental drift explains Australia's unique flora and fauna.

18. Explain why R. H. Whittaker's five-kingdom system has been replaced by a new system with three domains.

Student Misconceptions

1. Biologists have developed hypotheses for the origin of life by chemical evolution that can and have been tested in laboratory experiments. However, it is important to clarify to students that, although chemical evolution is an increasingly plausible hypothesis, there is no tangible evidence for the origin of life on Earth. Hypotheses for the origin of life describe steps that *could* have happened. There is still considerable room for speculation and alternative views. In contrast, evolutionary change of living things over the last 3.8 billion years is an incontrovertible fact.

2. Students may find it difficult to understand how natural selection could have acted on populations of protobionts, favoring stable protobionts with self-replicating, catalytic RNA. Explain that there are three conditions that are necessary and sufficient for natural selection to bring about evolutionary change in a population. If members of the population show variation, if that variation has a heritable basis, and if variant individuals differ in fitness, then natural selection will act to increase the proportion of favorable, heritable traits in the population. These conditions were met in populations of protobionts before the origin of life as we know it.

3. Metabolism evolved in prokaryotes. With remarkably few exceptions, the enormous diversity of metabolic reactions in living organisms arose in prokaryotes.

4. The generation of oxygen by oxygenic photosynthesis offered great opportunity and great risk to early prokaryotes. In its free molecular and ionized forms and in compounds such as hydrogen peroxide, oxygen attacks chemical bonds, inhibits enzymes, and damages cells. The increase in atmospheric oxygen likely doomed many prokaryote groups. Other prokaryotes harnessed the oxidizing power of oxygen in aerobic respiration to extract far more usable energy from organic molecules.

Chapter Guide to Teaching Resources

Overview: Changing life on a changing Earth

Concept 26.1 Conditions on early Earth made the origin of life possible

Transparencies

Figure 26.2   Can organic molecules form in a reducing atmosphere?

Figure 26.4   Laboratory versions of protobionts

Figure 26.5   A ribozyme capable of replicating RNA

Instructor and Student Media Resources

Activity: A scrolling geologic record

Video: Grand Canyon

Video: Volcanic eruption

Video: Lava flow

Concept 26.2 The fossil record chronicles life on Earth

Transparencies

Figure 26.7   Radiometric dating

Figure 26.8   Diversity of life and periods of mass extinction

Table 26.1   The geologic record

Figure 26.10 Clock analogy for some key events in Earth's history

Instructor and Student Media Resource

Video: Hydrothermal vent

Concept 26.3 As prokaryotes evolved, they exploited and changed young Earth

Concept 26.4 Eukaryotic cells arose from symbioses and genetic exchanges between prokaryotes

Transparency

Figure 26.13 A model of the origin of eukaryotes through serial endosymbiosis

Concept 26.5 Multicellularity evolved several times in eukaryotes

Transparencies

Figure 26.17   The Cambrian radiation of animals

Figure 26.18   Earth's major crustal plates

Figure 26.19   The history of continental drift during the Phanerozoic

Instructor and Student Media Resources

Activity: The history of life

Video: Tubeworms

Concept 26.6 New information has revised our understanding of the tree of life

Transparencies

Figure 26.21   Whittaker's five-kingdom system

Figure 26.22   One current view of biological diversity (part a)

Figure 26.22   One current view of biological diversity (part b)

Student Media Resource

Activity: Classification schemes

For additional resources such as digital images and lecture outlines, go to the Campbell Media Manager or the Instructor Resources section of **www.campbellbiology.com.**

Key Terms

colony
genetic annealing
geologic record
half-life
magnetic reversal

Pangaea
protobiont
radiometric dating
ribozyme
serial endosymbiosis

snowball Earth
  hypothesis
stromatolite
three-domain system

Word Roots

proto- = first (*protobionts:* aggregates of abiotically produced molecules)

stromato- = something spread out; **-lite** = a stone (*stromatolite:* rocks made of banded domes of sediment in which are found the most ancient forms of life)

CHAPTER 27

Prokaryotes

Teaching Objectives

Structural, Functional, and Genetic Adaptations Contribute to Prokaryotic Success

1. Explain why it might be said that the history of life on Earth is one long "age of prokaryotes."
2. Explain why prokaryotes are unable to grow in very salty or sugary foods, such as cured meats or jam.
3. State the function(s) of each of the following prokaryotic features:
   a. capsule
   b. fimbria
   c. sex pilus
   d. nucleoid
   e. plasmid
   f. endospore
4. Describe how prokaryotes carry out cellular respiration when they lack compartmentalized organelles such as mitochondria.
5. List the three domains of life.
6. Describe the structure, composition, and functions of prokaryotic cell walls.
7. Distinguish the structure and staining properties of gram-positive bacteria from those of gram-negative bacteria.
8. Explain why disease-causing gram-negative bacterial species are generally more deadly than disease-causing gram-positive bacteria.
9. Explain how the organization of prokaryotic genomes differs from that of eukaryotic genomes.
10. Describe the evidence of parallel adaptive evolution found in Lenski's experiments on *E. coli*.

Nutritional and Metabolic Diversity

11. Distinguish, with prokaryotic examples, among photoautotrophs, chemoautotrophs, photoheterotrophs, and chemoheterotrophs.
12. Distinguish among obligate aerobes, facultative anaerobes, and obligate anaerobes.
13. Explain the importance of nitrogen fixation to life on Earth.
14. Describe the specializations for nitrogen fixation in the cyanobacterium *Anabaena*.

A Survey of Prokaryotic Diversity

15. Explain why new assays for prokaryotic diversity that do not require researchers to culture microbes have been so fruitful.

16. Explain why some archaea are known as extremophiles. Describe the distinguishing features of methanogens, extreme halophiles, and extreme thermophiles.

The Ecological Impact of Prokaryotes

17. In general terms, describe the role of chemoheterotrophic and autotrophic prokaryotes in the cycling of chemical elements between the biological and chemical components of ecosystems.

18. Describe the mutualistic interaction between humans and *Bacteroides thetaiotaomicron*.

19. Distinguish among mutualism, commensalism, and parasitism. Provide an example of a prokaryote partner in each type of symbiosis.

20. Distinguish between exotoxins and endotoxins and give an example of each.

21. Describe the evidence that suggests that the dangerous *E. coli* strain O157:H7 arose through horizontal gene transfer.

22. Define *bioremediation*. Describe two examples of bioremediation involving prokaryotes.

Student Misconceptions

1. Many students simply do not appreciate the ubiquity, importance, and metabolic sophistication of prokaryotes. It is important to emphasize what recent findings have taught us about these abundant and capable organisms: that they live everywhere, that they are metabolically, structurally, and biochemically diverse, and that their biomass is an order of magnitude greater than the biomass of eukaryotes.

2. Emphasize to students how much is still unknown about the living world in general, and about prokaryotes in particular. Students often greatly overestimate the extent to which humans are capable stewards of life on Earth. Until the recent development of genetic prospecting techniques and the discovery of huge numbers of prokaryotes living deep underground, we did not even know of the existence of the majority of living biomass.

3. Discuss with your students that animal life—in fact, all life—is completely dependent on the metabolic activities of prokaryotes. Prokaryotes lived and evolved alone on Earth for well over a billion years. Eukaryotes would likely not survive a year in the absence of prokaryotes.

4. For many students, the terms *bacteria* and *prokaryote* are synonymous. Make sure that you call students' attention to the important differences between archaea and bacteria, differences that are far more basic than those between animals and plants. Ensure that your own use of the term *bacteria* is accurate and consistent.

5. Many students think of evolution as progressive, and view multicellular eukaryotes as "advanced" and thus far more capable than prokaryotes. Refer to this misconception when introducing nitrogen-fixing cyanobacteria as the

most self-sufficient of all organisms, requiring only light energy, CO_2, N_2, water, and some minerals to grow. With very few exceptions, all metabolic pathways evolved in prokaryotic organisms. Prokaryotes are far more metabolically diverse than eukaryotes.

Further Reading

Gould, Stephen Jay. 1996. The planet of the bacteria. *The Washington Post*, November 13 (available at http://www.stephenjaygould.org/library/gould_bacteria.html).

Chapter Guide to Teaching Resources

Overview: They're (almost) everywhere!

Concept 27.1 Structural, functional, and genetic adaptations contribute to prokaryotic success

Transparencies
Figure 27.3   Gram staining
Figure 27.6   Prokaryotic flagellum

Instructor and Student Media Resources
Activity: Prokaryotic cell structure and function
Video: Prokaryotic flagella
Video: Cyanobacteria

Concept 27.2 A great diversity of nutritional and metabolic adaptations have evolved in prokaryotes

Transparencies
Table 27.1   Major nutritional modes
Figure 27.10   Metabolic cooperation in a colonial prokaryote

Instructor and Student Media Resources
Investigation: What are the modes of nutrition in prokaryotes?
Video: Tubeworms

Concept 27.3 Molecular systematics is illuminating prokaryotic phylogeny

Transparencies
Figure 27.12   A simplified phylogeny of prokaryotes
Table 27.2   A comparison of the three domains of life
Figure 27.13   Major groups of bacteria

Student Media Resource
Activity: Classification of prokaryotes

Concept 27.4 Prokaryotes play crucial roles in the biosphere

Concept 27.5 Prokaryotes have both harmful and beneficial impacts on humans

For additional resources such as digital images and lecture outlines, go to the Campbell Media Manager or the Instructor Resources section of **www.campbellbiology.com.**

Key Terms

anaerobic respiration	extreme thermophile	obligate aerobe
biofilm	extremophile	obligate anaerobe
bioremediation	facultative anaerobe	parasite
capsule	fimbria	parasitism
chemoautotroph	Gram stain	peptidoglycan
chemoheterotroph	gram-negative	photoautotroph
commensalism	gram-positive	photoheterotroph
decomposer	host	pilus
endospore	methanogen	plasmid
endotoxin	mutualism	symbiont
exotoxin	nitrogen fixation	symbiosis
extreme halophile	nucleoid region	taxis

Word Roots

an- = without, not; **aero-** = the air (*anaerobic:* lacking oxygen; referring to an organism, environment, or cellular process that lacks oxygen and may be poisoned by it)

anti- = against; **-biot** = life (*antibiotic:* a chemical that kills bacteria or inhibits their growth)

bi- = two (*binary fission:* the type of cell division by which prokaryotes reproduce; each dividing daughter cell receives a copy of the single parental chromosome)

chemo- = chemical; **hetero-** = different (*chemoheterotroph:* an organism that must consume organic molecules for both energy and carbon)

endo- = inner, within (*endotoxin:* a component of the outer membranes of certain gram-negative bacteria responsible for generalized symptoms of fever and ache)

exo- = outside (*exotoxin:* a toxic protein secreted by a bacterial cell that produces specific symptoms even in the absence of the bacterium)

-gen = produce (*methanogen:* microorganisms that obtain energy by using carbon dioxide to oxidize hydrogen, producing methane as a waste product)

halo- = salt; **-philos** = loving (*halophile:* microorganisms that live in unusually highly saline environments such as the Great Salt Lake or the Dead Sea)

mutu- = reciprocal (*mutualism:* a symbiotic relationship in which both the host and the symbiont benefit)

-oid = like, form (*nucleoid:* a dense region of DNA in a prokaryotic cell)

photo- = light; **auto-** = self; **-troph** = food, nourish (*photoautotroph:* an organism that harnesses light energy to drive the synthesis of organic compounds from carbon dioxide)

sym- = with, together; **-bios** = life (*symbiosis:* an ecological relationship between organisms of two different species that live together in direct contact)

thermo- = temperature (*thermophiles:* microorganisms that thrive in hot environments, often 60–80°C)

CHAPTER 28

Protists

Teaching Objectives

Protists Are Extremely Diverse

1. Explain why the kingdom Protista is no longer considered a legitimate taxonomic group.

2. Describe the different nutritional strategies of protists.

3. Describe the three ecological categories of protists. Explain why the terms *protozoa* and *algae* are not useful as taxonomic categories.

4. Describe the evidence that supports the theory that mitochondria and plastids evolved by serial endosymbiosis. Explain which living organisms are likely relatives of the prokaryotes that gave rise to mitochondria and plastids.

5. Describe the evidence that suggests that mitochondria were acquired before plastids in eukaryotic evolution.

6. Explain the role of secondary endosymbiosis in the evolution of photosynthetic protists.

A Sample of Protistan Diversity

7. Describe the reduced mitochondria of diplomonads. Explain why this group is successful despite this feature.

8. Explain how trypanosomes avoid detection by the human immune system.

9. Explain why *Plasmodium* continues to pose a great risk to human health despite modern medical advances.

10. Describe the process and significance of conjugation in ciliate life cycles.

11. List three differences between oomycetes and fungi.

12. Describe the life cycle, ecology, and impact on humans of the following stramenopiles:

    a. downy mildew

    b. diatoms

    c. kelp

13. Describe how amoeboid protists move and feed.

14. Explain why foraminiferans and gymnamoebas are not considered to be closely related, although both are amoebas.

15. Compare the life cycles and ecology of plasmodial and cellular slime molds.

16. Explain the problem faced by *Dictyostelium* aggregates of constraining "cheaters" that never contribute to the stalk of the fruiting body. Discuss how

research on this topic may lead to insights into the evolution of multicellularity.

17. Explain the basis for the proposal for a new "plant" kingdom, Viridiplantae.

18. Describe three mechanisms by which large size and complexity have evolved in chlorophytes.

Student Misconceptions

1. Protists are tremendously diverse, varying greatly in size, complexity, habitat, mode of nutrition, and life history features. The variation in protists may overwhelm students. It is possible to help students make sense of this diversity by discussing the novel features that arose within eukaryotes—mitosis, meiotic sex, multicellularity, various specializations—and considering which lineages show particular features.

2. When they think of photosynthesis, students may think primarily or exclusively of land plants. Emphasize to your students that algal protists—seaweeds and phytoplankton—make a significant contribution to Earth's primary productivity.

3. Students may underestimate the complexity of unicellular protists. Point out to your students that a single-celled *Paramecium* is far more complex than any of the cells in their own bodies. As the textbook points out, protists include the most elaborate of all cells, cells that carry out the basic functions performed by all of the specialized cells, tissues, and organs of a multicellular organism.

4. Conjugation in ciliates is sexual, resulting in the production of two genetically novel individuals combining the genes of two parents. However, it is not reproduction, because no additional individuals are produced. The unusual life cycles of ciliates can be used to clarify for students the distinction between sex and reproduction.

5. Research addressing the problem faced by *Dictyostelium* aggregates of constraining "cheaters" that never contribute to the stalk of the fruiting body has led to insights into the evolution of multicellularity. Excellent time-lapse photographs of these fascinating protists can be used to introduce your students to the problem faced by all multicellular organisms—that of constraining "cheating" lineages or reducing their effect on the multicellular body.

Chapter Guide to Teaching Resources

Overview: A world in a drop of water

Concept 28.1 Protists are an extremely diverse assortment of eukaryotes

Transparency

Figure 28.3   Diversity of plastids produced by secondary endosymbiosis

Student Media Resource
Activity: Tentative phylogeny of eukaryotes

Concept 28.2 Diplomonads and parabasalids have modified mitochondria

Transparency
Figure 28.4   A tentative phylogeny of eukaryotes

Concept 28.3 Euglenozoans have flagella with a unique internal structure

Transparencies
Figure 28.6   Euglenozoan flagellum
Figure 28.8   *Euglena*, a euglenid commonly found in pond water

Instructor and Student Media Resources
Video: *Euglena*
Video: *Euglena* motion

Concept 28.4 Alveolates have sacs beneath the plasma membrane

Transparencies
Figure 28.11   The two-host life cycle of *Plasmodium*, the apicomplexan that causes malaria
Figure 28.12   Structure and function in the ciliate *Paramecium caudatum*

Instructor and Student Media Resources
Video: Dinoflagellate
Video: *Stentor*
Video: *Stentor* ciliate movement
Video: *Vorticella* cilia
Video: *Vorticella* detail
Video: *Vorticella* habitat
Video: *Paramecium* vacuole
Video: *Paramecium* cilia

Concept 28.5 Stramenopiles have "hairy" and smooth flagella

Transparencies
Figure 28.14   The life cycle of a water mold (layer 1)
Figure 28.14   The life cycle of a water mold (layer 2)
Figure 28.14   The life cycle of a water mold (layer 3)
Figure 28.21   The life cycle of *Laminaria*: An example of alternation of generations

Instructor and Student Media Resources
Video: Water mold oogonium
Video: Water mold zoospores
Video: Diatoms moving
Video: Various diatoms

Concept 28.6 Cercozoans and radiolarians have threadlike pseudopodia

Concept 28.7 Amoebozoans have lobe-shaped pseudopodia

Transparencies
Figure 28.26   The life cycle of a plasmodial slime mold
Figure 28.27   The life cycle of *Dictyostelium*, a cellular slime mold

Instructor and Student Media Resources
Video: Amoeba
Video: Amoeba pseudopodia
Video: Plasmodial slime mold streaming
Video: Plasmodial slime mold

Concept 28.8 Red algae and green algae are the closest relatives of land plants

Transparency
Figure 28.31   The life cycle of *Chlamydomonas*, a unicellular chlorophyte

Instructor and Student Media Resources
Video: *Chlamydomonas*
Video: *Volvox* colony
Video: *Volvox* daughter
Video: *Volvox* flagella
Investigation: What kinds of protists do various habitats support?

Review

Transparency
Table 28.1   A sample of protist diversity

For additional resources such as digital images and lecture outlines, go to the Campbell Media Manager or the Instructor Resources section of **www.campbellbiology.com.**

Key Terms

alternation of
  generations
amoeba
apicomplexan
blade
brown alga
cellular slime mold
ciliate
conjugation
diatom
dinoflagellate
diplomonad

euglenid
food vacuole
foraminiferan (foram)
golden alga
green alga
heteromorphic
holdfast
isomorphic
kinetoplastid
mixotroph
oomycete
parabasalid

plasmodial slime mold
plasmodium
protist
pseudopodium
radiolarian
red alga
secondary
  endosymbiosis
sporozoite
stipe
test
thallus

Word Roots

con- = with, together (*conjugation:* in ciliates, the transfer of micronuclei between two cells that are temporarily joined)

hetero- = different; **-morph** = form (*heteromorphic:* a condition in the life cycle of all modern plants in which the sporophyte and gametophyte generations differ in morphology)

iso- = same (*isomorphic:* alternating generations in which the sporophytes and gametophytes look alike, although they differ in chromosome number)

-phyte = plant (*gametophyte:* the multicellular haploid form in organisms undergoing alternation of generations)

pseudo- = false; **-podium** = foot (*pseudopodium:* a cellular extension of amoeboid cells used in moving and feeding)

thallos- = sprout (*thallus:* a seaweed body that is plantlike but lacks true roots, stems, and leaves)

CHAPTER 29

Plant Diversity I: How Plants Colonized Land

Teaching Objectives

An Overview of Land Plant Evolution

1. Describe four shared derived homologies that link charophyceans and land plants.
2. Distinguish among the kingdoms Plantae, Streptophyta, and Viridiplantae. Note which of these is used in the textbook.
3. Describe five characteristics that distinguish land plants from charophycean algae. Explain how these features are adaptive for life on land.
4. Define and distinguish among the stages of the alternation of generations life cycle.
5. Describe evidence that suggests that plants arose roughly 475 million years ago.

Bryophytes

6. List and distinguish among the three phyla of bryophytes. Briefly describe the characteristics of each group.
7. Distinguish between the phylum Bryophyta and the bryophytes.
8. Explain why bryophyte rhizoids are not considered roots.
9. Explain why most bryophytes grow close to the ground.
10. Diagram the life cycle of a bryophyte. Label the gametophyte and sporophyte stages and the locations of gamete production, fertilization, and spore production.
11. Describe the ecological and economic significance of bryophytes.

The Origin and Diversity of Vascular Plants

12. Describe the five traits that characterize modern vascular plants. Explain how these characteristics have contributed to their success on land.
13. Distinguish between microphylls and megaphylls.
14. Distinguish between the homosporous and heterosporous condition.
15. Explain why seedless vascular plants are most commonly found in damp habitats.
16. Name the two clades of living seedless vascular plants.
17. Explain how vascular plants differ from bryophytes.

18. Distinguish between giant and small lycophytes.

19. Explain why whisk ferns are no longer considered to be "living fossils."

20. Describe the production and dispersal of fern spores.

Student Misconceptions

1. Many students have difficulty in understanding the significance of derived characters that are shared between two extant groups. Just as many members of the general public have the mistaken notion that humans evolved from chimpanzees, some students will think that charophyceans are in some sense ancestral to plants or that charophyceans are identical to the last common ancestor that plants and charophyceans shared.

2. It is important to make sure that your students understand alternation of generations in bryophytes and seedless vascular plants. Plant life cycles are challenging for all students. Without a good understanding of the life cycles of plants with recognizable gametophytes and sporophytes, students will have great difficulty with gymnosperm and angiosperm life cycles.

3. Students tend to think of derived traits as "advanced." Be careful to avoid this term. Point out that organisms have a combination of primitive and derived traits, and that all living organisms have an equally long evolutionary history, dating back to the origin of life on Earth.

4. Many students are not very familiar with or knowledgeable about plants. Some of the terminology of plant life cycles can be confusing to such students. Clarify for students the meaning of these pairs of terms:

   a. homosporous and heterosporous

   b. bryophyte and phylum Bryophyta

   c. rhizoid and root

Chapter Guide to Teaching Resources

Overview: The greening of Earth

Concept 29.1 Land plants evolved from green algae

Concept 29.2 Land plants possess a set of derived terrestrial adaptations

Transparencies

Figure 29.4   Three clades that are candidates for designation as the plant kingdom

Figure 29.5   Derived traits of land plants: Apical meristems and alternation of generations

Figure 29.5   Derived traits of land plants: Walled spores produced in sporangia; multicellular gametangia; multicellular, dependent embryos

Table 29.1   Ten phyla of extant plants

Figure 29.7   Highlights of plant evolution

Student Media Resources

Activity: Terrestrial adaptations of plants

Activity: Highlights of plant phylogeny

Concept 29.3 The life cycles of mosses and other bryophytes are dominated by the gametophyte stage

Transparencies

Figure 29.8   The life cycle of a *Polytrichum* moss (layer 1)

Figure 29.8   The life cycle of a *Polytrichum* moss (layer 2)

Figure 29.8   The life cycle of a *Polytrichum* moss (layer 3)

Student Media Resource

Activity: Moss life cycle

Concept 29.4 Ferns and other seedless vascular plants formed the first forests

Transparencies

Figure 29.11   *Aglaophyton major*, an ancient relative of modern vascular plants

Figure 29.12   The life cycle of a fern

Figure 29.13   Hypotheses for the evolution of leaves

Student Media Resources

Activity: Fern life cycle

Investigation: What are the different stages of a fern life cycle?

For additional resources such as digital images and lecture outlines, go to the Campbell Media Manager or the Instructor Resources section of **www.campbellbiology.com.**

Key Terms

alternation of generations	calyptra	gametophyte
angiosperm	capsule	gymnosperm
antheridium	cuticle	heterosporous
apical meristem	embryophyte	homosporous
archegonium	foot	hornwort
bryophyte	gametangia	leaf
	gametophore	lignin

liverwort	protonema	sporocyte
lycophyte	pterophyte	sporophyll
megaphyll	rhizoid	sporophyte
megaspore	root	sporopollenin
microphyll	rosette cellulose-	stoma
microspore	synthesizing complex	strobili
moss	seed	tracheid
peat	seedless vascular plants	vascular plant
peristome	seta	vascular tissue
phloem	sorus	xylem
phragmoplast	sporangium	
placental transfer cell	spore	

Word Roots

-angio = vessel (*gametangia:* the reproductive organ of bryophytes, consisting of the male antheridium and female archegonium; a multichambered jacket of sterile cells in which gametes are formed)

bryo- = moss; **-phyte** = plant (*bryophytes:* the mosses, liverworts, and hornworts; a group of nonvascular plants that inhabit the land but lack many of the terrestrial adaptations of vascular plants)

gymno- = naked; **-sperm** = seed (*gymnosperm:* a vascular plant that bears naked seeds not enclosed in any specialized chambers)

hetero- = different; **-sporo** = a seed (*heterosporous:* referring to plants in which the sporophyte produces two kinds of spores that develop into unisexual gametophytes, either female or male)

homo- = like (*homosporous:* referring to plants in which a single type of spore develops into a bisexual gametophyte having both male and female sex organs)

mega- = large (*megaspores:* a spore from a heterosporous plant that develops into a female gametophyte bearing archegonia)

micro- = small; **-phyll** = leaf (*microphylls:* the small leaves of lycophytes that have only a single, unbranched vein)

peri- = around; **-stoma** = mouth (*peristome:* the upper part of the moss capsule often specialized for gradual spore discharge)

-phore = bearer (*gametophore:* the mature gamete-producing structure of a gametophyte body of a moss)

phragmo- = a partition; **-plast** = formed, molded (*phragmoplast:* an alignment of cytoskeletal elements and Golgi-derived vesicles across the midline of a dividing plant cell)

proto- = first; **-nema** = thread (*protonema:* a mass of green, branched, one-cell-thick filaments produced by germinating moss spores)

pter- = fern (*pteridophytes:* seedless plants with true roots with lignified vascular tissue; the group includes ferns, whisk ferns, and horsetails)

rhizo- = root; **-oid** = like, form (*rhizoids:* long, tubular single cells or filaments of cells that anchor bryophytes to the ground)

CHAPTER 30

Plant Diversity II:
The Evolution of Seed Plants

Teaching Objectives

Key Terrestrial Adaptations Were Crucial to the Success of Seed Plants

1. Name five terrestrial adaptations that contributed to the success of seed plants.
2. Compare the size and independence of the gametophytes of bryophytes with those of seed plants.
3. Describe the ovule of a seed plant.
4. Contrast the male gametophytes of bryophytes with those of seed plants.
5. Explain why pollen grains were an important adaptation for successful reproduction on land.
6. Explain how a seed can be said to include contributions from three distinct generations.
7. Compare spores with seeds as dispersal stages in plant life cycles.

Gymnosperms

8. Explain how climatic changes with the formation of the supercontinent Pangaea favored the spread of gymnosperms.
9. List and distinguish among the four phyla of gymnosperms.
10. Describe the life history of a pine. Indicate which structures are part of the gametophyte generation and which are part of the sporophyte generation.

Angiosperms (Flowering Plants)

11. Identify the following floral structures and describe a function for each:

    a. sepal   f. anther

    b. petal   g. stigma

    c. stamen   h. style

    d. carpel   i. ovary

    e. filament   j. ovule

12. Define *fruit*. Explain how fruits may be adapted to disperse seeds.
13. Explain why a cereal grain is a fruit rather than a seed.

14. Diagram the generalized life cycle of an angiosperm. Indicate which structures are part of the gametophyte generation and which are part of the sporophyte generation.

15. Describe the role of the generative cell and the tube cell within the angiosperm pollen grain.

16. Explain the process and function of double fertilization.

17. Explain the significance of *Archaefructus.*

18. Explain the significance of *Amborella.*

19. Distinguish between monocots and eudicots.

20. Explain how animals may have influenced the evolution of terrestrial plants and vice versa.

Plants and Human Welfare

21. Name the six angiosperms that are most important in the diet of the human species.

22. Describe the current threat to plant diversity caused by human population growth.

Student Misconceptions

1. Many students have great difficulty understanding the life cycles of seed plants in the context of alternation of gametophyte and sporophyte generations. There are a number of common problems that students may have with these life cycles:

   a. Some students may not recognize that meiosis in plants is not a sexual process. Such students think of the meiotic production of megaspores and microspores in seed plants as a step in the production of gametes and do not realize that it represents the asexual production of a new generation of gametophytes.

   b. Students may not recognize that the reduced gametophytes of seed plants are not equivalent to the gonads of animals, but rather represent a haploid generation that alternates with the larger sporophyte generation.

   c. Students may think of the embryonic sporophyte within the seed as the offspring of the sporophyte, and not recognize that it is actually the "grandchild" of that plant and the offspring of the reduced gametophyte generation.

   It is important to discuss alternation of generations in plants in simplified, generalized terms before considering the life cycles of specific plant taxa. In presenting this material, you may wish to contrast plant life cycles to the more familiar life cycles of animals, in order to confront and discuss some of the unacknowledged misconceptions that students may have.

2. Students may think of a seed as equivalent to an amniotic egg. Point out that although seeds and eggs both contain embryos, a seed includes contributions from three generations of plants. In addition to an embryonic sporophyte, a seed has a seed coat derived from the integuments of the "grandparent" sporophyte and a food supply derived from the tissues of the "parent" gametophyte.

Chapter Guide to Teaching Resources

Overview: Feeding the world

Concept 30.1 The reduced gametophytes of seed plants are protected in ovules and pollen grains

Transparencies
Figure 30.2   Gametophyte/sporophyte relationships
Figure 30.3   From ovule to seed

Concept 30.2 Gymnosperms bear "naked" seeds, typically on cones

Transparencies
Figure 30.5   A progymnosperm
Figure 30.6   The life cycle of a pine (layer 1)
Figure 30.6   The life cycle of a pine (layer 2)
Figure 30.6   The life cycle of a pine (layer 3)

Student Media Resource
Activity: Pine life cycle

Concept 30.3 The reproductive adaptations of angiosperms include flowers and fruits

Transparencies
Figure 30.7   The structure of an idealized flower
Figure 30.10   The life cycle of an angiosperm (layer 1)
Figure 30.10   The life cycle of an angiosperm (layer 2)
Figure 30.10   The life cycle of an angiosperm (layer 3)
Figure 30.11   A primitive flowering plant?
Figure 30.12   Angiosperm diversity: Basal angiosperms, hypothetical tree of flowering plants, magnoliids
Figure 30.12   Angiosperm diversity: Monocots and eudicots

Instructor and Student Media Resources
Activity: Angiosperm life cycle
Investigation: How are trees identified by their leaves?
Video: Flower blooming time lapse
Video: Time lapse of flowering plant life cycle
Video: Bee pollinating
Video: Bat pollinating agave plant

Concept 30.4 Human welfare depends greatly on seed plants

Transparency

Table 30.1   A sampling of medicines derived from seed plants

For additional resources such as digital images and lecture outlines, go to the Campbell Media Manager or the Instructor Resources section of **www.campbellbiology.com.**

Key Terms

anther	filament	pollen grain
basal angiosperm	flower	pollination
carpel	fruit	progymnosperm
conifer	integument	receptacle
cotyledon	magnoliid	seed
cross-pollination	micropyle	sepal
dicot	monocot	stamen
double fertilization	ovary	stigma
embryo sac	ovule	style
endosperm	pericarp	
eudicot	petal	

Word Roots

co- = with, together (*coevolution:* the mutual influence on the evolution of two different species interacting with each other and reciprocally influencing each other's adaptations)

endo- = inner (*endosperm:* a nutrient-rich tissue formed by the union of a sperm cell with two polar nuclei during double fertilization, which provides nourishment to the developing embryo in angiosperm seeds)

peri- = around; **-carp** = fruit (*pericarp:* the thickened wall of a fruit)

pro- = before; **gymno-** = naked; **-sperm** = seed (*progymnosperm:* an extinct group of plants that is probably ancestral to gymnosperms and angiosperms)

CHAPTER 31

Fungi

Teaching Objectives

Introduction to the Fungi

1. List the characteristics that distinguish fungi from members of other multicellular kingdoms.
2. Explain how fungi acquire their nutrients.
3. Describe the basic body plan of a fungus.
4. Describe the processes of plasmogamy and karyogamy in fungi.
5. Explain the significance of heterokaryotic stages in fungal life cycles.

Diversity of Fungi

6. Describe the evidence that suggests that Fungi and Animalia are sister kingdoms.
7. Explain the possible significance of the flagellated spores of members of the phylum Chytridiomycota.
8. Describe the life cycle of the black bread mold, *Rhizopus stolonifer.*
9. Describe two alternate hypotheses to explain the reduced mitochondria of the microsporidia.
10. Distinguish between ectomycorrhizae and endomycorrhizae.
11. Distinguish among the Zygomycota, Ascomycota, and Basidiomycota. Include a description of the sexual structure that characterizes each group and list some common examples of each group.

Ecological Impacts of Fungi

12. Describe some of the roles of fungi in ecosystems.
13. Describe the structure of a lichen. Explain the roles of the fungal component of the lichen.
14. Explain how lichens may act as pioneers on newly burned soil or volcanic rock.
15. Describe the role of fungi as agricultural pests.
16. Define mycosis, and describe some human mycoses.
17. Describe three commercial roles played by fungi.

Student Misconceptions

1. Many students do not appreciate the unique structure and the important ecological roles of fungi. Emphasize to your students that terrestrial communities have always been dependent on fungi, not only as decomposers but also as mycorrhizal symbionts with plants. Plants and fungi evolved together, and together they colonized the land. The extensive underground network of fungal mycelia is an essential component of all terrestrial communities.

2. Students are most familiar with animal life cycles. As a result, they think of meiosis as a sexual process, one that produces gametes that quickly fuse in syngamy. In teaching the variety of fungal life cycles, point out to your students that for fungi, meiosis is an asexual process that restores the haploid condition with the production of spores.

3. Fungal life cycles also present an excellent opportunity to introduce fascinating and controversial questions about the evolution of sex and diploidy. Students may wonder about the significance of the heterokaryotic condition and the importance of the transient diploid stage that follows karyogamy in fungi. Discussion of these events can lead to discussion of current theories about the costs and benefits of sex and the possible advantages of the diploid condition in eukaryotic life cycles.

Chapter Guide to Teaching Resources

Overview: Mighty mushrooms

Concept 31.1 Fungi are heterotrophs that feed by absorption

Transparencies
Figure 31.2   Structure of a multicellular fungus
Figure 31.3   Structure of hyphae
Figure 31.4   Specialized hyphae

Student Media Resource
Activity: Fungal reproduction and nutrition

Concept 31.2 Fungi produce spores through sexual or asexual life cycles

Transparencies
Figure 31.5   Generalized life cycle of fungi (layer 1)
Figure 31.5   Generalized life cycle of fungi (layer 2)
Figure 31.5   Generalized life cycle of fungi (layer 3)

Instructor and Student Media Resources

Video: *Phlyctochytrium* zoospore release

Video: *Allomyces* zoospore release

Concept 31.3 Fungi descended from an aquatic, single-celled, flagellated protist

Concept 31.4 Fungi have radiated into a diverse set of lineages

Transparencies

Figure 31.9   Phylogeny of fungi

Figure 31.11   Multiple evolutionary losses of flagella

Figure 31.12   The life cycle of the zygomycete *Rhizopus stolonifer* (black bread mold)

Figure 31.17   The life cycle of *Neurospora crassa*, an ascomycete

Figure 31.20   The life cycle of a mushroom-forming basidiomycete

Concept 31.5 Fungi have a powerful impact on ecosystems and human welfare

Transparency

Figure 31.24   Anatomy of an ascomycete lichen

Student Media Resource

Investigation: How does the fungus *Pilobolus* succeed as a decomposer?

Review

Transparency

Table 31.1   Review of fungal phyla

For additional resources such as digital images and lecture outlines, go to the Campbell Media Manager or the Instructor Resources section of **www.campbellbiology.com**.

Key Terms

arbuscular
  mycorrhizae
ascocarp
ascomycete
ascus
basidiocarp
basidiomycete
basidium
chitin
chytrid
club fungus
coenocytic
conidium
deuteromycete

dikaryotic
ectomycorrhizal
  fungi
endomycorrhizal
  fungi
exoenzyme
glomeromycete
haustorium
heterokaryon
hypha
imperfect fungi
karyogamy
lichen
mold

mycelium
mycorrhizae
mycosis
opisthokont
pheromone
plasmogamy
sac fungus
septum
soredia
yeast
zoospore
zygosporangium

Word Roots

coeno- = common; **-cyto** = cell (*coenocytic:* referring to a multinucleated condition resulting from the repeated division of nuclei without cytoplasmic division)

di- = two; **-karyo** = nucleus (*dikaryotic:* a mycelium with two haploid nuclei per cell, one from each parent)

exo- = out, outside (*exoenzymes:* powerful hydrolytic enzymes secreted by a fungus outside its body to digest food)

hetero- = different (*heterokaryon:* a mycelium formed by the fusion of two hyphae that have genetically different nuclei)

myco- = fungus; **rhizo-** = root (*mycorrhizae:* mutualistic associations of plant roots and fungi)

-osis = a condition of (*mycosis:* the general term for a fungal infection)

plasmo- = plasm; **-gamy** = marriage (*plasmogamy:* the fusion of the cytoplasm of cells from two individuals; occurs as one stage of syngamy)

CHAPTER 32

An Introduction to Animal Diversity

Teaching Objectives

What Is an Animal?

1. List the five characteristics that combine to define animals.
2. Describe the role of *Hox* genes in animal development.

The Origins of Animal Diversity

3. Describe the evidence that suggests animals may have first evolved about a billion years ago.
4. Explain the significance of the Cambrian explosion. Describe three hypotheses for the cause of the Cambrian explosion.
5. Outline the major grades of the animal kingdom based on symmetry, embryonic germ layers, the presence or absence and type of coelom, and protostome or deuterostome development.
6. Distinguish between radial and bilateral symmetry. Explain how animal symmetry may match the animal's way of life.
7. Distinguish among the acoelomate, pseudocoelomate, and coelomate grades. Explain the functions of a body cavity.
8. Distinguish between the following pairs of terms:
   a. diploblastic and triploblastic
   b. spiral and radial cleavage
   c. determinate and indeterminate cleavage
   d. schizocoelous and enterocoelous development
9. Compare the developmental differences between protostomes and deuterostomes, including:
   a. pattern of cleavage
   b. fate of the blastopore
   c. coelom formation
10. Name five major features of animal phylogeny that are supported by systematic analyses of morphological characters and recent molecular studies.
11. Distinguish between the ecdysozoans and the lophotrochozoans. Describe the characteristic features of each group.

Student Misconceptions

1. A surprisingly large number of students use the term *animal* as a synonym for *organism,* at least on occasion. Others confuse the terms *animal* and *vertebrate.* These students may be able to provide accurate definitions to these terms, but are careless and somewhat confused in their use and understanding of the words.

2. Students may have difficulty visualizing the differences between the morphological and developmental traits that distinguish animal body plans. Models can be very useful aids in teaching the students the difference between coelom and pseudocoelom, between spiral and radial cleavage, and between schizocoelous and enterocoelous development.

Chapter Guide to Teaching Resources

Overview: Welcome to your kingdom

Concept 32.1 Animals are multicellular, heterotrophic eukaryotes with tissues that develop from embryonic layers

Transparencies
Figure 32.2   Early embryonic development in animals (layer 1)
Figure 32.2   Early embryonic development in animals (layer 2)
Figure 32.2   Early embryonic development in animals (layer 3)

Concept 32.2 The history of animals may span more than a billion years

Transparencies
Figure 32.3   A choanoflagellate colony
Figure 32.4   One hypothesis for the origin of animals from a flagellated protist
Figure 32.6   A Cambrian seascape

Concept 32.3 Animals can be characterized by "body plans"

Transparencies
Figure 32.7   Body symmetry
Figure 32.8   Body plans of triploblastic animals
Figure 32.9   A comparison of protostome and deuterostome development

Concept 32.4 Leading hypotheses agree on major features of the animal phylogenetic tree

Transparencies

Figure 32.10   One hypothesis of animal phylogeny based mainly on morphological and developmental comparisons

Figure 32.11   One hypothesis of animal phylogeny based mainly on molecular data

Figure 32.13   Characteristics of lophotrochozoans: A trochophore larva

Student Media Resources

Activity: Animal phylogenetic tree

Investigation: How do molecular data fit traditional phylogenies?

For additional resources such as digital images and lecture outlines, go to the Campbell Media Manager or the Instructor Resources section of **www.campbellbiology.com.**

Key Terms

acoelomate	diploblastic	metamorphosis
anterior	dorsal	parazoan
archenteron	ecdysozoan	posterior
bilateral symmetry	ectoderm	protostome
bilaterian	Ediacaran fauna	development
blastopore	endoderm	pseudocoelomate
blastula	enterocoelous	radial cleavage
body cavity	eumetazoan	radial symmetry
body plan	gastrula	schizocoelous
Cambrian explosion	gastrulation	spiral cleavage
cephalization	germ layers	triploblastic
cleavage	grade	trochophore larva
coelom	indeterminate cleavage	ventral
coelomate	larva	
determinate cleavage	lophophore	
deuterostome	lophotrochozoan	
development	mesoderm	

Word Roots

a- = without; **-koilos** = a hollow (*acoelomate:* the condition of lacking a coelom)

arch- = ancient, beginning (*archenteron:* the endoderm-lined cavity, formed during the gastrulation process, that develops into the digestive tract of an animal)

bi- = two (*Bilateria:* the branch of eumetazoans possessing bilateral symmetry)

blast- = bud, sprout; **-pore** = a passage (*blastopore:* the opening of the archenteron in the gastrula that develops into the mouth in protostomes and the anus in deuterostomes)

cephal- = head (*cephalization:* an evolutionary trend toward the concentration of sensory equipment on the anterior end of the body)

deutero- = second (*deuterostome:* one of two lines of coelomates characterized by radial, indeterminate cleavage; enterocoelous formation of the coelom; and development of the anus from the blastopore)

di- = two (*diploblastic:* having two germ layers)

ecdys- = an escape (*Ecdysozoa:* one of two proposed clades within the protostomes; it includes the arthropods)

ecto- = outside; **-derm** = skin (*ectoderm:* the outermost of the three primary germ layers in animal embryos)

endo- = within (*endoderm:* the innermost of the three primary germ layers in animal embryos)

entero- = the intestine, gut (*enterocoelous:* the type of development found in deuterostomes; the coelomic cavities form when mesoderm buds from the wall of the archenteron and hollows out)

gastro- = stomach, belly (*gastrulation:* the formation of a gastrula from a blastula)

in- = into; **-gest** = carried (*ingestion:* a heterotrophic mode of nutrition in which other organisms or detritus are eaten whole or in pieces)

lopho- = a crest, tuft; **-trocho** = a wheel; (*Lophotrochozoa:* one of two proposed clades within the protostomes that includes annelids and mollusks)

meso- = middle (*mesoderm:* the middle primary germ layer of an early embryo)

meta- = boundary, turning point; **-morph** = form (*metamorphosis:* the resurgence of development in an animal larva that transforms it into a sexually mature adult)

para- = beside; **-zoan** = animal (*parazoan:* grade of body form lacking symmetry and tissues; describes the sponges)

proto- = first; **-stoma** = mouth (*protostomes:* a member of one of two distinct evolutionary lines of coelomates characterized by spiral, determinate cleavage; schizocoelous formation of the coelom; and development of the mouth from the blastopore)

pseudo- = false (*pseudocoelom:* a body cavity that is not completely lined by mesoderm)

radia- = a spoke, ray (*Radiata:* the radially symmetrical animal phyla, including cnidarians)

schizo- = split (*schizocoelous:* the type of development found in protostomes; initially, solid masses of mesoderm split to form coelomic cavities)

tri- = three (*triploblastic:* having three germ layers)

CHAPTER 33

Invertebrates

Teaching Objectives

Sponges

1. From a diagram, identify the parts of a sponge (including the spongocoel, porocyte, epidermis, choanocyte, mesohyl, amoebocyte, osculum, and spicules) and describe the function of each.

Eumetazoa

2. List the characteristics of the phylum Cnidaria that distinguish it from the other animal phyla.

3. Describe the specialized cells that are found in Cnidarians.

4. Describe the two basic body plans in Cnidaria and their role in Cnidarian life cycles.

5. List the four classes of Cnidaria and distinguish among them based on life cycle and morphological characteristics.

Bilateria

6. Distinguish between:

   a. diploblastic and triploblastic development

   b. acoelomates and coelomates

   c. gastrovascular cavity and alimentary canal

   d. protostome and deuterostome

7. List the characteristics of the phylum Platyhelminthes that distinguish it from the other animal phyla.

8. Distinguish among the four classes of Platyhelminthes and give examples of each.

9. Describe the generalized life cycle of a trematode and give an example of one fluke that parasitizes humans.

10. Explain how trematodes evade detection by the immune systems of their hosts.

11. Describe the anatomy and generalized life cycle of a tapeworm.

12. Describe unique features of rotifers that distinguish them from other pseudocoelomates.

13. Define *parthenogenesis* and describe asexual forms of rotifer reproduction.

14. Define *lophophore* and list three lophophorate phyla.

15. List the distinguishing characteristics of the phylum Nemertea.

16. Explain the relationship between nemerteans and flatworms.

17. List the characteristics that distinguish the phylum Mollusca from the other animal phyla.

18. Describe the basic body plan of a mollusc and explain how it has been modified in the Bivalvia, Cephalopoda, Gastropoda, and Polyplacophora.

19. List the characteristics that distinguish the phylum Annelida from other animal phyla.

20. Distinguish among the three classes of Annelida and give examples of each.

21. Describe the adaptations that enable some leeches to feed on blood.

22. List the characteristics of the phylum Nematoda that distinguish it from other wormlike animals.

23. Give examples of both parasitic and free-living species of nematodes.

24. List the characteristics of arthropods that distinguish them from the other animal phyla. List the three features that account for the success of this phylum.

25. Describe advantages and disadvantages of an exoskeleton.

26. Distinguish between hemocoel and coelom.

27. Define and distinguish between the major arthropod lines of evolution represented by:
    a. Cheliceriformes
    b. Hexapoda
    c. Crustacea
    d. Myriapoda

28. Describe three specialized features of spiders.

29. Describe two features that may account for the great diversity of insects.

Deuterostomia

30. List the characteristics of echinoderms that distinguish them from other animal phyla.

31. Distinguish among the six classes of echinoderms and give examples of each.

32. Explain why the phylum Chordata is included in a chapter on invertebrates.

33. Describe the developmental similarities between echinoderms and chordates.

Student Misconceptions

1. Students may find it difficult to recognize that echinoderms are our closest relatives within the animal kingdom, as members of the Deuterostome clade. It is important to emphasize the significance of the similarities in development between echinoderms and chordates, despite their very different adult forms.

2. Nematodes are unfamiliar to most students, who may not be aware of the great diversity and abundance of this ubiquitous and commercially important phylum.

3. The bdelloid rotifers have been reproducing asexually for over 35 million years. Tell your students about these rotifers and ask them to consider why it is that so few species are exclusively asexual. Why is sex the dominant—and often exclusive—means of reproduction in many animals, when sex is so costly?

Chapter Guide to Teaching Resources

Overview: Life without a backbone

Transparency
Figure 33.2   Review of animal phylogeny

Concept 33.1 Sponges are sessile and have a porous body and choanocytes

Transparency
Figure 33.4   Anatomy of a sponge

Concept 33.2 Cnidarians have radial symmetry, a gastrovascular cavity, and cnidocytes

Transparencies
Figure 33.5   Polyp and medusa forms of cnidarians
Figure 33.6   A cnidocyte of a hydra
Table 33.1   Classes of phylum Cnidaria
Figure 33.8   The life cycle of the hydrozoan *Obelia* (layer 1)
Figure 33.8   The life cycle of the hydrozoan *Obelia* (layer 2)
Figure 33.8   The life cycle of the hydrozoan *Obelia* (layer 3)

Instructor and Student Media Resources
Video: Hydra budding
Video: Hydra eating *Daphnia* (time-lapse)
Video: Hydra releasing sperm
Video: Jelly swimming
Video: Thimble jellies
Video: Coral reef
Video: Clownfish and anemone

Concept 33.3 Most animals have bilateral symmetry

Transparencies
Table 33.2   Classes of phylum Platyhelminthes
Figure 33.10   Anatomy of a planarian, a turbellian

Figure 33.11   The life cycle of a blood fluke (*Schistosoma mansonii*), a trematode

Figure 33.12   Anatomy of a tapeworm

Instructor and Student Media Resource

Video: Rotifer

Concept 33.4 Molluscs have a muscular foot, a visceral mass, and a mantle

Transparencies

Figure 33.16   The basic body plan of a mollusc

Table 33.3   Major classes of phylum Mollusca

Figure 33.19   The results of torsion in a gastropod

Figure 33.21   Anatomy of a clam

Instructor and Student Media Resource

Video: Nudibranchs

Concept 33.5 Annelids are segmented worms

Transparencies

Table 33.4   Classes of phylum Annelida

Figure 33.23   Anatomy of an earthworm

Instructor and Student Media Resources

Video: Earthworm locomotion

Video: Tubeworms

Concept 33.6 Nematodes are nonsegmented pseudocoelomates covered by a tough cuticle

Instructor and Student Media Resources

Video: *C. elegans* crawling

Video: *C. elegans* embryo development (time-lapse)

Concept 33.7 Arthropods are segmented coelomates that have an exoskeleton and jointed appendages

Transparencies

Figure 33.29   External anatomy of an arthropod

Table 33.5   Subphyla of phylum Arthropoda

Figure 33.32   Anatomy of a spider

Figure 33.35   Anatomy of a grasshopper, an insect

Figure 33.37   Insect diversity: Blattodea–Isoptera

Figure 33.37   Insect diversity: Lepidoptera–Trichoptera

Instructor and Student Media Resources
Investigation: How are insect species identified?
Video: Lobster mouth parts
Video: Bee pollinating
Video: Butterfly emerging

Concept 33.8 Echinoderms and chordates are deuterostomes

Transparencies
Figure 33.39   Anatomy of a sea star, an echinoderm
Table 33.6   Classes of phylum Echinodermata

Instructor and Student Media Resources
Activity: Characteristics of invertebrates
Video: Echinoderm tube feet

Review

Transparency
Table 33.7   Animal phyla

For additional resources such as digital images and lecture outlines, go
to the Campbell Media Manager or the Instructor Resources section of
www.campbellbiology.com.

Key Terms

alimentary canal	echinoderm	myriapod
ammonite	ectoproct	nematocyst
amoebocyte	eurypterid	open circulatory
arthropod	exoskeleton	system
book lung	foot	osculum
brachiopod	gastrovascular cavity	parthenogenesis
chelicera	hermaphrodite	phoronid
cheliceriform	hexapod	planarian
choanocyte	incomplete	polyp
closed circulatory	metamorphosis	radula
system	invertebrate	spongocoel
cnidocyte	isopod	suspension feeder
complete	mandible	torsion
metamorphosis	mantle	trilobite
copepod	mantle cavity	trochophore
crustacean	medusa	tube foot
cuticle	mesohyl	visceral mass
decapod	molting	water vascular system

Word Roots

arachn- = spider (*Arachnida:* the arthropod group that includes scorpions, spiders, ticks, and mites)

arthro- = jointed; **-pod** = foot (*Arthropoda:* segmented coelomates with exoskeletons and jointed appendages)

brachio- = the arm (*brachiopod:* also called lamp shells, these animals superficially resemble clams and other bivalve molluscs, but the two halves of the brachiopod shell are dorsal and ventral to the animal rather than lateral, as in clams)

bryo- = moss; **-zoa** = animal (*bryozoan:* colonial animals [phylum Ectoprocta] that superficially resemble mosses)

cheli- = a claw (*chelicerae:* clawlike feeding appendages characteristic of the cheliceriform group)

choano- = a funnel; **-cyte** = cell (*choanocyte:* flagellated collar cells of a sponge)

cnido- = a nettle (*cnidocytes:* unique cells that function in defense and prey capture in cnidarians)

-coel = hollow (*spongocoel:* the central cavity of a sponge)

cope- = an oar (*copepods:* a group of small crustaceans that are important members of marine and freshwater plankton communities)

cuti- = the skin (*cuticle:* the exoskeleton of an arthropod)

deca- = ten (*decapod:* a relatively large group of crustaceans that includes lobsters, crayfish, crabs, and shrimp)

diplo- = double (*Diplopoda:* the millipede group of animals)

echino- = spiny; **-derm** = skin (*echinoderm:* sessile or slow-moving animals with a thin skin that covers an exoskeleton; the group includes sea stars, sea urchins, brittle stars, crinoids, sea cucumbers, and sea daisies)

eury- = broad, wide; **-pter** = a wing, a feather, a fin (*eurypterid:* mainly marine and freshwater, extinct cheliceriforms; these predators, also called water scorpions, ranged up to 3 meters long)

exo- = outside (*exoskeleton:* a hard encasement on the surface of an animal)

gastro- = stomach; **-vascula** = a little vessel (*gastrovascular cavity:* the central digestive compartment, usually with a single opening that functions as both mouth and anus)

hermaphrod- = with both male and female organs (*hermaphrodite:* an individual that functions as both male and female in sexual reproduction by producing both sperm and eggs)

in- = without (*invertebrates:* animals without a backbone)

iso- = equal (*isopods:* one of the largest groups of crustaceans, primarily marine, but including pill bugs common under logs and moist vegetation next to the ground)

lopho- = a crest, tuft; **-phora** = to carry (*lophophore:* a horseshoe-shaped or circular fold of the body wall bearing ciliated tentacles that surround the mouth)

meso- = the middle; **-hyl** = matter (*mesohyl:* a gelatinous region between the two layers of cells of a sponge)

meta- = change; **-morph** = shape (*metamorphosis:* the resurgence of development in an animal larva that transforms it into a sexually mature adult)

nemato- = a thread; **-cyst** = a bag (*nematocysts:* the stinging capsules in cnidocytes, unique cells that function in defense and capture of prey)

nephri- = the kidney (*metanephridium:* in annelid worms, a type of excretory tubule with internal openings called nephrostomes that collect body fluids)

oscul- = a little mouth (*osculum:* a large opening in a sponge that connects the spongocoel to the environment)

partheno- = without fertilization; **-genesis** = producing (*parthenogenesis:* a type of reproduction in which females produce offspring from unfertilized eggs)

plan- = flat or wandering (*planarians:* flatworms that prey on smaller animals or feed on dead animals)

tri- = three; **-lobi** = a lobe (*trilobite:* an extinct group of arthropods with pronounced segmentation)

trocho- = a wheel (*trochophore:* a ciliated larva common to the life cycle of many molluscs, it is also characteristic of marine annelids and some other groups)

CHAPTER 34

Vertebrates

Teaching Objectives

Invertebrate Chordates and the Origin of Vertebrates

1. Distinguish between the phyla of deuterostomes.
2. Describe the four derived traits that define the phylum Chordata.
3. Distinguish among the three subphyla of the phylum Chordata and give examples of each.
4. Discuss the evidence for and against Garstang's hypothesis that vertebrates had a tunicate-like ancestor.
5. Explain what lancelets suggest about the evolution of the chordate brain.

Craniates Are Chordates with a Head

6. Discuss the importance of genetic duplication in chordate evolution.
7. Explain the fate of the neural crest cells in craniate development.
8. Explain what *Haikouella* and *Haikouichthys* tell us about craniate evolution.

Vertebrates Are Craniates with a Backbone

9. Describe the way of life and unique characters of the lamprey.
10. Describe conodonts, and explain why they are considered vertebrates.
11. Describe the trends in mineralized structures in early vertebrates.

Gnathostomes Are Vertebrates with Jaws

12. Explain one hypothesis for the evolution of the jaws of gnathostomes.
13. List the shared, derived characters that characterize gnathostomes.
14. Describe the evidence that suggests that the loss of bone in Chondrichthyes is a derived feature.
15. Describe the features of sharks that are adaptive for their active, predatory lifestyle.
16. Describe and distinguish between Chondrichthyes and Osteichthyes, noting the main traits of each group.
17. Identify and describe the main subgroups of Osteichthyes.
18. Name the three living lineages of lobe-fins.

Tetrapods Are Gnathostomes with Limbs and Feet

19. Define and distinguish between *gnathostomes, tetrapods,* and *amniotes.*
20. Explain what *Acanthostega* suggests about the origin of tetrapods.

21. Describe the common traits of amphibians and distinguish among the three orders of living amphibians.

Amniotes Have Amniotic Eggs

22. Describe an amniotic egg and explain its significance in the evolution of reptiles and mammals.

23. Explain why the reptile clade includes birds.

24. Describe a number of reptile features that are adaptive for life on land.

25. Explain why non-bird reptiles should be called "ectothermic" rather than "cold-blooded."

26. Define and describe the *parareptiles*.

27. Distinguish between the lepidosaurs and the archosaurs.

28. Compare the interpretations of dinosaurs as ectotherms or endotherms.

29. Describe the specialized adaptations of snakes that make them successful predators.

30. List the modifications of birds that are adaptive for flight.

31. Summarize the evidence supporting the hypothesis that birds evolved from theropod dinosaur ancestors.

32. Explain the significance of *Archaeopteryx*.

33. Describe the characteristic derived characters of mammals.

34. Describe the evolutionary origin of mammals.

35. Distinguish among monotreme, marsupial, and eutherian mammals.

36. Describe the adaptive radiation of mammals during the Cretaceous and early Tertiary periods.

37. Compare and contrast the four main evolutionary clades of eutherian mammals.

Primates and the Evolution of *Homo sapiens*

38. Describe the general characteristics of primates. Note in particular the features associated with an arboreal existence.

39. Distinguish between the two subgroups of primates and describe their early evolutionary relationship.

40. Distinguish between *hominoid* and *hominid*.

41. Explain what *Sahelanthropus* tells us about hominid evolution.

42. Describe the evolution of *Homo sapiens* from australopith ancestors. Clarify the order in which distinctive human traits arose.

Student Misconceptions

1. For a surprisingly large number of students, the term *animal* means vertebrate. Define the terms *organism, animal,* and *vertebrate* for students, and remind them to use these terms correctly.

2. Students may not appreciate the importance of genetic duplication in chordate and vertebrate evolution. Students find vertebrate evolution and diversity inherently interesting. This topic can provide an opportunity to discuss the

significance of the *Hox* gene clusters and the link between genetic and morphological complexity.

3. The evolution of tetrapods and the move of vertebrates to land provides an excellent opportunity to clarify for students that complex structures evolve by natural selection, and that such evolution must take place step-by-step, by modification of pre-existing variation, with each subsequent modification increasing the fitness of the organism displaying it.

4. Many students will likely be surprised to find birds included in the reptile clade. Discuss with them the shared, defined traits that characterize reptiles, and explain why birds cannot be excluded from this clade.

5. The study of human evolution has a number of possible points of confusion for students.

   a. Many students confuse the terms *hominid* and *hominoid.* Clarify that hominoids include apes and humans, while hominids include *Homo sapiens* and members of our lineage after the chimp and human lineages split.

   b. Some students will persist in thinking that humans evolved from chimpanzees. Clarify for students that, although chimps and humans share a recent common ancestor, that ancestor was neither chimp nor human.

   c. Discourage students from thinking of hominid evolution as an inevitable climb up the ladder of progress to *Homo sapiens.* Many hominid species arose over the last 6 million years, with all but one now extinct. Different hominid species had different combinations of ancestral and derived traits. The hominid lineage is more like a copiously branching bush than a ladder of progress.

Chapter Guide to Teaching Resources

Overview: Half a billion years of backbones

Concept 34.1 Chordates have a notochord and a dorsal, hollow nerve cord

Transparencies

Figure 34.2   Hypothetical phylogeny of chordates

Figure 34.3   Chordate characteristics

Figure 34.4   A tunicate, a urochordate

Figure 34.5   The lancelet *Branchiostoma,* a cephalochordate

Figure 34.6   Expression of developmental genes in lancelets and vertebrates

Concept 34.2 Craniates are chordates that have a head

Transparencies

Figure 34.7   The neural crest, embryonic source of many unique vertebrate characters

Figure 34.8   Fossils of primitive chordates

Concept 34.3 Vertebrates are craniates that have a backbone

Transparencies
Figure 34.11   A conodont
Figure 34.12   Jawless armored vertebrates

Concept 34.4 Gnathostomes are vertebrates that have jaws

Transparencies
Figure 34.13   Hypothesis for the evolution of vertebrate jaws
Figure 34.14   Early gnathostomes
Figure 34.16   Anatomy of a trout, an aquatic osteichthyan

Instructor and Student Media Resources
Video: Coral reef
Video: Clownfish and anemone
Video: Sea horses
Video: Manta ray

Concept 34.5 Tetrapods are gnathostomes that have limbs and feet

Transparencies
Figure 34.19   *Acanthostega,* a Devonian relative of tetrapods
Figure 34.20   The origin of tetrapods

Concept 34.6 Amniotes are tetrapods that have a terrestrially adapted egg

Transparencies
Figure 34.23   A phylogeny of amniotes
Figure 34.24   The amniotic egg
Figure 34.28   Form fits function: The avian wing and feather
Figure 34.29   *Archaeopteryx,* the earliest known bird

Instructor and Student Media Resources
Investigation: How does bone structure shed light on the origin of birds?
Video: Galápagos marine iguana
Video: Galápagos tortoise
Video: Snake ritual wrestling
Video: Swans taking flight
Video: Soaring hawk
Video: Flapping geese

Concept 34.7 Mammals are amniotes that have hair and produce milk

Transparencies

Figure 34.32   The evolution of the mammalian jaw and ear bones

Figure 34.35   Evolutionary convergence of marsupials and eutherians (placental mammals)

Figure 34.36   Mammalian diversity: Phylogenetic relationships of mammals

Figure 34.36   Mammalian diversity: Examples

Figure 34.38   A phylogenetic tree of primates

Instructor and Student Media Resources

Activity: Characteristics of chordates

Activity: Primate diversity

Video: Bat licking nectar

Video: Bat pollinating agave plant

Video: Galápagos sea lion

Video: Whale eating seal

Video: Wolves' agonistic behavior

Video: Gibbons brachiating

Video: Chimp agonistic behavior

Video: Chimp cracking nut

Concept 34.8 Humans are bipedal hominoids with a large brain

Transparency

Figure 34.41   A timeline for some hominid species

Student Media Resource

Activity: Human evolution

For additional resources such as digital images and lecture outlines, go to the Campbell Media Manager or the Instructor Resources section of **www.campbellbiology.com.**

Key Terms

acanthodian	cloaca	eutherian
amniote	conodont	extraembryonic
amphibian	craniate	membranes
anthropoid	diapsid	gnathostome
archosaur	dinosaur	hominid
chondrichthyan	ectothermic	hominoid
chordate	endothermic	lancelet

lateral line system	osteichthyan	ray-finned fish
lepidosaur	oviparous	reptile
lobe-fin	ovoviviparous	somites
mammal	paleoanthropology	spiral valve
marsupial	parareptile	swim bladder
monotreme	pharyngeal clefts	synapsid
mosaic evolution	pharyngeal slits	tetrapod
neural crest	placenta	theropod
notochord	placoderm	tunicate
operculum	pterosaur	vertebrate
opposable thumb	ratite	viviparous

Word Roots

aktin- = a ray; **-pterygi** = a fin (*Actinopterygii:* the class of ray-finned fishes)

arch- = ancient (*archosaurs:* the reptilian group which includes crocodiles, alligators, dinosaurs, and birds)

cephalo- = head (*cephalochordates:* a chordate without a backbone, represented by lancelets, tiny marine animals)

crani- = the skull (*craniata:* the chordate clade that possesses a cranium)

crocodil- = a crocodile (*Crocodilia:* the reptile group that includes crocodiles and alligators)

di- = two (*diapsids:* a group of amniotes distinguished by a pair of holes on each side of the skull)

dino- = terrible; **-saur** = lizard (*dinosaurs:* an extremely diverse group of ancient reptiles varying in body shape, size, and habitat)

endo- = inner; **-therm** = heat (*endotherm:* an animal that uses metabolic energy to maintain a constant body temperature, such as a bird or mammal)

eu- = good (*eutherians:* placental mammals; those whose young complete their embryonic development within the uterus, joined to the mother by the placenta)

extra- = outside, more (*extaembryonic membranes:* four membranes that support the developing embryo in reptiles and mammals)

gnatho- = the jaw; **-stoma** = the mouth (*gnathostomes:* the vertebrate clade that possesses jaws)

homin- = man (*hominid:* a term that refers to mammals that are more closely related to humans than to any other living species)

lepido- = a scale (*lepidosaurs:* the reptilian group which includes lizards, snakes, and tuatara)

marsupi- = a bag, pouch (*marsupial:* a mammal, such as a koala, kangaroo, or opossum, whose young complete their embryonic development inside a maternal pouch called the marsupium)

mono- = one (*monotremes:* an egg-laying mammal, represented by the platypus and the echidna)

neuro- = nerve (*neural crest:* a band of cells along the border where the neural tube pinches off from the ectoderm)

noto- = the back; **-chord** = a string (*notochord:* a longitudinal, flexible rod formed from dorsal mesoderm and located between the gut and the nerve cord in all chordate embryos)

opercul- = a covering, lid (*operculum:* a protective flap that covers the gills of fishes)

osteo- = bone; **-ichthy** = fish (*Osteichthyans:* the vertebrate clade that includes the ray-finned fishes and lobe-fins)

ostraco- = a shell; **-derm** = skin (*ostracoderm:* an extinct paraphyletic group of armored, fishlike vertebrates)

ovi- = an egg; **-parous** = bearing (*oviparous:* referring to a type of development in which young hatch from eggs laid outside the mother's body)

paedo- = a child; **-genic** = producing (*paedogenesis:* the precocious development of sexual maturity in a larva)

paleo- = ancient; **anthrop-** = man; **-ology** = the science of (*paleoanthropology:* the study of human origins and evolution)

placo- = a plate (*placoderm:* a member of an extinct group of gnathostomes that had jaws and were enclosed in a tough outer armor)

pro- = before; **-simi** = an ape (*prosimians:* a suborder of primates that probably resemble early arboreal primates)

ptero- = a wing (*pterosaurs:* winged reptiles that lived during the time of dinosaurs)

ratit- = flat-bottomed (*ratites:* the group of flightless birds)

soma- = body (*somites:* blocks of mesoderm that give rise to muscle segments in chordates)

syn- = together (*synapsids:* an amniote group distinguished by a single hole behind each eye socket)

tetra- = four; **-podi** = foot (*tetrapod:* a terrestrial lobe-fin possessing two pairs of limbs, such as amphibians, reptiles, and mammals)

tunic- = a covering (*tunicates:* members of the subphylum Urochordata)

uro- = the tail (*urochordate:* a chordate without a backbone, commonly called a tunicate, a sessile marine animal)

uro- = tail; **-del** = visible (*Urodela:* the order of salamanders that includes amphibians with tails)

vivi- = alive (*ovoviviparous:* referring to a type of development in which young hatch from eggs that are retained in the mother's uterus)

CHAPTER 35

Plant Structure, Growth, and Development

Teaching Objectives

The Plant Body

1. Describe and compare the three basic organs of vascular plants. Explain how these basic organs are interdependent.
2. List the basic functions of roots. Describe and compare the structures and functions of fibrous roots, taproots, root hairs, and adventitious roots.
3. Describe the basic structure of plant stems.
4. Explain the phenomenon of apical dominance.
5. Describe the structures and functions of four types of modified shoots.
6. Describe and distinguish between the leaves of monocots and those of eudicots.
7. Describe the three tissue systems that make up plant organs.
8. Describe and distinguish between the three basic cell types of plant tissues. For each tissue, describe one characteristic structural feature and explain its functional significance.
9. Explain the functional relationship between a sieve-tube member and its companion cell.

The Process of Plant Growth and Development

10. Distinguish between determinate and indeterminate growth. Give an example of each type of growth.
11. Distinguish among annual, biennial, and perennial plants.
12. Explain this statement: "In contrast to most animals, which have a stage of embryonic growth, plants have regions of embryonic growth."
13. Distinguish between the primary and secondary plant body.
14. Describe in detail the primary growth of the tissues of roots and shoots.
15. Describe in detail the secondary growth of the tissues of roots and shoots.
16. Name the cells that make up the tissue known as wood. Name the tissues that comprise the bark.

Mechanisms of Plant Growth and Development

17. Explain why *Arabidopsis* is an excellent model for the study of plant development.

18. Explain what each of these *Arabidopsis* mutants has taught us about plant development:

    a. *fass* mutant

    b. *gnom* mutant

    c. *KNOTTED-1* mutant

    d. *GLABRA-2* mutant

19. Define and distinguish between *morphogenesis, differentiation,* and *growth.*

20. Explain why (a) the plane and symmetry of cell division, (b) the orientation of cell expansion, and (c) cortical microtubules are important determinants of plant growth and development.

21. Explain how pattern formation may be determined in plants.

22. Give an example to demonstrate how a cell's location influences its developmental fate.

23. Explain how a vegetative shoot tip changes into a floral meristem.

24. Describe how three classes of organ identity genes interact to produce the spatial pattern of floral organs in *Arabidopsis.*

Student Misconceptions

1. Most students think of plants as static and unresponsive to their environment, in comparison to animals. Emphasize to your class that plants are flexible and plastic in their response to their environment, but that they respond primarily by modification of growth and morphology rather than by movement. Explain to your students that plants and animals differ fundamentally in their organization. Plants are modular organisms; most animals are unitary. Plant modules are represented by areas of meristematic growth and the tissues that these meristems produce. This modular organization of plants allows them considerable flexibility and plasticity.

2. Time-lapse films or lab demonstrations can demonstrate to your students that plants can be active and responsive. Plants turn to follow the sun over the course of a day. Fern antheridia open to release active sperm that cluster about mature archegonia in a teeming mass. Such illustrations may awaken an appreciation of plants in your students.

3. Point out to your students the important and varied roles that water plays in the life of plants. Water is essential to plant structure, to plant growth, and to the transport of materials within the plant body, in addition to its more familiar roles as a solvent and as a reactant.

Chapter Guide to Teaching Resources

Overview: No two plants are alike

Transparency
Figure 35.1   Fanwort (*Cabomba caroliniana*)

Concept 35.1 The plant body has a hierarchy of organs, tissues, and cells

Transparencies
Figure 35.2   An overview of a flowering plant
Figure 35.6   Simple versus compound leaves
Figure 35.8   The three tissue systems
Figure 35.9   Examples of differentiated plant cells

Student Media Resource
Activity: Root, stem, and leaf sections

Concept 35.2 Meristems generate cells for new organs

Transparencies
Figure 35.10   An overview of primary and secondary growth
Figure 35.11   Three years' past growth evident in a winter twig

Concept 35.3 Primary growth lengthens roots and shoots

Transparencies
Figure 35.12   Primary growth of a root
Figure 35.17   Leaf anatomy

Instructor and Student Media Resources
Video: Root growth in a radish seed (time-lapse)
Investigation: What are the functions of monocot tissues?

Concept 35.4 Secondary growth adds girth to stems and roots in woody plants

Transparencies
Figure 35.18   Primary and secondary growth of a stem (layer 1)
Figure 35.18   Primary and secondary growth of a stem (layer 2)
Figure 35.18   Primary and secondary growth of a stem (layer 3)
Figure 35.19   Cell division in the vascular cambium
Figure 35.20   Anatomy of a tree trunk

Student Media Resource
Activity: Primary and secondary growth

Concept 35.5 Growth, morphogenesis, and differentiation produce the plant body

Transparencies

Figure 35.21   *Arabidopsis thaliana*

Figure 35.22   The plane and symmetry of cell division influence development of form

Figure 35.23   The preprophase band and the plane of cell division

Figure 35.24   The orientation of plant cell expansion

Figure 35.31   The ABC hypothesis for the functioning of organ identity genes in flower development

For additional resources such as digital images and lecture outlines, go to the Campbell Media Manager or the Instructor Resources section of **www.campbellbiology.com.**

Key Terms

ABC model	guard cells	petiole
adventitious	heartwood	phase change
annual	herbaceous	phloem
apical dominance	indeterminate growth	pith
apical meristem	initials	plasticity
asymmetrical cell division	internode	polarity
axillary bud	lateral meristem	positional information
bark	lateral root	preprophase band
biennial	leaf	primary growth
blade	leaf primordia	primary plant body
bundle sheath	leaf trace	protoplast
collenchyma cell	lenticels	ray initials
companion cell	meristem	root
cork cambium	meristem identity gene	root cap
cortex	mesophyll	root hair
cuticle	morphogenesis	root system
derivatives	morphology	sapwood
dermal tissue system	node	sclereid
determinate growth	organ	sclerenchyma cell
endodermis	organ identity gene	secondary growth
epidermis	palisade mesophyll	secondary plant body
fiber	parenchyma cell	shoot system
fibrous root system	pattern formation	sieve plate
fusiform initials	perennial	sieve-tube member
ground tissue system	pericycle	spongy mesophyll
	periderm	stele

stem	tracheid	vessels
stoma	vascular bundle	xylem
systems biology	vascular cambium	zone of cell division
taproot system	vascular cylinder	zone of elongation
terminal bud	vascular tissue system	zone of maturation
tissue	vein	
tissue system	vessel element	

Word Roots

a- = not, without; **-symmetr** = symmetrical (*asymmetric cell division:* cell division in which one daughter cell receives more cytoplasm than the other during mitosis)

apic- = the tip; **meristo-** = divided (*apical meristems:* embryonic plant tissue on the tips of roots and in the buds of shoots that supplies cells for the plant to grow)

bienn- = every 2 years (*biennial:* a plant that requires two years to complete its life cycle)

coll- = glue; **-enchyma** = an infusion (*collenchyma cell:* a flexible plant cell type that occurs in strands or cylinders that support young parts of the plant without restraining growth)

endo- = inner; **derm-** = skin (*endodermis:* the innermost layer of the cortex in plants roots)

epi- = over (*epidermis:* the dermal tissue system in plants; the outer covering of animals)

fusi- = a spindle (*fusiform initials:* the cambrium cells within the vascular bundles; the name refers to the tapered ends of these elongated cells)

inter- = between (*internode:* the segment of a plant stem between the points where leaves are attached)

meso- = middle; **-phyll** = a leaf (*mesophyll:* the ground tissue of a leaf, sandwiched between the upper and lower epidermis and specialized for photosynthesis)

morpho- = form; **-genesis** = origin (*morphogenesis:* the development of body shape and organization during ontogeny)

perenni- = through the year (*perennial:* a plant that lives for many years)

peri- = around; **-cycle** = a circle (*pericycle:* a layer of cells just inside the endodermis of a root that may become meristematic and begin dividing again)

phloe- = the bark of a tree (*phloem:* the portion of the vascular system in plants consisting of living cells arranged into elongated tubes that transport sugar and other organic nutrients throughout the plant)

pro- = before (*procambium:* a primary meristem of roots and shoots that forms the vascular tissue)

proto- = first; **-plast** = formed, molded (*protoplast:* the contents of a plant cell exclusive of the cell wall)

quiesc- = quiet, resting (*quiescent center:* a region located within the zone of cell division in plant roots, containing meristematic cells that divide very slowly)

sclero- = hard (*sclereid:* a short, irregular sclerenchyma cell that occurs in nutshells and seed coats and is scattered through the parenchyma of some plants)

trachei- = the windpipe (*tracheids:* a water-conducting and supportive element of xylem composed of long, thin cells with tapered ends and walls hardened with lignin)

trans- = across (*transpiration:* the evaporative loss of water from a plant)

vascula- = a little vessel (*vascular tissue:* plant tissue consisting of cells joined into tubes that transport water and nutrients throughout the plant body)

xyl- = wood (*xylem:* the tube-shaped, nonliving portion of the vascular system in plants that carries water and minerals from the roots to the rest of the plant)

CHAPTER 36

Transport in Vascular Plants

Teaching Objectives

An Overview of Transport Mechanisms in Plants

1. Describe how proton pumps function in transport of materials across plant membranes, using the terms *proton gradient, membrane potential, cotransport,* and *chemiosmosis.*
2. Define *osmosis* and *water potential.* Explain how water potential is measured.
3. Explain how solutes and pressure affect water potential.
4. Explain how the physical properties of plant cells are changed when the plant is placed into solutions that have higher, lower, or the same solute concentration.
5. Define the terms *flaccid, plasmolyze, turgor pressure,* and *turgid.*
6. Explain how aquaporins affect the rate of water transport across membranes.
7. Name the three major compartments in vacuolated plant cells.
8. Distinguish between the symplast and the apoplast.
9. Describe three routes available for lateral transport in plants.
10. Define *bulk flow* and describe the forces that generate pressure in the vascular tissue of plants.
11. Relate the structure of sieve-tube cells, vessel cells, and tracheids to their functions in bulk flow.

Absorption of Water and Minerals by Roots

12. Explain what routes are available to water and minerals moving into the vascular cylinder of the root.
13. Explain how mycorrhizae enhance uptake of materials by roots.
14. Explain how the endodermis functions as a selective barrier between the root cortex and vascular cylinder.

Transport of Xylem Sap

15. Describe the potential and limits of root pressure to move xylem sap.
16. Define the terms *transpiration* and *guttation.*
17. Explain how transpirational pull moves xylem sap up from the root tips to the leaves.
18. Explain how cavitation prevents the transport of water through xylem vessels.
19. Explain this statement: "The ascent of xylem sap is ultimately solar powered."

The Control of Transpiration

20. Explain the importance and costs of the extensive inner surface area of a leaf.
21. Discuss the factors that may alter the stomatal density of a leaf.
22. Describe the role of guard cells in photosynthesis-transpiration.
23. Explain how and when stomata open and close. Describe the cues that trigger stomatal opening at dawn.
24. Explain how xerophytes reduce transpiration.
25. Describe crassulacean acid metabolism and explain why it is an important adaptation to reduce transpiration in arid environments.

Translocation of Phloem Sap

26. Define and describe the process of translocation. Trace the path of phloem sap from a primary sugar source to a sugar sink.
27. Describe the process of sugar loading and unloading.
28. Define *pressure flow.* Explain the significance of this process in angiosperms.

Student Misconceptions

1. Water potential is a difficult concept for many students. Remind students that water potential is a measure of the potential energy of water relative to the potential energy of pure, free water that is not bound to solutes or surfaces. Return to explanations of potential energy and explain that the potential energy of water refers to water's ability to perform work as it moves to a state of lower free energy.

2. Students may be confused about the mechanism of stomatal opening and closing. Stomata open when guard cells become turgid and close when guard cells are flaccid. Students may come to your course with the mistaken notion that this is because the cell walls of guard cells are thickened on the side of the stomatal opening and that the thinner walls bow out when the guard cells become turgid to close the stomata. Address this misunderstanding before discussing the role of the cellulose microfibrils in the guard cell walls. These microfibrils resist stretching and compression in the direction parallel to their orientation, causing the guard cells to increase more in length than in width as turgor increases. Because the two guard cells are attached at their tips, the increase in length causes buckling.

3. Some students may be confused if they construct their own analogies between animal circulation and plant transport. Some of the terminology of plant transport—vascular tissue, veins, bleeding of cut stems—can encourage such analogies. These students may develop mistaken notions about exchange of materials between phloem and xylem, and may not appreciate that xylem flow is unidirectional and that most of the water pulled up from the roots is lost through the leaves.

Chapter Guide to Teaching Resources

Overview: Pathways for survival

Concept 36.1 Physical forces drive the transport of materials in plants over a range of distances

Transparencies

Figure 36.2   An overview of transport in a vascular plant (layer 1)
Figure 36.2   An overview of transport in a vascular plant (layer 2)
Figure 36.2   An overview of transport in a vascular plant (layer 3)
Figure 36.2   An overview of transport in a vascular plant (layer 4)
Figure 36.3   Proton pumps provide energy for solute transport
Figure 36.4   Solute transport in plant cells
Figure 36.5   Water potential and water movement: An artificial model
Figure 36.6   Water relations in plant cells
Figure 36.8   Cell compartments and routes for short-distance transport

Instructor and Student Media Resources
Video: Plasmolysis
Video: Turgid *Elodea*

Concept 36.2 Roots absorb water and minerals from the soil

Transparency
Figure 36.9   Lateral transport of minerals and water in roots

Concept 36.3 Water and minerals ascend from roots to shoots through the xylem

Transparencies
Figure 36.12   The generation of transpirational pull in a leaf
Figure 36.13   Ascent of xylem sap

Student Media Resource
Activity: Transport of xylem sap

Concept 36.4 Stomata help regulate the rate of transpiration

Transparency
Figure 36.15   The mechanism of stomatal opening and closing

Student Media Resource
Investigation: How is the rate of transpiration calculated?

Concept 36.5 Organic nutrients are translocated through the phloem

Transparencies

Figure 36.17   Loading of sucrose into phloem

Figure 36.18   Pressure flow in a sieve tube

Student Media Resource

Activity: Translocation of phloem sap

For additional resources such as digital images and lecture outlines, go to the Campbell Media Manager or the Instructor Resources section of **www.campbellbiology.com.**

Key Terms

active transport	mycorrhizae	tonoplast
apoplast	osmosis	transfer cell
aquaporin	osmotic potential	translocation
bulk flow	passive transport	transpiration
Casparian strip	plasmolyze	transport protein
chemiosmosis	pressure potential	turgid
circadian rhythm	(Ψ_P)	turgor pressure
cotransport	proton pump	vacuolar membrane
endodermis	root pressure	water potential
flaccid	solute potential (Ψ_S)	wilting
guttation	sugar sink	xerophyte
megapascal (MPa)	sugar source	
membrane potential	symplast	

Word Roots

apo- = off, away; **-plast** = formed, molded (*apoplast:* in plants, the nonliving continuum formed by the extracellular pathway provided by the continuous matrix of cell walls)

aqua- = water; **-pori** = a pore, small opening (*aquaporin:* a transport protein in the plasma membranes of a plant or animal cell that specifically facilitates the diffusion of water across the membrane)

chemo- = chemical (*chemiosmosis:* the production of ATP using the energy of hydrogen-ion gradients across membranes to phosphorylate ADP)

circa- = a circle (*circadian rhythm:* a physiological cycle of about 24 hours, present in all eukaryotic organisms, that persists even in the absence of external cues)

co- = together; **trans-** = across; **-port** = a gate, door (*cotransport:* the coupling of the "downhill" diffusion of one substance to the "uphill" transport of another against its own concentration gradient)

endo- = within, inner; **-derm** = skin (*endodermis:* the innermost of the three primary germ layers in animal embryos)

gutt- = a drop (*guttation:* the exudation of water droplets caused by root pressure in certain plants)

mega- = large, great (*megapascal:* a unit of pressure equivalent to 10 atmospheres of pressure)

myco- = a fungus; **-rhizo** = a root (*mycorrhizae:* mutualistic associations of plant roots and fungi)

osmo- = pushing (*osmosis:* the diffusion of water across a selectively permeable membrane)

sym- = with, together (*symplast:* in plants, the continuum of cytoplasm connected by plasmodesmata between cells)

turg- = swollen (*turgor pressure:* the force directed against a cell wall after the influx of water and the swelling of a walled cell due to osmosis)

xero- = dry; **-phyto** = a plant (*xerophytes:* plants adapted to arid climates)

CHAPTER 37

Plant Nutrition

Teaching Objectives

Nutritional Requirements of Plants

1. Describe the ecological role of plants in transforming inorganic molecules into organic compounds.
2. Define the term *essential nutrient*.
3. Explain how hydroponic culture is used to determine which minerals are essential nutrients.
4. Distinguish between macronutrient and micronutrient.
5. Name the nine macronutrients required by plants.
6. List the eight micronutrients required by plants and explain why plants need only minute quantities of these elements.
7. Explain how a nutrient's role and mobility determine the symptoms of a mineral deficiency.

The Role of Soil in Plant Nutrition

8. Define soil texture and soil composition.
9. Explain how soil is formed.
10. Name the components of topsoil.
11. Describe the composition of loams and explain why they are the most fertile soils.
12. Explain how humus contributes to the texture and composition of soils.
13. Explain why plants cannot extract all of the water in soil.
14. Explain how the presence of clay in soil helps prevent the leaching of mineral cations.
15. Define *cation exchange*, explain why it is necessary for plant nutrition, and describe how plants can stimulate the process.
16. Explain why soil management is necessary in agricultural systems but not in natural ecosystems such as forests and grasslands. Describe an example of human mismanagement of soil.
17. List the three mineral elements that are most commonly deficient in agricultural soils.
18. Explain how soil pH determines the effectiveness of fertilizers and a plant's ability to absorb specific mineral nutrients.
19. Describe problems resulting from farm irrigation in arid regions.

20. Describe actions that can reduce loss of topsoil due to erosion.

21. Explain how phytoremediation can help detoxify polluted soil.

The Special Case of Nitrogen as a Plant Nutrient

22. Define nitrogen fixation and write an overall equation representing the conversion of gaseous nitrogen to ammonia.

23. Explain the importance of nitrogen-fixing bacteria to life on Earth.

24. Summarize the ecological role of each of the following groups of bacteria.

    a. ammonifying bacteria

    b. denitrifying bacteria

    c. nitrogen-fixing bacteria

    d. nitrifying bacteria

25. Explain why improving the protein yield of crops is a major goal of agricultural research.

Nutritional Adaptations: Symbiosis of Plants and Soil Microbes

26. Describe the development of a root nodule in a legume.

27. Explain how a legume protects its nitrogen-fixing bacteria from free oxygen, and explain why this protection is necessary.

28. Describe the basis for crop rotation.

29. Explain why a symbiosis between a legume and its nitrogen-fixing bacteria is considered to be mutualistic.

30. Explain why a symbiosis between a plant and a mycorrhizal fungus is considered to be mutualistic.

31. Distinguish between ectomycorrhizae and endomycorrhizae.

Nutritional Adaptations: Parasitism and Predation by Plants

32. Name one modification for nutrition in each of the following groups of plants:

    a. epiphytes

    b. parasitic plants

    c. carnivorous plants

Student Misconceptions

1. Some students have the mistaken idea that plants obtain "food" from their environment. Although these students understand that plants are photosynthetic, they consider a plant's uptake of water, minerals, and carbon dioxide as analogous to the feeding of animals. It is important to emphasize that the key ecological role of plants and other photoautotrophs is the synthesis of organic matter from inorganic precursors, using the energy from light. Clarify to students that, although plants take in raw materials from the air and soil, these inorganic nutrients are not energy sources and are not analogous to animal food.

2. This chapter provides an excellent opportunity to challenge student views of prokaryotes as important only because of their roles in "cheese and disease."

The crucial role of bacteria in the nitrogen cycle, especially in nitrogen fixation, can be used to reinforce the fact that all life on Earth depends on prokaryotic metabolism.

3. Mycorrhizal associations may be considered as plant oddities and not recognized as ubiquitous and essential to the majority of plants. Point out to your students that mycorrhizal associations are as old as plants themselves, that the great majority of plants have mycorrhizal associations, and that many plants, such as conifers, cannot survive without their fungal companions.

Chapter Guide to Teaching Resources

Overview: A nutritional network

Concept 37.1 Plants require certain chemical elements to complete their life cycle

Transparencies

Figure 37.2	The uptake of nutrients by a plant: A review
Figure 37.3	Hydroponic culture
Table 37.1	Essential elements in plants
Figure 37.6	The availability of soil water and minerals

Concept 37.2 Soil quality is a major determinant of plant distribution and growth

Student Media Resources

Activity: How plants obtain minerals from soil

Investigation: How does acid precipitation affect mineral deficiency?

Graph It: Global soil degradation

Concept 37.3 Nitrogen is often the mineral that has the greatest effect on plant growth

Transparencies

Figure 37.9	The role of soil bacteria in the nitrogen nutrition of plants (layer 1)
Figure 37.9	The role of soil bacteria in the nitrogen nutrition of plants (layer 2)
Figure 37.9	The role of soil bacteria in the nitrogen nutrition of plants (layer 3)

Student Media Resource

Activity: The nitrogen cycle

Concept 37.4 Plant nutritional adaptations often involve relationships with other organisms

Transparencies

Figure 37.11   Development of a soybean root nodule

Figure 37.12   Mycorrhizae

Instructor and Student Media Resource

Video: Sun dew trapping prey

For additional resources such as digital images and lecture outlines, go to the Campbell Media Manager or the Instructor Resources section of **www.campbellbiology.com.**

Key Terms

bacteroids	humus	nitrogen fixation
cation exchange	hydroponic culture	nitrogenase
crop rotation	inflorescence	nitrogen-fixing
ectomycorrhizae	loam	bacteria
endomycorrhizae	macronutrient	nodule
epiphyte	micronutrient	phytoremediation
essential element	mineral nutrient	sustainable agriculture
horizon	mycorrhizae	topsoil

Word Roots

ecto- = outside; **myco-** = a fungus; **-rhizo** = a root (*ectomycorrhizae:* a type of mycorrhizae in which the mycelium forms a dense sheath, or mantle, over the surface of the root; hyphae extend from the mantle into the soil, greatly increasing the surface area for water and mineral absorption)

endo- = inside (*endomycorrhizae:* a type of mycorrhizae that unlike ectomycorrhizae, do not have a dense mantle ensheathing the root; instead, microscopic fungal hyphae extend from the root into the soil)

macro- = large (*macronutrient:* elements required by plants and animals in relatively large amounts)

micro- = small (*micronutrient:* elements required by plants and animals in very small amounts)

-phyto = a plant (*phytoremediation:* an emerging, non-destructive technology that seeks to cheaply reclaim contaminated areas by taking advantage of the remarkable ability of some plant species to extract heavy metals and other pollutants from the soil and to concentrate them in easily harvested portions of the plant)

CHAPTER 38

Angiosperm Reproduction and Biotechnology

Teaching Objectives

Sexual Reproduction

1. In general terms, explain how the basic plant life cycle with alternation of generations is modified in angiosperms.
2. List four floral parts in order from outside to inside a flower.
3. From a diagram of an idealized flower, correctly label the following structures and describe the function of each structure:

   a. sepals

   b. petals

   c. stamen (filament and anther)

   d. carpel (style, ovary, ovule, and stigma)
4. Distinguish between:

   a. complete and incomplete flowers

   b. bisexual and unisexual flowers

   c. monoecious and dioecious plant species
5. Explain by which generation, structure, and process spores are produced.
6. Explain by which generation, structure, and process gametes are produced.
7. Name the structures that represent the male and female gametophytes of flowering plants.
8. Describe the development of an embryo sac and explain the fate of each of its cells.
9. Explain how pollen can be transferred between flowers.
10. Distinguish between pollination and fertilization.
11. Describe mechanisms that prevent self-pollination.
12. Outline the process of double fertilization. Explain the adaptive advantage of double fertilization in angiosperms.
13. Explain how fertilization in animals is similar to that in plants.
14. Describe the fate of the ovule and ovary after double fertilization. Note where major nutrients are stored as the embryo develops.
15. Describe the development and function of the endosperm. Distinguish between liquid endosperm and solid endosperm.

16. Describe the development of a plant embryo from the first mitotic division to the embryonic plant with rudimentary organs.

17. From a diagram, identify the following structures of a seed and state a function for each:

    a. seed coat

    b. proembryo

    c. suspensor

    d. hypocotyls

    e. radicle

    f. epicotyl

    g. plumule

    h. endosperm

    i. cotyledons

    j. shoot apex

18. Explain how a monocot and dicot seed differ.

19. Explain how fruit forms and ripens.

20. Distinguish among simple, aggregate, and multiple fruit. Give an example of each type of fruit.

21. Explain how selective breeding by humans has changed fruits.

22. Explain how seed dormancy can be advantageous to a plant. Describe some conditions for breaking dormancy.

23. Describe the process of germination in a garden bean.

Asexual Reproduction

24. Describe the natural mechanisms of vegetative reproduction in plants, including fragmentation and apomixis.

25. Explain the advantages and disadvantages of reproducing sexually and asexually.

26. Explain various methods that horticulturalists use to propagate plants from cuttings.

27. Explain how the technique of plant tissue culture can be used to clone and genetically engineer plants.

28. Describe the process of protoplast fusion and its potential agricultural impact.

Plant Biotechnology

29. Compare traditional plant-breeding techniques and genetic engineering, noting similarities and differences.

30. Describe two transgenic crops.

31. Describe some of the biological arguments for and against genetically modified crops.

Student Misconceptions

1. The angiosperm life cycle is very difficult for students to master. Many students find it hard to recognize that a tiny pollen grain and an embryo sac retained within the ovule of the sporophyte really represent a separate

generation. It is essential that students have a good understanding of the generalized alternation of generations life cycle in plants before they attempt to understand how this life cycle is modified in angiosperms.

2. Many students do not fully appreciate how fundamentally different plant life cycles are from the more familiar animal life cycles. Most students think of the embryo within the seed as the offspring of the sporophyte. They do not recognize that a seed actually contains structures contributed by three distinct generations of plants—the new sporophyte embryo, the remains of the female gametophyte, and the seed coat produced by the embryo's "grandparent."

3. Double fertilization is puzzling to many students. They are confused by the 3n condition of the endosperm, uncertain about how this triploid nucleus is produced, and unclear about the significance of this event to angiosperm reproduction.

Chapter Guide to Teaching Resources

Overview: To seed or not to seed

Concept 38.1 Pollination enables gametes to come together within a flower

Transparencies

Figure 38.2   An overview of angiosperm reproduction

Figure 38.3   Floral variations

Figure 38.4   The development of angiosperm gametophytes (pollen grains and embryo sacs)

Figure 38.5   "Pin" and "thrum" flower types reduce self-fertilization

Instructor and Student Media Resources

Activity: Angiosperm life cycle

Video: Time lapse of flowering plant life cycle

Video: Flower blooming time lapse

Video: Bee pollinating

Video: Bat pollinating agave plant

Concept 38.2 After fertilization, ovules develop into seeds and ovaries into fruits

Transparencies

Figure 38.6   Growth of the pollen tube and double fertilization

Figure 38.7   The development of a eudicot plant embryo

Figure 38.8   Seed structure

Figure 38.9   Developmental origin of fruits

Figure 38.10   Two common types of seed germination

Student Media Resources
Activity: Seed and fruit development
Investigation: What tells desert seeds when to germinate?

Concept 38.3 Many flowering plants clone themselves by asexual reproduction

Concept 38.4 Plant biotechnology is transforming agriculture

Student Media Resource
Activity: Making decisions about DNA technology: Golden rice

For additional resources such as digital images and lecture outlines, go to the Campbell Media Manager or the Instructor Resources section of **www.campbellbiology.com.**

Key Terms

aggregate fruit	fruit	receptacle
anther	hypocotyl	scion
apomixis	imbibition	scutellum
asexual reproduction	incomplete flower	seed coat
callus	inflorescence	self-incompatibility
carpel	megaspore	sepal
coleoptile	microspore	simple fruit
coleorhiza	monoecious	stamen
complete flower	multiple fruit	stigma
dioecious	ovary	stock
dormancy	ovule	style
double fertilization	petal	transgenic
endosperm	pistil	vegetative
epicotyl	protoplast fusion	reproduction
fragmentation	radicle	

Word Roots

a- = without; **-pomo** = fruit (*apomixis:* the asexual production of seeds)

anth- = a flower (*anther:* the terminal pollen sac of a stamen, inside which pollen grains with male gametes form in the flower of an angiosperm)

bi- = two (*bisexual flower:* a flower equipped with both stamens and carpels)

carp- = a fruit (*carpel:* the female reproductive organ of a flower, consisting of the stigma, style, and ovary)

coleo- = a sheath; **-rhiza** = a root (*coleorhiza:* the covering of the young root of the embryo of a grass seed)

di- = two (*dioecious:* referring to a plant species that has staminate and carpellate flowers on separate plants)

dorm- = sleep (*dormancy:* a condition typified by extremely low metabolic rate and a suspension of growth and development)

endo- = within (*endosperm:* a nutrient-rich tissue formed by the union of a sperm cell with two polar nuclei during double fertilization, which provides nourishment to the developing embryo in angiosperm seeds)

epi- = on, over (*epicotyl:* the embryonic axis above the point at which the cotyledons are attached)

gamet- = a wife or husband (*gametophyte:* the multicellular haploid form in organisms undergoing alternation of generations, which mitotically produces haploid gametes that unite and grow into the sporophyte generation)

hypo- = under (*hypocotyl:* the embryonic axis below the point at which the cotyledons are attached)

mega- = large (*megaspore:* a large, haploid spore that can continue to grow to eventually produce a female gametophyte)

micro- = small (*microspore:* a small, haploid spore that can give rise to a haploid male gametophyte)

mono- = one; **-ecious** = house (*monoecious:* referring to a plant species that has both staminate and carpellate flowers on the same individual)

peri- = around; **-carp** = a fruit (*pericarp:* the thickened wall of fruit)

proto- = first; **-plast** = formed, molded (*protoplast:* the contents of a plant cell exclusive of the cell wall)

scutell- = a little shield (*scutellum:* a specialized type of cotyledon found in the grass family)

sporo- = a seed; **-phyto** = a plant (*sporophyte:* the multicellular diploid form in organisms undergoing alternation of generations that results from a union of gametes and that meiotically produces haploid spores that grow into the gametophyte generation)

stam- = standing upright (*stamen:* the pollen-producing male reproductive organ of a flower, consisting of an anther and a filament)

uni- = one (*unisexual flower:* a flower missing either stamens or carpels)

CHAPTER 39

Plant Responses to Internal and External Signals

Teaching Objectives

Signal Transduction and Plant Responses

1. Compare the growth of a plant in darkness (etiolation) to the characteristics of greening (de-etiolation).

2. Describe the signal pathways associated with de-etiolation.

3. Describe the role of second messengers in the process of de-etiolation.

4. Describe the two main mechanisms by which a signaling pathway can activate an enzyme.

5. Explain, using several examples, what researchers have learned about the activity of plant hormones by study of mutant plants.

Plant Responses to Hormones

6. For the following scientists, describe their hypothesis, experiments, and conclusions about the mechanism of phototropism:

   a. Charles and Francis Darwin

   b. Peter Boysen-Jensen

   c. Frits Went

7. List six classes of plant hormones, describe their major functions, and note where they are produced in the plant.

8. Explain how a hormone may cause its effect on plant growth and development.

9. Describe a possible mechanism for the polar transport of auxin.

10. According to the acid growth hypothesis, explain how auxin can initiate cell elongation.

11. Explain why 2,4-D is widely used as a weed killer.

12. Explain how the ratio of cytokinin to auxin affects cell division and cell differentiation.

13. Describe the evidence that suggests that factors other than auxin from the terminal bud may control apical dominance.

14. Describe how stem elongation and fruit growth depend on a synergism between auxin and gibberellins.

15. Explain the probable mechanism by which gibberellins trigger seed germination.

16. Describe the functions of brassinosteroids in plants.

17. Describe how abscisic acid (ABA) helps prepare a plant for winter.

18. Describe the effects of ABA on seed dormancy and drought stress.

19. Describe the role of ethylene in the triple response to mechanical stress, apoptosis, leaf abscission, and fruit ripening.

Plant Responses to Light

20. Define *photomorphogenesis* and note which colors are most important to this process.

21. Compare the roles of blue-light photoreceptors and phytochromes.

22. Describe the phenomenon of chromophore photoreversibility and explain its role in light-induced germination of lettuce seeds.

23. Define *circadian rhythm* and explain what happens when an organism is artificially maintained in a constant environment.

24. List some common factors that entrain biological clocks.

25. Define *photoperiodism.*

26. Distinguish among short-day, long-day, and day-neutral plants. Explain why these names are misleading.

27. Explain what factors other than night length may control flowering and what is necessary for flowering to occur.

Plant Responses to Environmental Stimuli Other than Light

28. Describe how plants apparently tell up from down. Explain why roots display positive gravitropism and shoots exhibit negative gravitropism.

29. Distinguish between thigmotropism and thigmomorphogenesis.

30. Describe how motor organs can cause rapid leaf movements.

31. Provide a plausible explanation for how a stimulus that causes rapid leaf movement can be transmitted through the plant.

32. Describe the challenges posed by, and the responses of plants to, the following environmental stresses: drought, flooding, salt stress, heat stress, and cold stress.

Plant Defense: Responses to Herbivores and Pathogens

33. Explain how plants deter herbivores with physical and chemical defenses.

34. Describe the multiple ways that plants defend against pathogens.

Student Misconceptions

1. Many students think of plants as essentially passive and helpless in the face of environmental challenges. Despite being rooted in the soil, plants are neither passive nor defenseless. Like animals, plants detect environmental changes with cellular receptors. As in animals, plant receptors initiate signal transduction pathways. Unlike animals, few plants respond by movement. Instead, plants respond to environmental stimuli by modifying their morphology and/or physiology.

2. Regulation of circadian rhythms through a protein transcription factor that self-inhibits its own production provides an excellent and interesting example of feedback control and may help to clarify this concept for students.

3. Students are aware that plants have physical and chemical defenses against herbivores. However, they may be surprised to learn that some plants broadcast volatile chemicals to recruit parasitoids to attack insect herbivores or to warn other plants of herbivorous attack and give them time to mount their own chemical defense.

Chapter Guide to Teaching Resources

Overview: Stimuli and a stationary life

Concept 39.1 Signal transduction pathways link signal reception to response

Transparencies

Concept 39.2 Plant hormones help coordinate growth, development, and responses to stimuli

Transparencies

Instructor and Student Media Resources

Video: Phototropism

Activity: Leaf abscission

Investigation: What plant hormones affect organ formation?

Concept 39.3 Responses to light are critical for plant success

Transparencies

Figure 39.17   What wavelengths stimulate phototropic bending toward light?

Figure 39.19   Structure of a phytochrome

Figure 39.20   Phytochrome: A molecular switching mechanism

Figure 39.22   How does interrupting the dark period with a brief exposure to light affect flowering?

Figure 39.23   Is phytochrome the pigment that measures the interruption of dark periods in photoperiodic response?

Figure 39.24   Is there a flowering hormone?

Student Media Resource

Activity: Flowering lab

Concept 39.4 Plants respond to a wide variety of stimuli other than light

Instructor and Student Media Resources

Video: Gravitropism

Video: *Mimosa* leaf

Concept 39.5 Plants defend themselves against herbivores and pathogens

Transparencies

Figure 39.29   A maize leaf "recruits" a parasitoid wasp as a defensive response to an herbivore, an army-worm caterpillar

Figure 39.30   Gene-for-gene resistance of plants to pathogens: The receptor-ligand model

Figure 39.31   Defense responses against an avirulent pathogen

For additional resources such as digital images and lecture outlines, go to the Campbell Media Manager or the Instructor Resources section of **www.campbellbiology.com.**

Key Terms

abiotic
abscisic acid (ABA)
action potential
action spectrum
apoptosis
auxin
avirulent
biotic
blue-light
 photoreceptors
brassinosteroids
circadian rhythm
cytokinins
day-neutral plant
de-etiolation
elicitor
ethylene

etiolation
expansins
florigen
gene-for-gene
 recognition
gibberellins
gravitropism
heat-shock protein
hormone
hypersensitive
 response (HR)
jasmonic acid
long-day plant
oligosaccharin
photomorphogenesis
photoperiodism
phototropism

phytoalexin
phytochromes
PR protein
salicylic acid
second messenger
short-day plant
statolith
systemic acquired
 resistance (SAR)
thigmomorphogenesis
thigmotropism
triple response
tropism
vernalization
virulent

Word Roots

aux- = grow, enlarge (*auxins:* a class of plant hormones, including indoleacetic acid, having a variety of effects, such as phototropic response through the stimulation of cell elongation, stimulation of secondary growth, and the development of leaf traces and fruit)

circ- = a circle (*circadian rhythm:* a physiological cycle of about 24 hours, present in all eukaryotic organisms, that persists even in the absence of external cues)

crypto- = hidden; **-chromo** = color (*cryptochrome:* the name given to the unidentified blue-light photoreceptor)

cyto- = cell; **-kine** = moving (*cytokinins:* a class of related plant hormones that retard aging and act in concert with auxins to stimulate cell division, influence the pathway of differentiation, and control apical dominance)

gibb- = humped (*gibberellins:* a class of related plant hormones that stimulate growth in the stem and leaves, trigger the germination of seeds and breaking of bud dormancy, and stimulate fruit development with auxin)

hyper- = excessive (*hypersensitive response:* a vigorous, localized defense response to a pathogen that is avirulent based on an *R-Avr* match)

photo- = light; **-trop** = turn, change (*phototropism:* growth of a plant shoot toward or away from light)

phyto- = a plant; **-alexi** = to ward off (*phytoalexin:* an antibiotic, produced by plants, that destroys microorganisms or inhibits their growth)

stato- = standing, placed; **-lith** = a stone (*statolith:* specialized plastids that help a plant distinguish up from down)

thigmo- = a touch; **morpho-** = form; **-genesis** = origin (*thigmomorphogenesis:* a response in plants to chronic mechanical stimulation, resulting from increased ethylene production; an example is thickening stems in response to strong winds)

zea- = a grain; **-xantho** = yellow (*zeaxanthin:* a blue-light photoreceptor involved in stomatal opening)

CHAPTER 40

Basic Principles of
Animal Form and Function

Teaching Objectives

Functional Animal Anatomy: An Overview

1. Define *bioenergetics*.
2. Distinguish between anatomy and physiology. Explain how functional anatomy relates to these terms.

Body Plans and the External Environment

3. Explain how physical laws constrain animal form.
4. Explain how the size and shape of an animal's body affect its interactions with the environment.
5. Define *tissue*.
6. Distinguish among collagenous fibers, elastic fibers, and reticular fibers.
7. From micrographs or diagrams, correctly identify the following animal tissues, explain how their structure relates to their functions, and note examples of each type.
   a. Epithelial tissue
   b. Connective tissue
      i. Loose connective tissue
      ii. Adipose tissue
      iii. Fibrous connective tissue
      iv. Cartilage
      v. Bone
      vi. Blood
   c. Muscle tissue
      i. Skeletal (striated) muscle
      ii. Cardiac muscle
      iii. Smooth muscle
   d. Nervous tissue
      i. Neuron

Introduction to the Bioenergetics of Animals

8. Describe the basic sources of chemical energy and their fate in animal cells.

9. Define *biosynthesis.*

10. Define *metabolic rate* and explain how it can be determined for animals.

11. Distinguish between endothermic and exothermic animals.

12. Describe the relationship between metabolic rate and body size.

13. Distinguish between basal metabolic rate and standard metabolic rate. Describe the major factors that influence energy requirements.

14. Describe the natural variations found in the energy strategies of endotherms and ectotherms.

Regulating the Internal Environment

15. Distinguish between regulators and conformers for a particular environmental variable.

16. Define *homeostasis.* Describe the three functional components of a homeostatic control system.

17. Distinguish between positive and negative feedback mechanisms.

18. Define *thermoregulation.* Explain in general terms how endotherms and ectotherms manage their heat budgets.

19. Name four physical processes by which animals exchange heat with their environment.

20. Discuss the role of hair, feathers, and adipose tissue in insulation.

21. Explain the role of vasoconstriction and vasodilation in modifying the transfer of body heat with the environment.

22. Describe animal adaptations to facilitate evaporative cooling.

23. Describe thermoregulatory mechanisms utilized by endothermic invertebrates.

24. Explain how ectotherms and endotherms may acclimatize to changing environmental temperatures.

25. Explain the role of heat-shock proteins in helping cells to cope with severe temperature changes.

26. Define *torpor, hibernation, estivation,* and *daily torpor.*

Student Misconceptions

1. Students may not realize that the terms *regulator* and *conformer* describe how an animal copes with a specific environmental variable, and do not characterize the animal itself.

2. Many students confuse the terms *endotherm* and *ectotherm* with the concepts of regulators and conformers and the familiar terms *warm-blooded* and *cold-blooded.* Clarify for students that both endotherms and ectotherms may regulate their body temperature. They differ in the source of heat used to maintain body temperature, and the body temperatures of thermoregulating ectotherms may vary considerably more than those of endotherms. Discourage

students' use of the terms *warm-blooded* and *cold-blooded*. These nonscientific terms can be very misleading. Many ectotherms are able to use behavioral means to maintain body temperatures well above ambient temperatures.

3. Students may think of endothermy as "advanced" and ectothermy as "primitive," with the unspoken connotation that endothermy is a more successful strategy for thermoregulation. Point out to students that ectothermy is an effective and successful strategy under many conditions, and that ectotherms are considerably more abundant and diverse than endotherms.

Chapter Guide to Teaching Resources

Overview: Diverse forms, common challenges

Concept 40.1 Physical laws and the environment constrain animal size and shape

Transparencies
Figure 40.3   Contact with the environment
Figure 40.4   Internal exchange surfaces of complex animals

Instructor and Student Media Resource
Video: Galápagos sea lion

Concept 40.2 Animal form and function are correlated at all levels of organization

Transparencies
Figure 40.5   Structure and function in animal tissues: Epithelial tissue
Figure 40.5   Structure and function in animal tissues: Connective tissue
Figure 40.5   Structure and function in animal tissues: Muscle tissue
Table 40.1   Organ systems: Their main components and functions in mammals
Figure 40.6   Tissue layers of the stomach, a digestive organ

Student Media Resources
Activity: Overview of animal tissues
Activity: Epithelial tissue
Activity: Connective tissue
Activity: Nervous tissue
Activity: Muscle tissue

Concept 40.3 Animals use the chemical energy in food to sustain form and function

Transparencies

Figure 40.7   Bioenergetics of an animal: An overview

Figure 40.9   Maximum metabolic rates over different time spans

Figure 40.10 Energy budgets for four animals

Instructor and Student Media Resources

Video: Hydra eating *Daphnia*

Investigation: How does temperature affect metabolic rate in *Daphnia*?

Concept 40.4 Animals regulate their internal environment within relatively narrow limits

Transparency

Figure 40.11 A nonliving example of negative feedback: Control of room temperature

Student Media Resource

Activity: Regulation: Negative and positive feedback

Concept 40.5 Thermoregulation contributes to homeostasis and involves anatomy, physiology, and behavior

Transparencies

Figure 40.12 The relationship between body temperature and environmental temperature in an aquatic endotherm and ectotherm

Figure 40.13 Heat exchange between an organism and its environment

Figure 40.14 Mammalian integumentary system

Figure 40.15 Countercurrent heat exchangers

Figure 40.16 Thermoregulation in large, active bony fishes and sharks

Figure 40.17 Internal temperature in the winter moth

Figure 40.20 Preflight warmup in the hawkmoth

Figure 40.21 The thermostat function of the hypothalamus in human thermoregulation

Figure 40.22 Body temperature and metabolism during hibernation in Belding's ground squirrels

For additional resources such as digital images and lecture outlines, go to the Campbell Media Manager or the Instructor Resources section of **www.campbellbiology.com.**

Key Terms

abdominal cavity
acclimatization
adipose tissue
anatomy
basal metabolic rate
  (BMR)
basement membrane
bioenergetics
blood
bone
brown fat
cardiac muscle
cartilage
chondrocyte
collagenous fiber
columnar
conduction
conformer
connective tissue
convection
countercurrent heat
  exchanger
cuboidal
daily torpor
ectotherm
ectothermic
elastic fiber

endotherm
endothermic
epithelial tissue
estivation
evaporation
fibroblast
fibrous connective
  tissue
glandular epithelium
heat-shock protein
hibernation
homeostasis
integumentary system
interstitial fluid
ligament
loose connective tissue
macrophage
mesentery
metabolic rate
mucous membrane
muscle tissue
negative feedback
nervous tissue
neuron
nonshivering
  thermogenesis (NST)
organ

organ system
osteoblast
osteon
physiology
positive feedback
radiation
regulator
reticular fiber
simple epithelium
skeletal muscle
  (striated muscle)
smooth muscle
squamous
standard metabolic
  rate (SMR)
stratified epithelium
stress-induced protein
striated muscle
tendon
thermoregulation
thoracic cavity
tissue
torpor
vasoconstriction
vasodilation

Word Roots

chondro- = cartilage; **-cyte** = cell (*chondrocytes:* cartilage cells)

con- = with; **-vect** = carried (*convection:* the mass movement of warmed air or liquid to or from the surface of a body or object)

counter- = opposite (*countercurrent heat exchanger:* a special arrangement of blood vessels that helps trap heat in the body core and is important in reducing heat loss in many endotherms)

-dilat = expanded (*vasodilation:* an increase in the diameter of superficial blood vessels triggered by nerve signals that relax the muscles of the vessel walls)

ecto- = outside; **-therm** = heat (*ectotherm:* an animal, such as a reptile, fish, or amphibian, that must use environmental energy and behavioral adaptations to regulate its body temperature)

endo- = inner (*endotherm:* an animal, such as a bird or mammal, that uses metabolic energy to maintain a constant body temperature)

fibro- = a fiber (*fibroblast:* a type of cell in loose connective tissue that secretes the protein ingredients of the extracellular fibers)

homeo- = same; **-stasis** = standing, posture (*homeostasis:* the steady-state physiological condition of the body)

inter- = between (*interstitial fluid:* the internal environment of vertebrates, consisting of the fluid filling the space between cells)

macro- = large (*macrophage:* an amoeboid cell that moves through tissue fibers, engulfing bacteria and dead cells by phagocytosis)

osteo- = bone; **-blast** = a bud, sprout (*osteoblasts:* bone-forming cells that deposit a matrix of collagen)

CHAPTER 41

Animal Nutrition

Teaching Objectives

Nutritional Requirements of Animals

1. Compare the bioenergetics of animals when energy balance is positive and when it is negative.
2. Name the three nutrition needs that must be met by a nutritionally adequate diet.
3. Distinguish among undernourishment, overnourishment, and malnourishment.
4. Explain why fat hoarding may have provided a fitness advantage to our hunter-gatherer ancestors.
5. Explain the role of leptin in the regulation of fat storage and use.
6. Define *essential nutrients* and describe the four classes of essential nutrients.
7. Distinguish between water-soluble and fat-soluble vitamins.

Overview of Food Processing

8. Define and compare the four main stages of food processing.
9. Compare intracellular and extracellular digestion.

The Mammalian Digestive System

10. Describe the common processes and structural components of the mammalian digestive system.
11. Name three functions of saliva.
12. Compare where and how the major types of macromolecules are digested and absorbed within the mammalian digestive system.
13. Explain why pepsin does not digest the stomach lining.
14. Explain how the small intestine is specialized for digestion and absorption.
15. Describe the major functions of the large intestine.

Evolutionary Adaptations of Vertebrate Digestive Systems

16. Relate variations in dentition and length of the digestive system to the feeding strategies and diets of herbivores, carnivores, and omnivores.
17. Describe the roles of symbiotic microorganisms in vertebrate digestion.

Student Misconceptions

1. Students may have difficulty understanding that many features of human anatomy and physiology can be understood as adaptations to the selective pressures faced by our hunter-gatherer ancestors. Human fat hoarding and preference for high-salt foods are deadly today, but likely gave our ancestors a fitness advantage.

2. Students may not realize that essential nutrients vary from organism to organism, depending on their individual biosynthetic capabilities.

3. Point out to your students the enormous numbers—and important roles—of symbiotic bacteria in the human colon.

Chapter Guide to Teaching Resources

Overview: The need to feed

Instructor and Student Media Resources
Activity: Feeding mechanisms of animals
Video: Whale eating a seal
Video: Lobster mouth parts
Video: *Paramecium* vacuole
Video: *Paramecium* cilia-V

Concept 41.1 Homeostatic mechanisms manage an animal's energy budget

Transparencies
Figure 41.3   Homeostatic regulation of cellular fuel
Figure 41.5   A few of the appetite-regulating hormones

Concept 41.2 An animal's diet must supply carbon skeletons and essential nutrients

Transparencies
Figure 41.10   Essential amino acids from a vegetarian diet
Table 41.1   Vitamin requirements of humans
Table 41.2   Mineral requirements of humans

Student Media Resource
Activity: Analyzing food labels

Concept 41.3 The main stages of food processing are ingestion, digestion, absorption, and elimination

Transparencies

Figure 41.12   The four stages of food processing

Figure 41.13   Digestion in a hydra

Figure 41.14   Variation in alimentary canals

Instructor and Student Media Resource

Video: Hydra eating *Daphnia*

Concept 41.4 Each organ of the mammalian digestive system has specialized food-processing functions

Transparencies

Figure 41.15   The human digestive system

Figure 41.16   From mouth to stomach: The swallowing reflex and esophageal peristalsis (layer 1)

Figure 41.16   From mouth to stomach: The swallowing reflex and esophageal peristalsis (layer 2)

Figure 41.16   From mouth to stomach: The swallowing reflex and esophageal peristalsis (layer 3)

Figure 41.17   The stomach and gastric juice

Figure 41.19   The duodenum

Figure 41.20   Protease activation

Figure 41.21   Flowchart of enzymatic digestion in the human digestive system

Figure 41.22   Hormonal control of digestion

Figure 41.23   The structure of the small intestine

Figure 41.24   Digestion and absorption of fats

Student Media Resources

Activity: Digestive system function

Investigation: What role does amylase play in digestion?

Activity: Hormonal control of digestion

Concept 41.5 Evolutionary adaptations of vertebrate digestive systems are often associated with diet

Transparencies

Figure 41.26   Dentition and diet

Figure 41.27   The digestive tracts of a carnivore (coyote) and herbivore (koala) compared

Figure 41.28   Ruminant digestion

For additional resources such as digital images and lecture outlines, go to the Campbell Media Manager or the Instructor Resources section of **www.campbellbiology.com.**

Key Terms

absorption
acid chyme
alimentary canal
appendix
bile
bolus
bulk feeder
carnivore
cecum
chylomicron
colon
complete digestive
  tract
digestion
duodenum
elimination
enzymatic hydrolysis
epiglottis
esophagus
essential amino acid

essential fatty acids
essential nutrient
extracellular digestion
feces
fluid feeder
gallbladder
gastric juice
gastrovascular cavity
hepatic portal vein
herbivore
ingestion
intracellular digestion
lacteal
large intestine
liver
malnourished
microvillus
mineral
omnivore
oral cavity

overnourishment
pancreas
pepsin
pepsinogen
peristalsis
pharynx
pyloric sphincter
rectum
ruminant
salivary amylase
salivary glands
small intestine
sphincter
stomach
substrate feeder
suspension feeder
undernourishment
villus
vitamin

Word Roots

chylo- = juice; **-micro** = small (*chylomicron:* small globules composed of fats that are mixed with cholesterol and coated with special proteins)

chymo- = juice; **-trypsi** = wearing out (*chymotrypsin:* an enzyme found in the duodenum; it is specific for peptide bonds adjacent to certain amino acids)

di- = two (*dipeptidase:* an enzyme found attached to the intestinal lining; it splits small peptides)

entero- = the intestines (*enterogastrones:* a category of hormones secreted by the wall of the duodenum)

epi- = over; **-glotti** = the tongue (*epiglottis:* a cartilaginous flap that blocks the top of the windpipe, the glottis, during swallowing)

extra- = outside (*extracellular digestion:* the breakdown of food outside cells)

gastro- = stomach; **-vascula** = a little vessel (*gastrovascular cavities:* an extensive pouch that serves as the site of extracellular digestion and a passageway to disperse materials throughout most of an animal's body)

herb- = grass; **-vora** = eat (*herbivore:* a heterotrophic animal that eats plants)

hydro- = water; **-lysis** = to loosen (*hydrolysis:* a chemical process that lyses or splits molecules by the addition of water)

intra- = inside (*intracellular digestion:* the joining of food vacuoles and lysosomes to allow chemical digestion to occur within the cytoplasm of a cell)

micro- = small; **-villi** = shaggy hair (*microvilli:* many fine, fingerlike projections of the epithelial cells in the lumen of the small intestine that increase its surface area)

omni- = all (*omnivore:* a heterotrophic animal that consumes both meat and plant material)

peri- = around; **-stalsis** = a constriction (*peristalsis:* rhythmic waves of contraction of smooth muscle that push food along the digestive tract)

CHAPTER 42

Circulation and Gas Exchange

Teaching Objectives

Circulation in Animals

1. Describe the need for circulatory and respiratory systems due to increasing animal body size.
2. Explain how a gastrovascular cavity functions in part as a circulatory system.
3. Distinguish between open and closed circulatory systems. List the three basic components common to both systems.
4. List the structural components of a vertebrate circulatory system and relate their structure to their functions.
5. Describe the general relationship between metabolic rates and the structure of the vertebrate circulatory system.
6. Using diagrams, compare and contrast the circulatory systems of fish, amphibians, non-bird reptiles, and mammals or birds.
7. Distinguish between pulmonary and systemic circuits and explain the functions of each.
8. Explain the advantage of double circulation over a single circuit.
9. Define a *cardiac cycle*, distinguish between systole and diastole, and explain what causes the first and second heart sounds.
10. Define *cardiac output* and describe two factors that influence it.
11. List the four heart valves, describe their location, and explain their functions.
12. Define *heart murmur* and explain its cause.
13. Define *sinoatrial (SA) node* and describe its location in the heart.
14. Distinguish between a myogenic heart and a neurogenic heart.
15. Describe the origin and pathway of the action potential (cardiac impulse) in the normal human heart.
16. Explain how the pace of the SA node can be modulated by nerves, hormones, body temperature, and exercise.
17. Relate the structures of capillaries, arteries, and veins to their functions.
18. Explain why blood flow through capillaries is substantially slower than it is through arteries and veins.
19. Define *blood pressure* and describe how it is measured.
20. Explain how peripheral resistance and cardiac output affect blood pressure.

21. Explain how blood returns to the heart even though it must sometimes travel from the lower extremities against gravity.

22. Explain how blood flow through capillary beds is regulated.

23. Explain how osmotic pressure and hydrostatic pressure regulate the exchange of fluid and solutes across capillaries.

24. Describe the composition of lymph and explain how the lymphatic system helps the normal functioning of the circulatory system. Explain the role of lymph nodes in body defense.

25. Describe the composition and functions of plasma.

26. Relate the structure of erythrocytes to their function.

27. List the five main types of white blood cells and characterize their functions.

28. Describe the structure of platelets.

29. Outline the formation of erythrocytes from their origin from stem cells in the red marrow of bones to their destruction by phagocytic cells.

30. Describe the hormonal control of erythrocyte production.

31. Outline the sequence of events that occurs during blood clotting and explain what prevents spontaneous clotting in the absence of injury.

32. Distinguish between a heart attack and a stroke.

33. Distinguish between low-density lipoproteins (LDLs) and high-density lipoproteins (HDLs).

34. List the factors that have been correlated with an increased risk of cardiovascular disease.

Gas Exchange in Animals

35. Define *gas exchange* and distinguish between a respiratory medium and a respiratory surface.

36. Describe the general requirements for a respiratory surface and list a variety of respiratory organs that meet these requirements.

37. Describe respiratory adaptations of aquatic animals.

38. Describe the advantages and disadvantages of water as a respiratory medium.

39. Describe countercurrent exchange and explain why it is more efficient than the concurrent flow of water and blood.

40. Describe the advantages and disadvantages of air as a respiratory medium and explain how insect tracheal systems are adapted for efficient gas exchange in a terrestrial environment.

41. For the human respiratory system, describe the movement of air through air passageways to the alveolus, listing the structures that air must pass through on its journey.

42. Compare positive and negative pressure breathing. Explain how respiratory movements in humans ventilate the lungs.

43. Distinguish between tidal volume, vital capacity, and residual volume.

44. Explain how the respiratory systems of birds and mammals differ.

45. Explain how breathing is controlled in humans.

46. Define *partial pressure* and explain how it influences diffusion across respiratory surfaces.

47. Describe the adaptive advantage of respiratory pigments in circulatory systems. Distinguish between hemocyanin and hemoglobin as respiratory pigments.

48. Draw the Hb-oxygen dissociation curve, explain the significance of its shape, and explain how the affinity of hemoglobin for oxygen changes with oxygen concentration.

49. Describe how carbon dioxide is picked up at the tissues and deposited in the lungs.

50. Describe the respiratory adaptations of the pronghorn that give it great speed and endurance.

51. Describe respiratory adaptations of diving mammals and the role of myoglobin.

Student Misconceptions

1. The velocity of blood slows greatly as blood flows from arterioles into capillaries. This slow blood flow in the capillaries increases the efficiency of transfer of material between blood and tissues, by providing more time for diffusion. Many students think that the blood slows because the narrow capillaries offer great resistance to blood flow. These students are not aware that the rate of fluid flow is determined by the total cross-sectional area of the vessels. In the circulatory system, the total cross-sectional area of the capillaries greatly exceeds that of the wider vessels, allowing flow velocity in the capillaries to remain low.

2. Some students have the mistaken idea that exchange of material between the blood and the tissues takes place by mass flow of materials from the blood. Emphasize to your students that diffusion is the most important process accounting for this exchange, as nutrients and oxygen diffuse into the tissues along the full length of the capillary. The branching of the capillaries, their thin walls, and the slow flow of blood through the capillaries all serve to facilitate diffusion.

3. Some students think of the three-chambered hearts of amphibians and most non-bird reptiles as inferior to the four-chambered hearts of mammals and birds. Students may consider the three-chambered heart to be a transitional stage in a progressive evolutionary sequence. Point out to your students that this intermediate heart evolved almost 400 million years ago. The extent of mixing of oxygen-rich and oxygen-poor blood in the circulatory systems of animals with three-chambered hearts varies considerably. These hearts are facultative, rather than inferior, and are able to adjust blood flow depending on circumstances. This may allow diversion of blood from the lungs when they are not the primary site of oxygen uptake: when the animal is submerged, or when oxygen is taken up across gills or skin.

4. Remind your students that insects do not transport oxygen or carbon dioxide in their blood.

Further Reading

Michael, J. A., M. P. Wenderoth, H. I. Modell, W. Cliff, B. Horwitz, P. McHale, D. Richardson, D. Silverthorn, S. Williams, and S. Whitescarver. 2002. Undergraduate's understanding of cardiovascular phenomena. *Advances in Physiology Education, 26(2)*, 72–84.

Yip, D. Y. 1999. Teachers' misconceptions of the circulatory system. *Journal of Biological Education, 32(3)*, 207–215.

Chapter Guide to Teaching Resources

Overview: Trading with the environment

Concept 42.1 Circulatory systems reflect phylogeny

Transparencies

Figure 42.2   Internal transport in the cnidarian *Aurelia*

Figure 42.3   Open and closed circulatory systems

Figure 42.4   Vertebrate circulatory systems

Concept 42.2 Double circulation in mammals depends on the anatomy and pumping cycle of the heart

Transparencies

Figure 42.5   The mammalian cardiovascular system: An overview

Figure 42.6   The mammalian heart: A closer look

Figure 42.7   The cardiac cycle

Figure 42.8   The control of heart rhythm

Student Media Resource

Activity: Mammalian cardiovascular system structure

Concept 42.3 Physical principles govern blood circulation

Transparencies

Figure 42.9   The structure of blood vessels

Figure 42.10   Blood flow in veins

Figure 42.11   The interrelationship of blood flow velocity, cross-sectional area of blood vessels, and blood pressure

Figure 42.12   Measurement of blood pressure (layer 1)

Figure 42.12   Measurement of blood pressure (layer 2)

Figure 42.12   Measurement of blood pressure (layer 3)

Figure 42.12   Measurement of blood pressure (layer 4)

Figure 42.13   Blood flow in capillary beds

Figure 42.14   Fluid exchange between capillaries and the interstitial fluid

Student Media Resources

Activity: Path of blood flow in mammals

Activity: Mammalian cardiovascular system function

Biology Labs On-Line: CardioLab

Concept 42.4 Blood is a connective tissue with cells suspended in plasma

Transparencies

Figure 42.15   The composition of mammalian blood

Figure 42.16   Differentiation of blood cells

Figure 42.17   Blood clotting

Student Media Resource

Investigation: How is cardiovascular fitness measured?

Concept 42.5 Gas exchange occurs across specialized respiratory surfaces

Transparencies

Figure 42.19   The role of gas exchange in bioenergetics

Figure 42.20   Diversity in the structure of gills, external body surfaces functioning in gas exchange

Figure 42.21   The structure and function of fish gills

Figure 42.22   Tracheal systems

Figure 42.23   The mammalian respiratory system

Figure 42.24   Negative pressure breathing

Figure 42.25   The avian respiratory system

Student Media Resource

Activity: The human respiratory system

Concept 42.6 Breathing ventilates the lungs

Transparency

Figure 42.26   Automatic control of breathing

Concept 42.7 Respiratory pigments bind and transport gases

Transparencies

Figure 42.27   Loading and unloading of respiratory gases

Figure 42.28   Hemoglobin loading and unloading of O_2

Figure 42.29   Dissociation curves for hemoglobin

Figure 42.30   Carbon dioxide transport in the blood

Student Media Resource

Biology Labs On-Line: HemoglobinLab

Review

Transparency

Page 897   Dissociation curves for two hemoglobins

For additional resources such as digital images and lecture outlines, go to the Campbell Media Manager or the Instructor Resources section of **www.campbellbiology.com.**

Key Terms

alveolus
arteriole
artery
atherosclerosis
atrioventricular (AV) node
atrioventricular valve
atrium
blood
blood pressure
blood vessels
Bohr shift
breathing
breathing control center
bronchiole
bronchus
capillary
capillary bed
cardiac cycle
cardiac output
cardiovascular disease
cardiovascular system
closed circulatory system
countercurrent exchange
diaphragm
diastole
diastolic pressure
dissociation curve
double circulation
electrocardiogram (ECG or EKG)
endothelium
erythrocyte

erythropoietin (EPO)
fibrin
fibrinogen
gas exchange
gill
gill circulation
heart
heart attack
heart murmur
heart rate
hemocyanin
hemoglobin
hemolymph
hemophilia
high-density lipoprotein (HDL)
hypertension
larynx
leukocyte
low-density lipoprotein (LDL)
lung
lymph
lymph node
lymphatic system
myogenic heart
myoglobin
negative pressure breathing
neurogenic heart
open circulatory system
pacemaker
parabronchus
partial pressure
peripheral resistance

plasma
platelet
positive pressure breathing
pulmocutaneous circuit
pulmonary circuit
pulse
red blood cell
residual volume
respiratory medium
respiratory pigment
respiratory surface
semilunar valve
sinoatrial (SA) node
sinus
stem cell
stroke
stroke volume
systemic circuit
systemic circulation
systole
systolic pressure
thrombus
tidal volume
trachea
tracheal system
vein
ventilation
ventricle
venule
vital capacity
vocal cord
white blood cell

Word Roots

alveol- = a cavity (*alveoli:* one of the dead-end, multilobed air sacs that constitute the gas exchange surface of the lungs)

atrio- = a vestibule; **-ventriculo** = ventricle (*atrioventricular node:* a region of specialized muscle tissue between the right atrium and right ventricle; it generates electrical impulses that primarily cause the ventricles to contract)

cardi- = heart; **-vascula** = a little vessel (*cardiovascular system:* the closed circulatory system characteristic of vertebrates)

counter- = opposite (*countercurrent exchange:* the opposite flow of adjacent fluids that maximizes transfer rates)

endo- = inner (*endothelium:* the innermost, simple squamous layer of cells lining the blood vessels; the only constituent structure of capillaries)

erythro- = red; **-poiet** = produce (*erythropoietin:* a hormone produced in the kidney when tissues of the body do not receive enough oxygen. This hormone stimulates the production of erythrocytes)

fibrino- = a fiber; **-gen** = produce (*fibrinogen:* the inactive form of the plasma protein that is converted to the active form fibrin, which aggregates into threads that form the framework of a blood clot)

hemo- = blood; **-philia** = loving (*hemophilia:* a human genetic disease caused by a sex-linked recessive allele, characterized by excessive bleeding following injury)

leuko- = white; **-cyte** = cell (*leukocyte:* a white blood cell)

myo- = muscle (*myoglobin:* an oxygen-storing, pigmented protein in muscle cells)

para- = beside, near (*parabronchi:* the sites of gas exchange in bird lungs; they allow air to flow past the respiratory surface in just one direction)

pluri- = more, several; **-potent** = powerful (*pluripotent stem cell:* a cell within bone marrow that is a progenitor for any kind of blood cell)

pulmo- = a lung; **-cutane** = skin (*pulmocutaneous:* the route of circulation that directs blood to the skin and lungs)

semi- = half; **-luna** = moon (*semilunar valve:* a valve located at the two exits of the heart, where the aorta leaves the left ventricle and the pulmonary artery leaves the right ventricle)

thrombo- = a clot (*thrombus:* a clump of platelets and fibrin that blocks the flow of blood through a blood vessel)

CHAPTER 43

The Immune System

Teaching Objectives

Nonspecific Defenses Against Infection

1. Explain what is meant by nonspecific defense and list the nonspecific lines of defense in the vertebrate body.

2. Distinguish between:
   a. innate and acquired immunity
   b. humoral and cell mediated response

3. Explain how the physical barrier of skin is reinforced by chemical defenses.

4. Define *phagocytosis*. Name four types of phagocytic leukocytes.

5. Explain how interferon limits cell-to-cell spread of viruses.

6. Describe the inflammation response, including how it is triggered.

7. Describe the factors that influence phagocytosis during the inflammation response.

8. Explain how the action of natural killer cells differs from the action of phagocytes.

9. Explain what occurs during the condition known as septic shock.

10. Describe the roles of antimicrobial proteins in innate immunity.

How Specific Immunity Arises

11. Distinguish between antigens and antibodies.

12. Distinguish between antigen and epitope.

13. Explain how B lymphocytes and T lymphocytes recognize specific antigens.

14. Explain how the particular structure of a lymphocyte's antigen binding site forms during development. Explain the role of recombinase in generating the staggering variability of lymphocytes.

15. Explain why the antigen receptors of lymphocytes are tested for self-reactivity during development. Predict the consequences that would occur if such testing did not take place.

16. Describe the mechanism of clonal selection. Distinguish between effector cells and memory cells.

17. Distinguish between primary and secondary immune responses.

18. Describe the cellular basis for immunological memory.

19. Describe the variation found in the major histocompatibility complex (MHC) and its role in the rejection of tissue transplants. Explain the adaptive advantage of this variation.

20. Compare the structures and functions of cytotoxic T cells and helper T cells.

21. Compare the production and functions of class I MHC and class II MHC molecules.

Immune Responses

22. Distinguish between humoral immunity and cell-mediated immunity.

23. Describe the roles of helper T lymphocytes in both humoral and cell-mediated immunity.

24. Describe the functions of the proteins CD4 and CD8.

25. Explain how cytotoxic T cells and natural killer cells defend against tumors.

26. Distinguish between T-dependent antigens and T-independent antigens.

27. Explain why macrophages are regarded as the main antigen-presenting cells in the primary response but memory B cells are the main antigen-presenting cells in the secondary response.

28. Explain how antibodies interact with antigens.

29. Diagram and label the structure of an antibody and explain how this structure allows antibodies to (a) recognize and bind to antigens, and (b) assist in the destruction and elimination of antigens.

30. Distinguish between the variable (V) and constant (C) regions of an antibody molecule.

31. Describe the production and uses of monoclonal antibodies.

32. Compare the processes of neutralization, opsonization, and agglutination.

Immunity in Health and Disease

33. Distinguish between active and passive immunity and describe examples of each.

34. Explain how the immune response to Rh factor differs from the response to A and B blood antigens.

35. Describe the potential problem of Rh incompatibility between a mother and her unborn fetus and explain what precautionary measures may be taken.

36. Explain what is done medically to reduce the risk of tissue transplant rejection due to differences in the MHC. Explain what is unique about the source of potential immune rejection in bone marrow grafts.

37. Describe an allergic reaction, including the roles of IgE, mast cells, and histamine.

38. Explain what causes anaphylactic shock and how it can be treated.

39. List three autoimmune disorders and describe possible mechanisms of autoimmunity.

40. Distinguish between inborn and acquired immunodeficiency.

41. Explain how general health and mental well-being might affect the immune system.

42. Describe the infectious agent that causes AIDS and explain how it enters a susceptible cell.

43. Explain how HIV is transmitted and describe its incidence throughout the world. Note strategies that can reduce a person's risk of infection.

Student Misconceptions

1. The immune system is complex and difficult for students to understand. Take particular care in clarifying the many terms that students encounter in this chapter. Make sure your students can distinguish between members of the following pairs of terms:

   a. leukocyte; lymphocyte

   b. antigen; antibody

   c. B lymphocyte; T lymphocyte

   d. cytotoxic T cell; helper T cell

2. In discussing vertebrate immune systems, emphasize the incredible diversity of lymphocytes. Ensure that your students understand how gene rearrangement generates this diversity. Ask probing questions to encourage students to understand why such a complex mechanism has arisen. Why don't vertebrates simply code for the necessary lymphocytes? Encourage students to think about why this system is economical and why natural selection has favored this complicated mechanism.

3. Students can become confused in sorting out the many targets of the vertebrate immune response. Review the similarities and differences between the immune system's adaptive responses to pathogens and to defective or infected cells that are "nonself," and its occasional maladaptive autoimmune response to normal cells that are "self."

Chapter Guide to Teaching Resources

Overview: Reconnaissance, recognition, and response

Concept 43.1 Innate immunity provides broad defenses against infection

Transparencies

Figure 43.2	Overview of vertebrate defenses against bacteria, viruses, and other pathogens
Figure 43.4	Phagocytosis
Figure 43.5	The human lymphatic system
Figure 43.6	Major events in the local inflammatory response

Concept 43.2 In acquired immunity, lymphocytes provide specific defenses against infection

Transparencies

Figure 43.7	Epitopes (antigenic determinants)
Figure 43.8	Antigen receptors on lymphocytes

Concept 43.3 Humoral and cell-mediated immunity defend against different types of threats

Transparencies

Instructor and Student Media Resources

Video: T cell receptors

Activity: Immune responses

Concept 43.4 The immune system's ability to distinguish self from nonself limits tissue transplantation

Transparency

Concept 43.5 Exaggerated, self-directed, or diminished immune responses can cause disease

Transparency

Student Media Resources

Activity: HIV reproductive cycle

Investigation: What causes infections in AIDS patients?

Investigation: Why do AIDS rates differ across the U.S.?

For additional resources such as digital images and lecture outlines, go to the Campbell Media Manager or the Instructor Resources section of **www.campbellbiology.com.**

Key Terms

acquired immunity
active immunity
acquired
  immunodeficiency
  syndrome (AIDS)
anaphylactic shock
antibody
antigen
antigen presentation
antigen receptor
antigen-presenting cell
apoptosis
autoimmune disease
B cell receptor
B lymphocyte (B cell)
CD4
CD8
cell-mediated immune
  response
chemokine
class I MHC molecules
class II MHC
  molecules
clonal selection
complement system

cytokine
cytotoxic T cell
dendritic cell
effector cell
eosinophil
epitope
graft versus host
  reaction
heavy chain
helper T cell
histamine
human
  immunodeficiency
  virus (HIV)
humoral immune
  response
immunization
immunoglobulin
inflammatory response
innate immunity
interferon
light chain
lymphocyte
lysozyme
macrophage

major
  histocompatibility
  complex (MHC)
mast cell
membrane attack
  complex (MAC)
memory cell
monoclonal antibody
monocyte
natural killer (NK) cell
neutrophil
passive immunity
phagocytosis
plasma cell
primary immune
  response
Rh factor
secondary immune
  response
T cell receptor
T lymphocyte (T cell)
thymus
vaccination

Word Roots

agglutinat- = glued together (*agglutination:* an antibody-mediated immune response in which bacteria or viruses are clumped together, effectively neutralized, and opsonized)

an- = without; **-aphy** = suck (*anaphylactic shock:* an acute, life threatening, allergic response)

anti- = against; **-gen** = produce (*antigen:* a foreign macromolecule that does not belong to the host organism and that elicits an immune response)

chemo- = chemistry; **-kine** = movement (*chemokine:* a group of about 50 different proteins secreted by blood vessel endothelial cells and monocytes; these molecules bind to receptors on many types of leukocytes and induce numerous changes central to inflammation)

cyto- = cell (*cytokines:* in the vertebrate immune system, protein factors secreted by macrophages and helper T cells as regulators of neighboring cells)

epi- = over; **-topo** = place (*epitope:* a localized region on the surface of an antigen that is chemically recognized by anitobodies)

immuno- = safe, free; **-glob** = globe, sphere (*immunoglobulin:* one of the class of proteins comprising the antibodies)

inter- = between; **leuko-** = white (*interleukin-2:* a cytokine which helps B cells that have contacted antigen differentiate into antibody-secreting plasma cells)

macro- = large; **-phage** = eat (*macrophage:* an amoeboid cell that moves through tissue fibers, engulfing bacteria and dead cells by phagocytosis)

mono- = one (*monocyte:* an agranular leukocyte that is able to migrate into tissues and transform into a macrophage)

neutro- = neutral; **-phil** = loving (*neutrophil:* the most abundant type of leukocyte; neutrophils tend to self destruct as they destroy foreign invaders, limiting their lifespan to but a few days)

perfora- = bore through (*perforin:* a protein that forms pores in a target cell's membrane)

CHAPTER 44

Osmoregulation and Excretion

Teaching Objectives

An Overview of Osmoregulation

1. Define *osmoregulation* and *excretion.*
2. Define *osmolarity* and distinguish among isoosmotic, hyperosmotic, and hypoosmotic solutions.
3. Distinguish between osmoregulators and osmoconformers. Explain why osmoregulation has an energy cost.
4. Distinguish between stenohaline and euryhaline animals, and explain why euryhaline animals include both osmoconformers and osmoregulators.
5. Discuss the osmoregulatory strategies of marine animals.
6. Explain how the osmoregulatory problems of freshwater animals differ from those of marine animals.
7. Describe anhydrobiosis as an adaptation that helps tardigrades and nematodes to survive periods of dehydration.
8. Describe some adaptations that reduce water loss in terrestrial animals.
9. Describe the ultimate function of osmoregulation. Explain how hemolymph and interstitial fluids are involved in this process.
10. Explain the role of transport epithelia in osmoregulation and excretion.

Water Balance and Waste Disposal

11. Describe the production and elimination of ammonia. Explain why ammonia excretion is most common in aquatic species.
12. Compare the strategies to eliminate waste as ammonia, urea, or uric acid. Note which animal groups are associated with each process and why a particular strategy is most adaptive for a particular group.
13. Compare the amounts of nitrogenous waste produced by endotherms and ectotherms, and by predators and herbivores.

Excretory Systems

14. Describe the key steps in the process of urine production.
15. Describe how a flame-bulb (protonephridial) excretory system functions.
16. Explain how the metanephridial excretory tubule of annelids functions. Compare the structure to the protonephridial system.
17. Describe the Malpighian tubule excretory system of insects.

18. Using a diagram, identify and give the function of each structure in the mammalian excretory system.

19. Using a diagram, identify and describe the function of each region of the nephron.

20. Describe and explain the relationships among the processes of filtration, reabsorption, and secretion in the mammalian kidney.

21. Distinguish between cortical and juxtamedullary nephrons. Explain the significance of the juxtamedullary nephrons of birds and mammals.

22. Explain how the loop of Henle enhances water conservation by the kidney.

23. Explain how the loop of Henle functions as a countercurrent multiplier system.

24. Describe the nervous and hormonal controls involved in the regulation of the kidney.

25. Explain how the feeding habits of the South American vampire bat illustrate the versatility of the mammalian kidney.

26. Describe the structural and physiological adaptations in the kidneys of nonmammalian species that allow them to osmoregulate in different environments.

Student Misconceptions

1. Some students do not realize that *hyperosmotic, isoosmotic,* and *hypoosmotic* are relative terms. A solution is not hyperosmotic; it is hyperosmotic in relation to a reference solution.

2. Students may think—mistakenly—that the majority of the water reabsorbed from the glomerular filtrate moves back into the blood as the filtrate moves through the loop of Henle and the collecting duct. Clarify for your students that water reabsorption in the collecting duct is under hormonal control and that this region of the nephron plays a crucial role in regulating water uptake and thus controlling osmolarity of the blood. However, the majority of the water reabsorbed from the filtrate moves into the blood by osmosis from the proximal tubule, accompanying the reabsorption of nutrients and salts.

3. Some students think of mammalian urine as hyperosmotic to blood. These students may be surprised to find that mammals can also produce large amounts of hypoosmotic urine, at times when salt is scarce and fluid intake is high.

4. Many students have difficulty understanding the countercurrent multiplier system involving the loop of Henle and its role in the formation of concentrated urine. This material is challenging, and students may find it easier to master if you teach about a simpler countercurrent system earlier in your course, before the topic of osmoregulation and excretion is dealt with.

Chapter Guide to Teaching Resources

Overview: A balancing act

Concept 44.1 Osmoregulation balances the uptake and loss of water and solutes

Transparencies

Figure 44.3   Osmoregulation in marine and freshwater bony fishes: A comparison
Figure 44.5   Water balance in two terrestrial mammals
Figure 44.6   What role does fur play in water conservation by camels?
Figure 44.7   Salt-excreting glands in birds

Concept 44.2 An animal's nitrogenous wastes reflect its phylogeny and habitat

Transparency

Figure 44.8   Nitrogenous wastes

Concept 44.3 Diverse excretory systems are variations on a tubular theme

Transparencies

Figure 44.9   Key functions of excretory systems: An overview
Figure 44.10   Protonephridia: The flame-bulb system of a planarian
Figure 44.11   Metanephridia of an earthworm
Figure 44.12   Malpighian tubules of insects

Concept 44.4 Nephrons and associated blood vessels are the functional units of the mammalian kidney

Transparencies

Figure 44.13   The mammalian excretory system
Figure 44.14   The nephron and collecting duct: Regional functions of the transport epithelium

Student Media Resources

Activity: Structure of the human excretory system
Activity: Nephron function

Concept 44.5 The mammalian kidney's ability to conserve water is a key terrestrial adaptation

Transparencies

Figure 44.15   How the human kidney concentrates urine: The two-solute model (layer 1)

Figure 44.15   How the human kidney concentrates urine: The two-solute model (layer 2)

Figure 44.15   How the human kidney concentrates urine: The two-solute model (layer 3)

Figure 44.16   Hormonal control of the kidney by negative feedback circuits

Student Media Resources

Activity: Control of water reabsorption

Investigation: What affects urine production?

Concept 44.6 Diverse adaptations of the vertebrate kidney have evolved in different environments

Transparency

Figure 44.18   Environmental adaptations of the vertebrate kidney

For additional resources such as digital images and lecture outlines, go to the Campbell Media Manager or the Instructor Resources section of **www.campbellbiology.com.**

Key Terms

afferent arteriole
aldosterone
ammonia
angiotensin II
anhydrobiosis
antidiuretic hormone (ADH)
atrial natriuretic factor (ANF)
Bowman's capsule
collecting duct
cortical nephrons
countercurrent multiplier system
distal tubule
efferent arteriole
euryhaline
excretion

filtrate
filtration
glomerulus
juxtaglomerular apparatus (JGA)
juxtamedullary nephrons
loop of Henle
Malpighian tubule
metanephridium
nephron
osmoconformer
osmolarity
osmoregulation
osmoregulator
peritubular capillaries
protonephridium
proximal tubule

renal artery
renal cortex
renal medulla
renal pelvis
renal vein
renin-angiotensin-aldosterone system (RAAS)
secretion
selective reabsorption
stenohaline
transport epithelium
urea
ureter
urethra
uric acid
urinary bladder
vasa recta

Word Roots

an- = without; **hydro-** = water; **-bios** = life (*anhydrobiosis:* the ability to survive in a dormant state when an organism's habitat dries up)

anti- = against; **-diure** = urinate (*antidiuretic hormone:* a hormone that helps regulate water balance)

eury- = broad, wide; **-halin** = salt (*euryhaline:* organisms that can tolerate substantial changes in external osmolarity)

glomer- = a ball (*glomerulus:* a ball of capillaries surrounded by Bowman's capsule in the nephron and serving as the site of filtration in the vertebrate kidney)

homeo- = like, same; **-stasis** = standing (*homeostasis:* the steady-state physiological condition of the body)

juxta- = near to (*juxtaglomerular apparatus:* a specialized tissue located near the afferent arteriole that supplies blood to the glomerulus)

meta- = with; **-nephri** = kidney (*metanephridium:* in annelid worms, a type of excretory tubule with internal openings called nephrostomes that collect body fluids and external openings called nephridiopores)

osmo- = pushing; **-regula** = regular (*osmoregulation:* adaptations to control the water balance in organisms living in hyperosmotic, hypoosmotic, or terrestrial environments)

peri- = around (*peritubular capillaries:* the network of tiny blood vessels that surrounds the proximal and distal tubules in the kidney)

podo- = foot; **-cyte** = cell (*podocytes:* specialized cells of Bowman's capsule that are permeable to water and small solutes but not to blood cells or large molecules such as plasma proteins)

proto- = first (*protonephridium:* an excretory system, such as the flame-cell system of flatworms, consisting of a network of closed tubules having external openings called nephridiopores and lacking internal openings)

reni- = a kidney; **-angio** = a vessel; **-tens** = stretched (*renin-angiotensin-aldosterone system:* a part of a complex feedback circuit that normally partners with antidiuretic hormone in osmoregulation)

steno- = narrow (*stenohaline:* organisms that cannot tolerate substantial changes in external osmolarity)

vasa- = a vessel; **-recta** = straight (*vasa recta:* the capillary system that serves the loop of Henle)

CHAPTER 45

Hormones and the Endocrine System

Teaching Objectives

An Introduction to Regulatory Systems

1. Compare the response times of the two major systems of internal communication: the nervous system and the endocrine system.

2. Explain how neurosecretory cells, epinephrine, and control of day/night cycles illustrate the integration of the endocrine and nervous systems.

3. Describe the organization of a stimulus, receptor, control center, efferent signal, and effector in a simple endocrine pathway.

4. Describe an example of a negative feedback loop in an endocrine pathway involved in maintaining homeostasis.

5. Explain why the neurohormone pathway that regulates the release of milk by a nursing mother is an example of positive feedback.

Chemical Signals and Their Modes of Action

6. List the three major classes of molecules that function as hormones in vertebrates.

7. Name the three key events involved in signaling by vertebrate hormones.

8. Explain what changes may be triggered by a signal transduction pathway initiated by the binding of a water-soluble hormone to a receptor in the plasma membrane of a target cell.

9. Discuss how and why different target cells exposed to the same hormone may respond in different ways.

10. Describe the nature and location of intracellular receptors for hormones that pass easily through cell membranes. Explain how their role compares to the signal-transduction pathway noted above, and describe the changes they are likely to trigger within the target cell.

11. Explain the role of local regulators in paracrine signaling. Describe the diverse functions of cytokines, growth factors, nitric oxide, and prostaglandins.

The Vertebrate Endocrine System

12. Explain how the hypothalamus and pituitary glands interact and how they coordinate the endocrine system.

13. Describe the location of the pituitary. List and explain the functions of the hormones released from the anterior and posterior lobes.

14. Explain the role of tropic hormones in coordinating endocrine signaling throughout the body. Distinguish between releasing hormones and inhibiting hormones.

15. List the hormones of the thyroid gland and explain their roles in development and metabolism. Explain the causes and symptoms of hyperthyroidism, hypothyroidism, and goiter.

16. Note the location of the parathyroid glands and describe the hormonal control of calcium homeostasis.

17. Distinguish between alpha and beta cells in the pancreas and explain how their antagonistic hormones (insulin and glucagon) regulate carbohydrate metabolism.

18. Distinguish between type I diabetes mellitus and type II diabetes mellitus.

19. List the hormones of the adrenal medulla, describe their functions, and explain how their secretions are controlled.

20. List the hormones of the adrenal cortex and describe their functions.

21. List the hormones of three categories of steroid hormones produced by the gonads. Describe variations in their production between the sexes. Note the functions of each category of steroid and explain how secretions are controlled.

22. Describe the location of the pineal gland. Explain the significance of its secretion of melatonin.

23. Describe several examples of invertebrate hormones that function in the control of reproduction and development.

Student Misconceptions

1. Some students think of endocrine and nervous regulation as entirely separate control mechanisms. Emphasize to your students that these important systems work together to regulate a number of physiological processes, that some molecules function both as hormones in the endocrine system and as chemical messengers in the nervous system, and that the hypothalamus and pituitary gland serve to integrate the endocrine and nervous systems of vertebrates.

2. Students can be overwhelmed by the large number of human endocrine glands and hormones. Encourage your students to look for patterns in this information. Students should recognize the basic hormonal control pathways, similarities in means of regulation, and the various chemical classes of hormone.

Chapter Guide to Teaching Resources

Overview: The body's long-distance regulators

Concept 45.1 The endocrine system and the nervous system act individually and together in regulating an animal's physiology

Transparency

Figure 45.2   Basic patterns of simple hormonal control pathways

Concept 45.2 Hormones and other chemical signals bind to target cell receptors, initiating pathways that culminate in specific cell responses

Transparencies

Figure 45.3   Mechanisms of hormonal signaling: A review

Figure 45.4   One chemical signal, different effects

Student Media Resources

Activity: Overview of cell signaling

Activity: Peptide hormone action

Activity: Steroid hormone action

Concept 45.3 The hypothalamus and pituitary integrate many functions of the vertebrate endocrine system

Transparencies

Table 45.1   Major human endocrine glands and some of their hormones (hypothalamus–parathyroid glands)

Table 45.1   Major human endocrine glands and some of their hormones (pancreas–pineal gland)

Figure 45.6   Human endocrine glands surveyed in this chapter

Figure 45.7   Production and release of posterior pituitary hormones

Figure 45.8   Production and release of anterior pituitary hormones

Concept 45.4 Nonpituitary hormones help regulate metabolism, homeostasis, development, and behavior

Transparencies

Figure 45.9   Feedback regulation of T_3 and T_4 secretion from the thyroid gland

Figure 45.11   Hormonal control of calcium homeostasis in mammals

Figure 45.12   Maintenance of glucose homeostasis by insulin and glucagon

Figure 45.13   Stress and the adrenal gland

Student Media Resources

Activity: Human endocrine glands and hormones

Investigation: How do thyroxine and TSH affect metabolism?

Concept 45.5 Invertebrate regulatory systems also involve endocrine and nervous system interactions

Transparencies

Figure 45.15   Hormonal regulation of insect development (layer 1)

Figure 45.15   Hormonal regulation of insect development (layer 2)

Figure 45.15   Hormonal regulation of insect development (layer 3)

For additional resources such as digital images and lecture outlines, go to the Campbell Media Manager or the Instructor Resources section of **www.campbellbiology.com.**

Key Terms

adenohypophysis
adrenal gland
adrenocorticotropic hormone (ACTH)
androgen
anterior pituitary
antidiuretic hormone (ADH)
brain hormone
calcitonin
catecholamine
corticosteroid
cytokine
diabetes mellitus
ecdysone
endocrine gland
endocrine system
endorphin
epinephrine
estrogen
follicle-stimulating hormone (FSH)
glucagon

glucocorticoid
gonadotropin
growth factor
growth hormone (GH)
hormone
hypothalamus
insulin
insulin-like growth factor (IGF)
islets of Langerhans
juvenile hormone
luteinizing hormone (LH)
melanocyte-stimulating hormone (MSH)
melatonin
mineralocorticoid
negative feedback
neurohypophysis
neurosecretory cell
nitric oxide (NO)
norepinephrine

oxytocin
pancreas
parathyroid gland
parathyroid hormone (PTH)
pineal gland
pituitary gland
posterior pituitary
progestin
prolactin (PRL)
prostaglandin (PG)
signal transduction pathway
testosterone
thyroid gland
thyroid-stimulating hormone (TSH)
thyroxine (T_4)
triiodothyronine (T_3)
tropic hormone
vitamin D

Word Roots

adeno- = gland; **-hypo** = below (*adenohypophysis:* also called the anterior pituitary, a gland positioned at the base of the hypothalamus)

andro- = male; **-gen** = produce (*androgens:* the principal male steroid hormones, such as testosterone, which stimulate the development and maintenance of the male reproductive system and secondary sex characteristics)

anti- = against; **-diure** = urinate (*antidiuretic hormone:* a hormone that helps regulate water balance)

cata- = down; **-chol** = anger (*catecholamines:* a class of compounds, including epinephrine and norepinephrine, that are synthesized from the amino acid tyrosine)

-cortico = the shell; **-tropic** = to turn or change (*adrenocorticotropic hormone:* a peptide hormone released from the anterior pituitary, it stimulates the production and secretion of steroid hormones by the adrenal cortex)

ecdys- = an escape (*ecdysone:* a steroid hormone that triggers molting in arthropods)

endo- = inside (*endorphin:* a hormone produced in the brain and anterior pituitary that inhibits pain perception)

epi- = above, over (*epinephrine:* a hormone produced as a response to stress; also called adrenaline)

gluco- = sweet (*glucagon:* a peptide hormone secreted by pancreatic endocrine cells that raises blood glucose levels; an antagonistic hormone to insulin)

lut- = yellow (*luteinizing hormone:* a gonadotropin secreted by the anterior pituitary)

melan- = black (*melatonin:* a modified amino acid hormone secreted by the pineal gland)

neuro- = nerve (*neurohypophysis:* also called the posterior pituitary, it is an extension of the brain)

oxy- = sharp, acid (*oxytocin:* a hormone that induces contractions of the uterine muscles and causes the mammary glands to eject milk during nursing)

para- = beside, near (*parathyroid glands:* four endocrine glands, embedded in the surface of the thyroid gland, that secrete parathyroid hormone and raise blood calcium levels)

pro- = before; **-lact** = milk (*prolactin:* a hormone produced by the anterior pituitary gland, it stimulates milk synthesis in mammals)

tri- = three; **-iodo** = violet (*triiodothyronine:* one of two very similar hormones produced by the thyroid gland and derived from the amino acid tyrosine)

CHAPTER 46

Animal Reproduction

Teaching Objectives

Overview of Animal Reproduction

1. Distinguish between asexual and sexual reproduction.

2. List and describe four mechanisms of asexual reproduction.

3. Describe several adaptive advantages of asexual reproduction. Discuss the conditions that may favor the occurrence of asexual reproduction.

4. Explain the advantages of periodic reproduction. Describe factors that may control the timing of reproductive events.

5. Describe an example of an animal life cycle that alternates between asexual and sexual reproduction.

6. Define *parthenogenesis* and describe the conditions that favor its occurrence. Note examples of invertebrate and vertebrate species that use this form of reproduction.

7. Explain how hermaphroditism may be advantageous in sessile or burrowing animals that have difficulty encountering a member of the opposite sex.

8. Distinguish between male-first and female-first sequential hermaphroditism. Note the adaptive advantages of these reproductive systems.

Mechanisms of Sexual Reproduction

9. Describe mechanisms that increase the probability that mature sperm will encounter fertile eggs of the same species in organisms that use external fertilization.

10. Explain the function of pheromones in mate attraction.

11. Compare reproductive systems using internal and external fertilization on the basis of the relative number of zygotes and protection of the embryos.

12. List and describe various methods of egg and embryo protection.

13. Compare the reproductive systems of a polychaete worm, a parasitic flatworm, an insect, a common nonmammalian vertebrate, and a mammal.

Mammalian Reproduction

14. Using a diagram, identify and give the function of each component of the reproductive system of the human male.

15. Using a diagram, identify and give the function of each component of the reproductive system of the human female.

16. Describe the two physiological reactions common to sexual arousal in both sexes.

17. Describe the four phases of the sexual response cycle.

18. Compare menstrual cycles and estrous cycles.

19. Describe the stages of the human female reproductive cycle.

20. Explain how the uterine cycle and ovarian cycle are synchronized in female mammals. Note in detail the functions of the hormones involved.

21. Describe human oogenesis.

22. Describe spermatogenesis and the structure and function of mature sperm.

23. Describe three major differences between oogenesis and spermatogenesis.

24. Describe human menopause. Describe a possible evolutionary explanation for human menopause.

25. Describe the influence of androgens on primary and secondary sex characteristics and behavior.

26. Compare the patterns of hormone secretion and reproductive events in male and female mammals.

27. Define *conception, gestation,* and *parturition.*

28. Compare the length of pregnancies in humans, rodents, dogs, cows, and elephants.

29. Describe the changes that occur in the mother and the developing embryo during each trimester of a human pregnancy.

30. Explain the role of embryonic hormones during the first few months of pregnancy.

31. Describe the stages of parturition.

32. Describe the control of lactation.

33. Describe mechanisms that may help prevent the mother's immune system from rejecting the developing embryo.

34. List the various methods of contraception and explain how each works.

35. Describe techniques that allow us to learn about the health and genetics of a fetus.

36. Explain how and when *in vitro* fertilization, zygote intrafallopian transfer, and gamete intrafallopian transfer may be used.

Student Misconceptions

1. Explain to your students the fundamental difference between sex and reproduction. Sex is the creation of genetically novel individuals, with a genetic contribution from two parents. Reproduction is the creation of new individuals. Thus, sexual reproduction is the creation of new, genetically novel individuals with two parents. Asexual reproduction is the creation of new individuals whose genes all come from a single parent.

2. Clarify for your students the basic biological difference between male and female. A male is an individual who produces many small, motile gametes; a female is an individual who produces few large, nonmotile gametes.

3. In discussing animal reproduction, explain to your students the role of meiosis in producing haploid animal gametes, but also point out that meiosis is not a sexual process in the other multicellular kingdoms. In plants and fungi, meiosis is the process for production of haploid, asexual spores.

Chapter Guide to Teaching Resources

Overview: Doubling up for sexual reproduction

Concept 46.1 Both asexual and sexual reproduction occur in the animal kingdom

Transparency

Figure 46.3   Sexual behavior in parthenogenetic lizards

Instructor and Student Media Resources

Video: Hydra budding

Video: Hydra releasing sperm

Concept 46.2 Fertilization depends on mechanisms that help sperm meet eggs of the same species

Transparencies

Figure 46.7   Reproductive anatomy of a parasitic flatworm

Figure 46.8   Insect reproductive anatomy

Concept 46.3 Reproductive organs produce and transport gametes: focus on humans

Transparencies

Figure 46.9   Reproductive anatomy of the human female (part 1)

Figure 46.9   Reproductive anatomy of the human female (part 2)

Figure 46.10   Reproductive anatomy of the human male (part 1)

Figure 46.10   Reproductive anatomy of the human male (part 2)

Student Media Resources

Activity: Reproductive system of the human female

Activity: Reproductive system of the human male

Investigation: What might obstruct the male urethra?

Concept 46.4 In humans and other mammals, a complex interplay of hormones regulates gametogenesis

Transparencies

Figure 46.11   Human oogenesis

Figure 46.12   Human spermatogenesis

Figure 46.13   The reproductive cycle of the human female

Figure 46.14   Hormonal control of the testes

Concept 46.5 In humans and other placental mammals, an embryo grows into a newborn in the mother's uterus

Transparencies

Figure 46.15   Formation of the zygote and early postfertilization events

Figure 46.16   Placental circulation

Figure 46.18   A model for the induction of labor

Figure 46.19   The three stages of labor

Figure 46.20   Mechanisms of some contraceptive methods

Instructor and Student Media Resources

Video: Ultrasound of human fetus 1

Video: Ultrasound of human fetus 2

Review

Page 986   The distribution of care behavior

For additional resources such as digital images and lecture outlines, go to the Campbell Media Manager or the Instructor Resources section of **www.campbellbiology.com.**

Key Terms

abortion	ejaculation	internal fertilization
acrosome	ejaculatory duct	labia majora
asexual reproduction	endometrium	labia minora
assisted reproductive technology (ART)	epididymis	labor
	estrous cycle	lactation
baculum	estrus	Leydig cell
barrier method	external fertilization	luteal phase
Bartholin's glands	fertilization	mammary glands
birth control pills	fetus	menopause
blastocyst	fission	menstrual cycle
budding	follicle	menstrual flow phase
bulbourethral gland	follicular phase	menstruation
cervix	fragmentation	myotonia
cleavage	gamete	natural family planning
clitoris	gametogenesis	
cloaca	gestation	oogenesis
coitus	glans penis	oogonia
conception	gonads	organogenesis
condom	hermaphroditism	orgasm
contraception	human chorionic gonadotropin (HCG)	ovarian cycle
corpus luteum		ovary
diaphragm	hymen	oviduct
egg	*in vitro* fertilization	ovulation

ovum
parthenogenesis
parturition
penis
pheromone
placenta
pregnancy
prepuce
primary oocyte
proliferative phase
prostate gland
regeneration
rhythm method
scrotum

secondary oocyte
secretory phase
semen
seminal vesicle
seminiferous tubule
sequential
 hermaphroditism
sexual reproduction
sperm
spermatheca
spermatogenesis
spermatogonia
testis
trimester

trophoblast
tubal ligation
urethra
uterine cycle
uterus
vagina
vas deferens
vasectomy
vasocongestion
vestibule
vulva
zygote

Word Roots

a- = not, without (*asexual reproduction:* a type of reproduction involving only one parent that produces genetically identical offspring)

acro- = tip; **-soma** = body (*acrosome:* an organelle at the tip of a sperm cell that helps the sperm penetrate the egg)

bacul- = a rod (*baculum:* a bone that is contained in, and helps stiffen, the penis of rodents, raccoons, walruses, and several other mammals)

blasto- = produce; **-cyst** = sac, bladder (*blastocyst:* a hollow ball of cells produced one week after fertilization in humans)

coit- = a coming together (*coitus:* the insertion of a penis into a vagina, also called sexual intercourse)

contra- = against (*contraception:* the prevention of pregnancy)

-ectomy = cut out (*vasectomy:* the cutting of each vas deferens to prevent sperm from entering the urethra)

endo- = inside (*endometrium:* the inner lining of the uterus, which is richly supplied with blood vessels)

epi- = above, over (*epididymis:* a coiled tubule located adjacent to the testes where sperm are stored)

labi- = lip; **major-** = larger (*labia majora:* a pair of thick, fatty ridges that enclose and protect the labia minora and vestibule)

lact- = milk (*lactation:* the production of milk)

menstru- = month (*menstruation:* the shedding of portions of the endometrium during a menstrual cycle)

minor- = smaller (*labia minora:* a pair of slender skin folds that enclose and protect the vestibule)

myo- = muscle (*myotonia:* increased muscle tension)

oo- = egg; **-genesis** = producing (*oogenesis:* the process in the ovary that results in the production of female gametes)

partheno- = a virgin (*parthenogenesis:* a type of reproduction in which females produce offspring from unfertilized eggs)

partur- = giving birth (*parturition:* the expulsion of a baby from the mother, also called birth)

-theca = a cup, case (*spermatheca:* a sac in the female reproductive system where sperm are stored)

tri- = three (*trimester:* a three-month period)

vasa- = a vessel (*vasocongestion:* the filling of a tissue with blood caused by increased blood flow through the arteries of that tissue)

CHAPTER 47

Animal Development

Teaching Objectives

The Stages of Embryonic Development in Animals

1. Compare the concepts of preformation and epigenesis.
2. List the two functions of fertilization.
3. Describe the acrosomal reaction and explain how it ensures that gametes are conspecific.
4. Describe the cortical reaction.
5. Explain how the fast and slow blocks to polyspermy function sequentially to prevent multiple sperm from fertilizing the egg.
6. Describe the changes that occur in an activated egg and explain the importance of cytoplasmic materials to egg activation.
7. Compare fertilization in a sea urchin and in a mammal.
8. Describe the general process of cleavage.
9. Explain the importance of embryo polarity during cleavage. Compare the characteristics of the animal hemisphere, vegetal hemisphere, and gray crescent in amphibian embryos.
10. Describe the formation of a blastula in sea urchin, amphibian, and bird embryos. Distinguish among meroblastic cleavage, holoblastic cleavage, and the formation of the blastoderm.
11. Describe the product of cleavage in an insect embryo.
12. Describe the process of gastrulation and explain its importance. Explain how this process rearranges the embryo. List adult structures derived from each of the primary germ layers.
13. Compare gastrulation in a sea urchin, a frog, and a chick.
14. Describe the formation of the notochord, neural tube, and somites in a frog.
15. Describe the significance and fate of neural crest cells. Explain why neural crest cells have been called a "fourth germ layer."
16. List and explain the functions of the extraembryonic membranes in reptile eggs.
17. Describe the events of cleavage in a mammalian embryo. Explain the significance of the inner cell mass.
18. Explain the role of the trophoblast in implantation of a human embryo.
19. Explain the functions of the extraembryonic membranes in mammalian development.

The Cellular and Molecular Basis of Morphogenesis and Differentiation in Animals

20. Describe the significance of changes in cell shape and cell position during embryonic development. Explain how these cellular processes occur. Describe the process of convergent extension.

21. Describe the role of the extracellular matrix in embryonic development.

22. Describe the locations and functions of cell adhesion molecules.

23. Describe the two general principles that integrate our knowledge of the genetic and cellular mechanisms underlying differentiation.

24. Describe the process of fate mapping and the significance of fate maps.

25. Describe the two important conclusions that have resulted from the experimental manipulation of parts of embryos and the use of fate maps.

26. Explain how the three body axes are established in early amphibian and chick development.

27. Explain the significance of Spemann's organizer in amphibian development.

28. Explain what is known about the molecular basis of induction.

29. Explain pattern formation in a developing chick limb, including the roles of the apical ectodermal ridge and the zone of polarizing activity.

30. Explain how a limb bud is directed to develop into either a forelimb or a hind limb.

Student Misconceptions

1. Some students think of fertilization as a mechanical drilling of sperm into egg. Emphasize to your students the complex choreography of the events of fertilization, in which contact between conspecific egg and sperm initiates a series of metabolic reactions within egg and sperm that trigger the onset of embryonic development.

2. As with any complex biological process, some students find it easier to learn the complex details than to understand the significance of the events of development. Ensure that your students know the events, but also understand the significance of cleavage, gastrulation, and organogenesis in animal development.

3. Students may not appreciate the importance of gastrulation and the reorganization that allows the germ layers in the gastrula to interact with each other in new ways. Remind them of Lewis Wolpert's famous quote: "It is not birth, marriage, or death, but gastrulation, which is truly the most important time in your life."

4. Many students have great difficulty visualizing the events of development, especially the rearrangements of cell layers during gastrulation and neurulation. Use models and time-lapse film to help students understand these complex events.

5. Students may find it difficult to appreciate the homology of the four extraembryonic membranes in mammals and reptiles. Ensure that your students understand the common ancestry of these membranes, despite their derived structure and function in mammals.

Chapter Guide to Teaching Resources

Overview: A body-building plan for animals

Concept 47.1 After fertilization, embryonic development proceeds through cleavage, gastrulation, and organogenesis

Transparencies

Figure 47.3   The acrosomal and cortical reactions during sea urchin fertilization

Figure 47.4   What is the effect of sperm binding on Ca^{2+} distribution in the egg?

Figure 47.5   Timeline for the fertilization of sea urchin eggs

Figure 47.6   Early events of fertilization in mammals

Figure 47.8   The body axes and their establishment in an amphibian

Figure 47.9   Cleavage in a frog embryo

Figure 47.10   Cleavage in a chick embryo

Figure 47.11   Gastrulation in a sea urchin embryo (layer 1)

Figure 47.11   Gastrulation in a sea urchin embryo (layer 2)

Figure 47.11   Gastrulation in a sea urchin embryo (layer 3)

Figure 47.12   Gastrulaton in a frog embryo

Figure 47.13   Gastrulation in a chick embryo

Figure 47.14   Early organogenesis in a frog embryo

Figure 47.15   Organogenesis in a chick embryo

Figure 47.16   Adult derivatives of the three embryonic germ layers in vertebrates

Figure 47.17   Extraembryonic membranes in birds and other reptiles

Figure 47.18   Four stages in early embryonic development of a human

Instructor and Student Media Resources

Activity: Sea urchin development

Video: Sea urchin embryonic development

Investigation: What determines cell differentiation in the sea urchin?

Activity: Frog development

Video: Frog embryo development

Video: *C. elegans* embryo development (time-lapse)

Video: Ultrasound of human fetus 1

Video: Ultrasound of human fetus 2

Concept 47.2 Morphogenesis in animals involves specific changes in cell shape, position, and adhesion

Transparencies

Figure 47.19   Change in cellular shape during morphogenesis

Figure 47.20   Convergent extension of a sheet of cells

Concept 47.3 The developmental fate of cells depends on their history and on inductive signals

Transparencies

Figure 47.23   Fate mapping for two chordates

Figure 47.24   How does distribution of the gray crescent at the first cleavage affect the potency of the two daughter cells?

Figure 47.25   Can the dorsal tip of the blastopore induce cells in another part of the amphibian embryo to change their developmental fate?

Figure 47.26   Vertebrate limb development

Figure 47.27   What role does the zone of polarizing activity (ZPA) play in limb pattern formation in vertebrates?

For additional resources such as digital images and lecture outlines, go to the Campbell Media Manager or the Instructor Resources section of **www.campbellbiology.com.**

Key Terms

acrosomal reaction
acrosome
allantois
amnion
amniote
animal pole
apical ectodermal ridge (AER)
archenteron
blastocoel
blastocyst
blastoderm
blastomere
blastopore
blastula
cadherins
cell adhesion molecules (CAMs)
cell differentiation
chorion
cleavage
convergent extension
cortical granules

cortical reaction
cytoplasmic determinants
dorsal lip
ectoderm
endoderm
extraembryonic membranes
fast block to polyspermy
fate map
fertilization envelope
gastrula
gastrulation
germ layers
gray crescent
holoblastic cleavage
induction
inner cell mass
invagination
involution
meroblastic cleavage
mesoderm

morphogenesis
morula
neural crest
neural tube
notochord
organogenesis
pattern formation
positional information
primitive streak
slow block to polyspermy
somites
totipotent
trophoblast
vegetal pole
yolk
yolk plug
yolk sac
zona pellucida
zone of polarizing activity (ZPA)

Word Roots

acro- = the tip (*acrosomal reaction:* the discharge of a sperm's acrosome when the sperm approaches an egg)

arch- = ancient, beginning (*archenteron:* the endoderm-lined cavity, formed during the gastrulation process, that develops into the digestive tract of an animal)

blast- = bud, sprout; **-pore** = a passage (*blastopore:* the opening of the archenteron in the gastrula that develops into the mouth in protostomes and the anus in deuterostomes)

blasto- = produce; **-mere** = a part (*blastomeres:* small cells of an early embryo)

cortex- = shell (*cortical reaction:* a series of changes in the cortex of the egg cytoplasm during fertilization)

ecto- = outside; **-derm** = skin (*ectoderm:* the outermost of the three primary germ layers in animal embryos)

endo- = within (*endoderm:* the innermost of the three primary germ layers in animal embryos)

epi- = above; **-genesis** = origin, birth (*epigenesis:* the progressive development of form in an embryo)

extra- = beyond (*extraembryonic membrane:* four membranes that support the developing embryo in reptiles, birds, and mammals)

fertil- = fruitful (*fertilization:* the union of haploid gametes to produce a diploid zygote)

gastro- = stomach, belly (*gastrulation:* the formation of a gastrula from a blastula)

holo- = whole (*holoblastic cleavage:* a type of cleavage in which there is complete division of the egg)

in- = into; **vagin-** = a sheath (*invagination:* the infolding of cells)

involut- = wrapped up (*involution:* cells rolling over the edge of a lip into the interior)

mero- = a part (*meroblastic cleavage:* a type of cleavage in which there is incomplete division of yolk-rich egg, characteristic of avian development)

meso- = middle (*mesoderm:* the middle primary germ layer of an early embryo)

morul- = a little mulberry (*morula:* a solid ball of blastomeres formed by early cleavage)

noto- = the back; **-chord** = a string (*notochord:* a long, flexible rod that runs along the dorsal axis of the body in the future position of the vertebral column)

poly- = many (*polyspermy:* fertilization by more than one sperm)

soma- = a body (*somites:* paired blocks of mesoderm just lateral to the notochord of a vertebrate embryo)

tropho- = nourish (*trophoblast:* the outer epithelium of the blastocyst, which forms the fetal part of the placenta)

zona = a belt; **pellucid-** = transparent (*zona pellucida:* the extracellular matrix of a mammalian egg)

CHAPTER 48

Nervous Systems

Teaching Objectives

An Overview of Nervous Systems

1. Compare and contrast the nervous systems of the following animals and explain how variations in design and complexity relate to their phylogeny, natural history, and habitat: hydra, sea star, planarian, insect, squid, and vertebrate.
2. Name the three stages in the processing of information by nervous systems.
3. Distinguish among sensory neurons, interneurons, and motor neurons.
4. List and describe the major parts of a neuron and explain the function of each.
5. Describe the function of astrocytes, radial glia, oligodendrocytes, and Schwann cells.

The Nature of Nerve Signals

6. Define a *membrane potential* and a *resting potential*.
7. Describe the factors that contribute to a membrane potential.
8. Explain why the membrane potential of a resting neuron is typically around -60 to -80 mV.
9. Explain the role of the sodium-potassium pump in maintaining the resting potential.
10. Distinguish between gated and ungated ion channels and among stretch-gated ion channels, ligand-gated ion channels, and voltage-gated ion channels.
11. Define a *graded potential* and explain how it is different from a resting potential or an action potential.
12. Describe the characteristics of an *action potential*. Explain the role of voltage-gated ion channels in this process.
13. Describe the two main factors that underlie the repolarizing phase of the action potential.
14. Define the *refractory period*.
15. Explain how an action potential is propagated along an axon.
16. Describe the factors that affect the speed of action potentials along an axon and describe adaptations that increase the speed of propagation. Describe saltatory conduction.
17. Compare an electrical synapse and a chemical synapse.
18. Describe the structures of a chemical synapse and explain how they transmit an action potential from one cell to another.

19. Explain how excitatory postsynaptic potentials (EPSPs) and inhibitory postsynaptic potentials (IPSPs) affect the postsynaptic membrane potential.

20. Define *summation* and distinguish between temporal and spatial summation. Explain how summation applies to EPSPs and IPSPs.

21. Explain the role of the axon hillock.

22. Describe the role of signal transduction pathways in indirect synaptic transmission.

23. Describe the specific properties of the neurotransmitters acetylcholine and biogenic amines.

24. Identify and describe the functions of the four amino acids and several neuropeptides that work as neurotransmitters.

25. Explain how endorphins function as natural analgesics.

26. Describe the roles of nitric oxide and carbon monoxide as local regulators.

Vertebrate Nervous Systems

27. Compare the structures and functions of the central nervous system and the peripheral nervous system.

28. Distinguish between the functions of the autonomic nervous system and the somatic nervous system.

29. Describe the embryonic development of the vertebrate brain.

30. Describe the structures and functions of the following brain regions: medulla oblongata, pons, midbrain, cerebellum, thalamus, epithalamus, hypothalamus, and cerebrum.

31. Describe the specific functions of the reticular system.

32. Explain how the suprachiasmatic nuclei (SCN) function as a mammalian biological clock.

33. Relate the specific regions of the cerebrum to their functions.

34. Distinguish between the functions of the left and right hemispheres of the cerebrum.

35. Describe the specific functions of the brain regions associated with language, speech, emotions, memory, and learning.

36. Explain the possible role of long-term potentiation in memory storage and learning in the vertebrate brain.

37. Describe our current understanding of human consciousness.

38. Explain how research on stem cells and neural development may lead to new treatments for injuries and disease.

39. Describe current treatments for schizophrenia.

40. Distinguish between bipolar disorder and major depression.

41. Describe the symptoms and brain pathology that characterize Alzheimer's disease. Discuss possible treatments for this disease.

42. Explain the cause of Parkinson's disease.

Student Misconceptions

1. The sequence of events during the generation of an action potential can be confusing to some students. Your students may have some or all of these common misconceptions:

   a. Students may think that the sodium-potassium pump causes the falling phase of the action potential by pumping Na^+ ions back out of the neuron.

   b. Many students imagine a massive influx and efflux of ions across the neuron's plasma membrane during the conduction of the action potential. These students do not realize the small number of ions that are involved.

   c. Some students use imagery of electricity moving down a wire in considering the conduction of an action potential. This comparison may have some uses, but it can also confuse students. Ions, rather than electrons, are responsible for the conduction of an action potential; an action potential is conducted at speeds far lower than those of electricity; electrons are carried along a wire, while ions move across the neuron membrane.

   d. Many students do not realize that resting membrane potentials characterize all living cells.

2. Students may think of the membrane potential as an absolute value, rather than recognizing that it is a difference in electrical potential (voltage) across the neuron's plasma membrane. The negative membrane potential indicates that the inside of the cell is negative relative to the outside. To test for this misunderstanding, ask your students what happens to the membrane potential of a neuron if the membrane potential decreases. Students who think of membrane potential as an absolute number will answer that the potential becomes more negative.

Further Reading

Silverthorn, D. U. 2002. Uncovering misconceptions about the resting membrane potential. *Advances in Physiology Education, 26(2),* 69–71.

Chapter Guide to Teaching Resources

Overview: Command and control center

Concept 48.1 Nervous systems consist of circuits of neurons and supporting cells

Transparencies

Figure 48.2   Organization of some nervous systems

Figure 48.3   Overview of information processing by nervous systems

Figure 48.4   The knee-jerk reflex

Figure 48.5   Structure of a vertebrate neuron

Figure 48.6   Structural diversity of vertebrate neurons

Figure 48.8   Schwann cells and the myelin sheath

Student Media Resource

Activity: Neuron structure

Concept 48.2 Ion pumps and ion channels maintain the resting potential of a neuron

Transparencies

Figure 48.9   Intracellular recording

Figure 48.10   Ionic gradients across the plasma membrane of a mammalian neuron

Figure 48.11   Modeling a mammalian neuron

Concept 48.3 Action potentials are the signals conducted by axons

Transparencies

Figure 48.12   Graded potentials and an action potential in a neuron

Figure 48.13   The role of voltage-gated ion channels in the generation of an action potential (layer 1)

Figure 48.13   The role of voltage-gated ion channels in the generation of an action potential (layer 2)

Figure 48.13   The role of voltage-gated ion channels in the generation of an action potential (layer 3)

Figure 48.13   The role of voltage-gated ion channels in the generation of an action potential (layer 4)

Figure 48.13   The role of voltage-gated ion channels in the generation of an action potential (layer 5)

Figure 48.14   Conduction of an action potential

Figure 48.15   Saltatory conduction

Student Media Resources

Activity: Nerve signals: Action potentials

Investigation: What triggers nerve impulses?

Concept 48.4 Neurons communicate with other cells at synapses

Transparencies

Figure 48.17   A chemical synapse

Figure 48.18   Summation of postsynaptic potentials

Table 48.1   Major neurotransmitters

Concept 48.5 The vertebrate nervous system is regionally specialized

Transparencies

Concept 48.6 The cerebral cortex controls voluntary movement and cognitive functions

Transparencies

Concept 48.7 CNS injuries and diseases are the focus of much research

Transparency

For additional resources such as digital images and lecture outlines, go to the Campbell Media Manager or the Instructor Resources section of **www.campbellbiology.com.**

Key Terms

acetylcholine
action potential
Alzheimer's disease
aspartate
astrocyte
autonomic nervous system
axon
axon hillock
basal nuclei
biogenic amine
biological clock
bipolar disorder
blood-brain barrier
brainstem
cell body
central canal
central nervous system (CNS)
cerebellum
cerebral cortex
cerebral hemisphere
cerebrospinal fluid
cerebrum
corpus callosum
cranial nerve
dendrite
depolarization
dopamine
effector cell
endorphin
enteric division
epinephrine
epithalamus
equilibrium potential (E_{ion})
excitatory postsynaptic potential (EPSP)
forebrain

gamma aminobutyric acid (GABA)
ganglion
gated ion channel
glia
glutamate
glycine
graded potential
gray matter
growth cone
hindbrain
hyperpolarization
hypothalamus
inhibitory postsynaptic potential (IPSP)
interneuron
lateralization
ligand-gated ion channel
limbic system
long-term memory
long-term potentiation (LTP)
major depression
medulla oblongata
membrane potential
midbrain
motor neuron
myelin sheath
neocortex
nerve
nerve net
neuron
neuropeptide
neurotransmitter
norepinephrine
oligodendrocyte
parasympathetic division

Parkinson's disease
peripheral nervous system (PNS)
pons
postsynaptic cell
presynaptic cell
radial glia
reflex
refractory period
resting potential
reticular formation
saltatory conduction
schizophrenia
Schwann cell
sensory neuron
serotonin
short-term memory
somatic nervous system
spatial summation
spinal nerve
stretch-gated ion channel
substance P
suprachiasmatic nuclei (SCN)
sympathetic division
synapse
synaptic cleft
synaptic terminal
synaptic vesicle
temporal summation
thalamus
threshold
ventricle
voltage-gated ion channel
white matter

Word Roots

astro- = a star; **-cyte** = cell (*astrocytes:* glial cells that provide structural and metabolic support for neurons)

auto- = self (*autonomic nervous system:* the branch of the peripheral nervous system of vertebrates that regulates the internal environment)

bio- = life; **-genic** = producing (*biogenic amines:* neurotransmitters derived from amino acids)

cephalo- = head (*cephalization:* the clustering of sensory neurons and other nerve cells to form a brain near the anterior end and mouth of animals with elongated, bilaterally symmetrical bodies)

de- = down, out (*depolarization:* an electrical state in an excitable cell whereby the inside of the cell is made less negative relative to the outside)

dendro- = tree (*dendrite:* one of usually numerous, short, highly branched processes of a neuron that receive signals from other neurons)

endo- = within (*endorphin:* a hormone produced in the brain and anterior pituitary that inhibits pain perception)

epi- = above, over (*epithalamus:* a brain region, derived from the diencephalon, that contains several clusters of capillaries that produce cerebrospinal fluid; it is located above the thalamus)

glia = glue (*glia:* supporting cells that are essential for the structural integrity of the nervous system and for the normal functioning of neurons)

hyper- = over, above, excessive (*hyperpolarization:* an electrical state whereby the inside of the cell is made more negative relative to the outside than at the resting membrane potential)

hypo- = below (*hypothalamus:* the ventral part of the vertebrate forebrain that functions in maintaining homeostasis, especially in coordinating the endocrine and nervous systems; it is located below the thalamus)

inter- = between (*interneurons:* an association neuron; a nerve cell within the central nervous system that forms synapses with sensory and motor neurons and integrates sensory input and motor output)

neuro- = nerve; **trans-** = across (*neurotransmitter:* a chemical messenger released from the synaptic terminal of a neuron at a chemical synapse that diffuses across the synaptic cleft and binds to and stimulates the postsynaptic cell)

oligo- = few, small (*oligodendrocytes:* glial cells that form insulating myelin sheaths around the axons of neurons in the central nervous system)

para- = near (*parasympathetic division:* one of three divisions of the autonomic nervous system)

post- = after (*postsynaptic cell:* the target cell at a synapse)

pre- = before (*presynaptic cell:* the transmitting cell at a synapse)

salta- = leap (*saltatory conduction:* rapid transmission of a nerve impulse along an axon resulting from the action potential jumping from one node of Ranvier to another, skipping the myelin-sheathed regions of membrane)

soma- = body (*somatic nervous system:* the branch of the vertebrate peripheral nervous system that carries signals to and from skeletal muscles in response to external stimuli)

supra- = above, over (*suprachiasmatic nuclei:* a pair of structures in the hypothalamus of mammals that functions as a biological clock)

syn- = together (*synapse:* the locus where a neuron communicates with a postsynaptic cell in a neural pathway)

CHAPTER 49

Sensory and Motor Mechanisms

Teaching Objectives

Sensing, Acting, and Brains
1. Differentiate between sensation and perception.

Introduction to Sensory Reception
2. Explain the difference between exteroreceptors and interoreceptors.
3. Describe the four general functions of receptor cells as they convert energy stimuli into changes in membrane potentials and then transmit signals to the central nervous system.
4. Distinguish between sensory transduction and receptor potential.
5. Explain the importance of sensory adaptation.
6. List the five types of sensory receptors and explain the energy transduced by each type.

Hearing and Equilibrium
7. Explain the role of mechanoreceptors in hearing and balance.
8. Describe the structure and function of invertebrate statocysts.
9. Explain how insects may detect sound.
10. Refer to a diagram of the human ear and give the function of each structure.
11. Explain how the mammalian ear functions as a hearing organ.
12. Explain how the mammalian ear functions to maintain body balance and equilibrium.
13. Describe the hearing and equilibrium systems of nonmammalian vertebrates.

Chemoreception: Taste and Smell
14. Explain how the chemoreceptors involved with taste function in insects and humans.
15. Describe what happens after an odorant binds to an odorant receptor on the plasma membrane of the olfactory cilia.
16. Explain the basis of the sensory discrimination of human smell.

Photoreceptors and Vision
17. Compare the structures of, and processing of light by, the eyecups of *Planaria*, the compound eye of insects, and the single-lens eyes of molluscs.

18. Refer to a diagram of the vertebrate eye to identify and give the function of each structure.

19. Describe the functions of the rod cells and cone cells of the vertebrate eye.

20. Explain and compare how the rods and cones of the retina transduce stimuli into action potentials.

21. Explain how the retina assists the cerebral cortex in the processing of visual information.

Movement and Locomotion

22. Describe three functions of a skeleton.

23. Describe how hydrostatic skeletons function and explain why they are not found in large terrestrial organisms.

24. Distinguish between an exoskeleton and an endoskeleton.

25. Explain how the structure of the arthropod exoskeleton provides both strength and flexibility.

26. Explain how a skeleton combines with an antagonistic muscle arrangement to provide a mechanism for movement.

27. Explain how body proportions and posture impact physical support on land.

28. Using a diagram, identify the components of a skeletal muscle cell.

29. Explain the sliding-filament model of muscle contraction.

30. Explain how muscle contraction is controlled.

31. Explain how the nervous system produces graded contraction of whole muscles.

32. Explain the adaptive advantages of slow and fast muscle fibers.

33. Distinguish among skeletal muscle, cardiac muscle, and smooth muscle.

34. List the advantages and disadvantages associated with moving through:

    a. an aquatic environment

    b. a terrestrial environment

    c. air

35. Discuss the factors that affect the energy cost of locomotion.

Student Misconceptions

1. Some students do not realize how greatly the sensory worlds of various animals differ. Try to convey to your students how a bat, a shark, or even the family pooch perceives the world.

2. The story of the evolution of the middle ear bones in mammals is one of the best-understood and best-supported examples of homology and modification of structures. This story can be used to explain to students how new structures arise as organisms adapt to new environments, how structures change function step-by-step over evolutionary time, and how each intermediate structure is functional and contributes to fitness.

Chapter Guide to Teaching Resources

Overview: Sensing and acting

Concept 49.1 Sensory receptors transduce stimulus energy and transmit signals to the central nervous system

Transparencies

Figure 49.2   Sensory reception: Two mechanisms
Figure 49.3   Sensory receptors in human skin

Concept 49.2 The mechanoreceptors involved with hearing and equilibrium detect settling particles or moving fluid

Transparencies

Figure 49.6   The statocyst of an invertebrate
Figure 49.7   An insect ear
Figure 49.8   The structure of the human ear
Figure 49.9   Transduction in the cochlea
Figure 49.10   How the cochlea distinguishes pitch
Figure 49.11   Organs of equilibrium in the inner ear
Figure 49.12   The lateral line system in a fish

Student Media Resource

Activity: Structure and function of the eye

Concept 49.3 The senses of taste and smell are closely related in most animals

Transparencies

Figure 49.13   How do insects detect different tastes?
Figure 49.14   Sensory transduction by a sweetness receptor
Figure 49.15   Smell in humans

Concept 49.4 Similar mechanisms underlie vision throughout the animal kingdom

Transparencies

Figure 49.16   Ocelli and orientation behavior of a planarian
Figure 49.17   Compound eyes
Figure 49.18   Structure of the vertebrate eye
Figure 49.19   Focusing in the mammalian eye
Figure 49.20   Rod structure and light absorption
Figure 49.21   Production of a receptor potential in a rod

Figure 49.22   The effect of light on synapses between rod cells and bipolar cells

Figure 49.23   Cellular organization of the vertebrate regina

Figure 49.24   Neural pathways for vision

Concept 49.5 Animal skeletons function in support, protection, and movement

Transparencies

Figure 49.25   Peristaltic locomotion in an earthworm

Figure 49.26   Bones and joints of the human skeleton (part 1)

Figure 49.26   Bones and joints of the human skeleton (part 2)

Student Media Resource

Activity: Human skeleton

Concept 49.6 Muscles move skeletal parts by contracting

Transparencies

Figure 49.27   The interaction of muscles and skeletons in movement

Figure 49.28   The structure of skeletal muscle

Figure 49.29   The sliding-filament model of muscle contraction

Figure 49.30   Myosin-actin interactions underlying muscle fiber contraction (layer 1)

Figure 49.30   Myosin-actin interactions underlying muscle fiber contraction (layer 2)

Figure 49.30   Myosin-actin interactions underlying muscle fiber contraction (layer 3)

Figure 49.30   Myosin-actin interactions underlying muscle fiber contraction (layer 4)

Figure 49.31   The role of regulatory proteins and calcium in muscle fiber contraction

Figure 49.32   The roles of the sarcoplasmic reticulum and T tubules in muscle fiber contraction

Figure 49.33   Review of contraction in a skeletal muscle fiber

Figure 49.34   Motor units in a vertebrate skeletal muscle

Figure 49.35   Summation of twitches

Table 49.1   Types of skeletal muscle fibers

Student Media Resources

Activity: Skeletal muscle structure

Activity: Muscle contraction

Investigation: How do electrical stimuli affect muscle contraction?

Concept 49.7 Locomotion requires energy to overcome friction and gravity

Transparency

Figure 49.37   What are the energy costs of locomotion?

Instructor and Student Media Resources

Video: Jelly swimming

Video: Thimble jellies

Video: Echinoderm tube feet

Video: Manta ray

Video: Coral reef

Video: Clownfish and anemone

Video: Earthworm locomotion

Video: *C. elegans*

Video: Gibbons brachiating

Video: Soaring hawk

Video: Swans taking flight

Video: Flapping geese

For additional resources such as digital images and lecture outlines, go to the Campbell Media Manager or the Instructor Resources section of **www.campbellbiology.com.**

Key Terms

A band	Eustachian tube	lateral line system
accommodation	exoskeleton	lens
amacrine cell	exteroreceptor	locomotion
amplification	eye cup	malleus
aqueous humor	fovea	mechanoreceptor
bipolar cell	ganglion cell	middle ear
cardiac muscle	gustation	motor unit
chemoreceptor	hair cell	muscle spindle
chitin	horizontal cell	myofibril
choroid	hydrostatic skeleton	myofilaments
ciliary body	I band	myoglobin
cochlea	incus	nociceptor
compound eye	inner ear	olfaction
cone cell	intercalated disk	ommatidium
conjunctiva	interoreceptor	opsin
cornea	iris	optic chiasm
electromagnetic receptor	lateral geniculate nuclei	organ of Corti
endoskeleton	lateral inhibition	outer ear

oval window
pain receptor
perception
peristalsis
photopsin
photoreceptor
pitch
primary visual cortex
pupil
receptor potential
recruitment
retina
retinal
rhodopsin
rod cell
round window

saccule
sarcomere
sarcoplasmic reticulum
  (SR)
sclera
semicircular canals
sensation
sensory adaptation
sensory reception
sensory receptor
sensory transduction
single-lens eye
skeletal muscle
  (striated muscle)
sliding-filament model
smooth muscle

stapes
statocyst
statolith
taste buds
tetanus
thermoreceptor
thick filament
thin filament
transverse (T) tubules
tropomyosin
troponin complex
tympanic membrane
utricle
vitreous humor
Z lines

Word Roots

ama- = together (*amacrine cell:* neurons of the retina that help integrate information before it is sent to the brain)

aqua- = water (*aqueous humor:* the clear, watery solution that fills the anterior cavity of the eye)

bi- = two (*bipolar cell:* neurons that synapse with the axons of rods and cones in the retina of the eye)

chemo- = chemical (*chemoreceptor:* a receptor that transmits information about the total solute concentration in a solution or about individual kinds of molecules)

coch- = a snail (*cochlea:* the complex, coiled organ of hearing that contains the organ of Corti)

electro- = electricity (*electromagnetic receptor:* receptors of electromagnetic energy, such as visible light, electricity, and magnetism)

endo- = within (*endoskeleton:* a hard skeleton buried within the soft tissues of an animal)

exo- = outside (*exoskeleton:* a hard encasement on the surface of an animal that provides protection and points of attachment for muscles)

extero- = outside (*exteroreceptor:* sensory receptors that detect stimuli outside the body, such as heat, light, pressure, and chemicals)

fovea = a pit (*fovea:* the center of the visual field of the eye)

gusta- = taste (*gustatory receptors:* taste receptors)

hydro- = water (*hydrostatic skeleton:* a skeletal system composed of fluid held under pressure in a closed body compartment; the main skeleton of most cnidarians, flatworms, nematodes, and annelids)

inter- = between; **-cala** = insert (*intercalated disks:* specialized junctions between cardiac muscle cells which provide direct electrical coupling among cells)

intero- = inside (*interoreceptor:* sensory receptors that detect stimuli within the body, such as blood pressure and body position)

mechano- = an instrument (*mechanoreceptor:* a sensory receptor that detects physical deformations in the body's environment associated with pressure, touch, stretch, motion, and sound)

myo- = muscle; **-fibro** = fiber (*myofibril:* a fibril collectively arranged in longitudinal bundles in muscle cells; composed of thin filaments of actin and a regulatory protein and thick filaments of myosin)

noci- = harm (*nociceptor:* pain receptors in the epidermis of the skin)

olfact- = smell (*olfactory receptor:* smell receptors)

omma- = the eye (*ommatidia:* the facets of the compound eye of arthropods and some polychaete worms)

peri- = around; **-stalsis** = a constriction (*peristalsis:* rhythmic waves of contraction of smooth muscle that push food along the digestive tract)

photo- = light (*photoreceptor:* receptors of light)

rhodo- = red (*rhodopsin:* a visual pigment consisting of retinal and opsin)

sacc- = a sack (*saccule:* a chamber in the vestibule behind the oval window that participates in the sense of balance)

sarco- = flesh; **-mere** = a part (*sarcomere:* the fundamental, repeating unit of striated muscle, delimited by the Z lines)

sclero- = hard (*sclera:* a tough, white outer layer of connective tissue that forms the globe of the vertebrate eye)

semi- = half (*semicircular canals:* a three-part chamber of the inner ear that functions in maintaining equilibrium)

stato- = standing; **-lith** = a stone (*statolith:* sensory organs that contain mechanoreceptors and function in the sense of equilibrium)

tetan- = rigid, tense (*tetanus:* the maximal, sustained contraction of a skeletal muscle, caused by a very fast frequency of action potentials elicited by continual stimulation)

thermo- = heat (*thermoreceptor:* an interoreceptor stimulated by either heat or cold)

trans- = across; **-missi** = send (*transmission:* the conduction of impulses to the central nervous system)

tropo- = turn, change (*tropomyosin:* the regulatory protein that blocks the myosin binding sites on the actin molecules)

tympan- = a drum (*tympanic membrane:* another name for the eardrum)

utric- = a leather bag (*utricle:* a chamber behind the oval window that opens into the three semicircular canals)

vitre- = glass (*vitreous humor:* the jellylike material that fills the posterior cavity of the vertebrate eye)

CHAPTER 50

An Introduction to Ecology and the Biosphere

Teaching Objectives

The Scope of Ecology

1. Define *ecology*. Identify the two features of organisms studied by ecologists.
2. Describe the relationship between ecology and evolutionary biology.
3. Distinguish between abiotic and biotic components of the environment.
4. Distinguish among organismal ecology, population ecology, community ecology, ecosystem ecology, and landscape ecology.
5. Clarify the difference between ecology and environmentalism.

Interactions Between Organisms and the Environment Affect the Distribution of Species

6. Define *biogeography*.
7. Describe the questions that might be asked in a study addressing the limits of the geographic distribution of a particular species.
8. Describe the problems caused by introduced species and illustrate with a specific example.
9. Explain how habitat selection may limit distribution of a species within its range of suitable habitats.
10. Describe, with examples, how biotic and abiotic factors may affect the distribution of organisms.
11. List the four abiotic factors that are the most important components of climate.
12. Distinguish between macroclimate and microclimate patterns.
13. Provide an example of a microclimate.
14. Explain, with examples, how a body of water and a mountain range might affect regional climatic conditions.
15. Describe how an ecologist might predict the effect of global warming on distribution of a tree species.
16. Name three ways in which marine biomes affect the biosphere.

Aquatic and Terrestrial Biomes

17. Describe the characteristics of the major aquatic biomes: lakes, wetlands, streams, rivers, estuaries, intertidal biomes, oceanic pelagic biomes, coral reefs, and marine benthic biomes.

18. Define the following characteristics of lakes: seasonal turnover, thermal stratification, thermocline, photic zone.

19. Explain why the following statement is false: "All communities on Earth are based on primary producers that capture light energy by photosynthesis."

20. Describe the characteristics of the major terrestrial biomes: tropical forest, desert, savanna, chaparral, temperate grassland, coniferous forest, temperate broadleaf forest, and tundra.

21. Give an example of a biome characterized by periodic disturbance.

Student Misconceptions

1. Some students—and many members of the general public—do not understand the difference between *ecology* and *environmentalism*. The distinction is clarified in the text, but bears repeating in class. Point out to students that ecologists and environmentalists often work together. Use specific cases to illustrate how ecologists have provided scientific evidence that has been crucial in planning environmental management or advocating for environmental protection. Point out that many areas of applied ecology study human effects on the environment.

2. Students tend to underestimate the interdependence of populations within communities. Individual species may be seen as fundamentally independent of one another. Predators are recognized to influence the species they prey on, but the importance of the network of interactions among organisms is generally undervalued.

3. Many students overemphasize the importance of "balance" in communities, ecosystems, and biomes. They do not realize that many species have evolved to cope with or benefit from environmental perturbation, and that some biomes are characterized by periodic natural disturbances. As a result of this misunderstanding, students may take the gloomy view that biological communities are unable to recover from human damage or natural disaster. To counter these views, describe specific cases of communities that have recovered from major disturbances.

Chapter Guide to Teaching Resources

Overview: The scope of ecology

Concept 50.1 Ecology is the study of interactions between organisms and the environment

Transparency

Figure 50.2   Distribution and abundance of the red kangaroo in Australia, based on aerial surveys

Student Media Resource

Activity: Science, technology, and society: DDT

Concept 50.2 Interactions between organisms and the environment limit the distribution of species

Transparencies

Figure 50.5   Biogeographic realms

Figure 50.6   Flowchart of factors limiting geographic distribution

Figure 50.7   Spread of breeding populations of the great-tailed grackle in the United States from 1974 to 1996

Figure 50.8   Does feeding by sea urchins and limpets affect seaweed distribution?

Figure 50.10   Global climate patterns: Latitudinal variation in sunlight density

Figure 50.10   Global climate patterns: Seasonal variation in sunlight intensity

Figure 50.10   Global climate patterns: Global air circulation and precipitation patterns

Figure 50.10   Global climate patterns: Global wind patterns

Figure 50.11   Moderating effects of large bodies of water on climate

Figure 50.12   How mountains affect rainfall

Figure 50.13   Lake stratification and seasonal turnover (layer 1)

Figure 50.13   Lake stratification and seasonal turnover (layer 2)

Figure 50.13   Lake stratification and seasonal turnover (layer 3)

Figure 50.13   Lake stratification and seasonal turnover (layer 4)

Figure 50.14   Current range and predicted range for the American beech (*Fagus grandifolia*) under two scenarios of climate change over the next century

Instructor and Student Media Resources

Activity: Adaptations to biotic and abiotic factors

Investigation: How do abiotic factors affect distribution of organisms?

Video: Clownfish and anemone

Video: Tubeworms

Video: Hydrothermal vent

Concept 50.3 Abiotic and biotic factors influence the structure and dynamics of aquatic biomes

Transparencies

Figure 50.15   The distribution of major aquatic biomes

Figure 50.16   Zonation in aquatic environments

Instructor and Student Media Resources

Activity: Aquatic biomes

Video: Coral reef

Concept 50.4 Climate largely determines the distribution and structure of terrestial biomes

Transparencies

Figure 50.18   A climograph for some major types of biomes in North America

Figure 50.19   The distribution of major terrestrial biomes

Instructor and Student Media Resources

Activity: Terrestrial biomes

Video: Flapping geese

Video: Swans taking flight

For additional resources such as digital images and lecture outlines, go to the Campbell Media Manager or the Instructor Resources section of **www.campbellbiology.com.**

Key Terms

abiotic	desert	organismal ecology
abyssal zone	detritus	patchiness
aphotic zone	dispersal	permafrost
benthic zone	ecology	photic zone
benthos	ecosystem	population
biome	ecosystem ecology	population ecology
biosphere	ecotone	precautionary
biota	estuary	principle
biotic	eutrophic lake	savanna
canopy	intertidal zone	streams and rivers
chaparral	landscape ecology	temperate broadleaf
climate	limnetic zone	forest
climograph	littoral zone	temperate grassland
community	macroclimate	thermocline
community ecology	marine benthic zone	tropical rain forest
coniferous forest	microclimate	tropics
coral reef	neritic zone	tundra
deep-sea hydrothermal	oceanic pelagic biome	turnover
vent	oligotrophic lake	wetland

Word Roots

a- = without; **bio-** = life (*abiotic components:* nonliving chemical and physical factors in the environment)

abyss- = deep, bottomless (*abyssal zone:* the very deep benthic communities near the bottom of the ocean; this region is characterized by continuous cold, extremely high water pressure, low nutrients, and near or total absence of light)

bentho- = the depths of the sea (*benthic zone:* the bottom surfaces of aquatic environments)

estuar- = the sea (*estuary:* the area where a freshwater stream or river merges with the ocean)

eu- = good, well; **troph-** = food, nourishment (*eutrophic:* shallow lakes with high nutrient content in the water)

geo- = the Earth (*biogeography:* the study of the past and present distribution of species)

hydro- = water; **therm-** = heat (*deep-sea hydrothermal vents:* a dark, hot, oxygen-deficient environment associated with volcanic activity; the food producers are chemoautotrophic prokaryotes)

inter- = between (*intertidal zone:* the shallow zone of the ocean where land meets water)

limn- = a lake (*limnetic zone:* the well-lit, open surface waters of a lake farther from shore)

littor- = the seashore (*littoral zone:* the shallow, well-lit waters of a lake close to shore)

oligo- = small, scant (*oligotrophic lake:* a nutrient-poor, clear, deep lake with minimum phytoplankton)

micro- = small (*microclimate:* very fine scale variations of climate, such as the specific climatic conditions underneath a log)

pelag- = the sea (*oceanic pelagic biome:* most of the ocean's waters far from shore, constantly mixed by ocean currents)

perman- = remaining (*permafrost:* a permanently frozen stratum below the arctic tundra)

-photo = light (*aphotic zone:* the part of the ocean beneath the photic zone, where light does not penetrate sufficiently for photosynthesis to occur)

profund- = deep (*profundal zone:* the deep, aphotic region of a lake)

thermo- = heat; **-clin** = slope (*thermocline:* a narrow stratum of rapid temperature change in the ocean and in many temperate-zone lakes)

CHAPTER 51

Behavioral Ecology

Teaching Objectives

Introduction to Behavior and Behavioral Ecology

1. Define *behavior*.
2. Distinguish between proximate and ultimate questions about behavior. Ask a proximate question and an ultimate question about bird song.
3. Explain how the classical discipline of ethology led to the modern study of behavioral ecology.
4. Define *fixed action patterns* and give an example.
5. Define *imprinting*. Suggest a proximate cause and an ultimate cause for imprinting in young geese.

Many Behaviors Have a Genetic Component

6. Explain how genes and environment contribute to behavior. Explain what is unique about innate behavior.
7. Distinguish between kinesis and taxis.
8. Distinguish between signal and pheromone.
9. Explain how Berthold's research demonstrated a genetic basis for blackcap migration.
10. Describe Insel's research on the genetic and physiological controls on parental behavior of prairie voles. Describe Bester-Meredith and Marler's research on the influence of social behavior on parental behavior of California mice.

Learning

11. Explain how habituation may influence behavior.
12. Describe Tinbergen's classic experiment on spatial learning in digger wasps.
13. Distinguish between landmarks and cognitive maps.
14. Describe how associative learning might help a predator to avoid toxic prey.
15. Distinguish between classical conditioning and operant conditioning.
16. Describe an experiment that demonstrates problem solving in nonhuman animals.

Behavioral Traits Can Evolve by Natural Selection

17. Explain how Hedrick and Riechert's experiments demonstrated that behavioral differences between populations might be the product of natural selection.

18. Use an example to show how researchers can demonstrate the evolution of behavior in laboratory experiments.

19. Explain optimal foraging theory.

20. Explain how behavioral ecologists carry out cost-benefit analyses to determine how an animal should forage optimally. Explain how Zach demonstrated that crows feed optimally on whelks.

21. Explain how predation risk may affect the foraging behavior of a prey species.

22. Define and distinguish among *promiscuous, monogamous,* and *polygamous* mating relationships. Define and distinguish between *polygyny* and *polyandry.*

23. Describe how the certainty of paternity influences the development of mating systems.

24. Explain why males are more likely than females to provide parental care in fishes.

25. Suggest an ultimate explanation for a female stalk-eyed fly's preference for mates with relatively long eyestalks.

26. Agonistic behavior in males is often a ritualized contest rather than combat. Suggest an ultimate explanation for this.

27. Explain how game theory may be used to evaluate alternative behavioral strategies.

28. Define *inclusive fitness* and *reciprocal altruism.* Discuss conditions that would favor the evolution of altruistic behavior.

29. Relate the coefficient of relatedness to the concept of altruism.

30. Define *Hamilton's rule* and the concept of *kin selection.*

Social Learning and Sociobiology

31. Define *social learning* and *culture.*

32. Explain why mate choice copying by a female may increase her fitness.

33. State the main premise of sociology.

Student Misconceptions

1. Clarify to your students that proximate and ultimate questions are both legitimate approaches to the study of behavior. "How" (proximate) and "why" (ultimate) questions about animal behavior are related in their evolutionary basis. Proximate mechanisms were favored by natural selection because they produce behaviors that increase fitness in some way.

2. Provide examples to your students to show them that the answer to "nature or nurture?" is usually "nature and nurture."

3. Students may have difficulty understanding that our genetic makeup influences human social behaviors, but does not rigidly determine that behavior. Some students may entirely discount the genetic basis of complex human behaviors. Other students may take the opposite view, imagining that there are single genes determining complex human behavioral traits such as depression, alcoholism, or overeating leading to obesity.

Chapter Guide to Teaching Resources

Overview: Studying behavior

Concept 51.1 Behavioral ecologists distinguish between proximate and ultimate causes of behavior

Transparencies

Figure 51.3   Sign stimuli in a classic fixed action pattern

Figure 51.4   Proximate and ultimate perspectives on aggressive behavior by male sticklebacks

Figure 51.5   Proximate and ultimate perspectives on imprinting in graylag geese

Figure 51.6   Imprinting for conservation

Instructor and Student Media Resources

Investigation: How can pillbug responses to environments be tested?

Video: Ducklings

Concept 51.2 Many behaviors have a strong genetic component

Transparencies

Figure 51.7   A kinesis and a taxis

Figure 51.9   Minnows responding to the presence of an alarm substance

Figure 51.10   Are the different songs of closely related green lacewing species under genetic control?

Concept 51.3 Environment, interacting with an animal's genetic makeup, influences the development of behaviors

Transparencies

Figure 51.12   How does dietary environment affect mate choice by female *Drosophila mojavensis*?

Table 51.1   Influence of cross-fostering on male mice

Figure 51.14   Does a digger wasp use landmarks to find her nest?

Figure 51.15   Associative learning in zebrafish

Instructor and Student Media Resource

Video: Chimp cracking nut

Concept 51.4 Behavioral traits can evolve by natural selection

Transparencies

Figure 51.19   Aggressiveness of funnel web spiders (*Agelenopsis aperta*) living in two environments

Figure 51.20 Evolution of foraging behavior by laboratory populations of *Drosophila melanogaster*

Figure 51.21 Evidence of a genetic basis for migratory orientation

Concept 51.5 Natural selection favors behaviors that increase survival and reproductive success

Transparencies

Figure 51.22 Energy costs and benefits in foraging behavior

Figure 51.23 Feeding by bluegill sunfish

Figure 51.24 Risk of predation and use of foraging areas by mule deer

Figure 51.28 Sexual selection influenced by imprinting

Figure 51.31 Male polymorphism in the marine intertidal isopod *Paracerceis sculpta*

Instructor and Student Media Resources

Video: Snake wrestle ritual

Video: Albatross courtship ritual

Video: Blue-footed boobies' courtship ritual

Video: Chimp agonistic behavior

Video: Wolves' agonistic behavior

Video: Giraffe courtship ritual

Concept 51.6 The concept of inclusive fitness can account for most altruistic social behavior

Transparencies

Figure 51.34 The coefficient of relatedness between siblings

Figure 51.35 Kin selection and altruism in Belding's ground squirrel

Figure 51.36 Mate choice copying by female guppies (*Poecilia reticulata*)

Instructor and Student Media Resource

Video: Bee pollinating

For additional resources such as digital images and lecture outlines, go to the Campbell Media Manager or the Instructor Resources section of **www.campbellbiology.com.**

Key Terms

agonistic behavior	behavioral ecology	cognition
altruism	classical conditioning	cognitive ethology
associative learning	coefficient of	cognitive map
behavior	relatedness	communication

culture
ethology
fixed action pattern
  (FAP)
foraging
game theory
habituation
Hamilton's rule
imprinting
inclusive fitness
innate behavior
kin selection

kinesis
landmark
learning
mate choice copying
monogamous
operant conditioning
optimal foraging
  theory
pheromone
polyandry
polygamous
polygyny

promiscuous
proximate question
reciprocal altruism
sensitive period
sign stimulus
signal
social learning
sociobiology
spatial learning
taxis
ultimate question

Word Roots

agon- = a contest (*agonistic behavior:* a type of behavior involving a contest of some kind that determines which competitor gains access to some resource, such as food or mates)

andro- = a man (*polyandry:* a polygamous mating system involving one female and many males)

etho- = custom, habit (*ethology:* the study of animal behavior in natural conditions)

gyno- = a woman (*polygyny:* a polygamous mating system involving one male and many females)

kine- = move (*kinesis:* a change in activity rate in response to a stimulus)

mono- = one; **-gamy** = reproduction (*monogamous:* a type of relationship in which one male mates with just one female)

poly- = many (*polygamous:* a type of relationship in which an individual of one sex mates with several of the other sex)

socio- = a companion (*sociobiology:* the study of social behavior based on evolutionary theory)

CHAPTER 52

Population Ecology

Teaching Objectives

Characteristics of Populations

1. Distinguish between density and dispersion of a population.
2. Explain how ecologists may estimate the density of a species.
3. Describe conditions that may result in clumped dispersion, uniform dispersion, and random dispersion of individuals in a population.
4. Explain how a life table is constructed.
5. Distinguish between a life table and a reproductive table.
6. Describe the characteristics of populations that exhibit Type I, Type II, and Type III survivorship curves.

Life Histories

7. Define and distinguish between *semelparity* and *iteroparity*. Explain what factors may favor the evolution of each life history strategy.
8. Explain, with examples, how limited resources and trade-offs may affect life histories.

Population Growth

9. Compare the exponential model of population growth with the logistic model.
10. Explain how an environment's carrying capacity affects the per capita rate of increase of a population.
11. Explain the meaning of each of the following terms in the logistic model of population growth:

    a. r_{max}

    b. $K - N$

    c. $(K - N)/K$

12. Distinguish between *r*-selected populations and *K*-selected populations.

Population-Limiting Factors

13. Explain how density-dependent factors affect population growth.
14. Explain, with examples, how biotic and abiotic factors may work together to control a population's growth.
15. Describe boom-and-bust population cycles, explaining possible causes of lynx/hare fluctuations.

Human Population Growth

16. Describe the history of human population growth.

17. Define the *demographic transition.*

18. Compare the age structures of Italy, Afghanistan, and the United States. Describe the possible consequences for each country.

19. Describe the problems associated with estimating Earth's carrying capacity for the human species.

Student Misconceptions

1. Students who are weak in math may not fully understand the exponential and logistic models of population growth. Make sure that your students can define and explain the significance of all terms in these equations.

2. Many students do not recognize that any positive *r* term in the exponential growth model results in exponential growth. Some students think that *r* must be >1.0 to produce exponential growth.

3. Make sure that your students understand that estimates of global carrying capacity for the human race depend not only on population size but also on resource use per capita.

4. Students recognize that living things are adapted to survive and reproduce in the environments in which they live. Point out an equally important concept: that the metabolic activities of living things also modify the environment. Some of these changes—such as increasing levels of oxygen and decreasing levels of carbon dioxide—have been very beneficial to the majority of living things. In a very real sense, life itself has created the world in which we live.

Chapter Guide to Teaching Resources

Overview: Earth's fluctuating populations

Concept 52.1 Dynamic biological processes influence population density, dispersion, and demography

Transparencies

Figure 52.2   Population dynamics

Table 52.1   Life table for Belding's ground squirrels (*Spermophilus beldingi*) at Tioga Pass, in the Sierra Nevada Mountains of California

Figure 52.4   Survivorship curves for male and female Belding's ground squirrels

Figure 52.5   Idealized survivorship curves: Types I, II, and III

Table 52.2   Reproductive table for Belding's ground squirrels at Tioga Pass

Student Media Resources
Activity: Techniques for estimating population density and size
Activity: Investigating survivorship curves

Concept 52.2 Life history traits are products of natural selection

Transparency
Figure 52.7   How does caring for offspring affect parental survival in kestrels?

Concept 52.3 The exponential model describes population growth in an idealized, unlimited environment

Transparencies
Figure 52.9   Population growth predicted by the exponential model
Figure 52.10   Exponential growth in the African elephant population of Kruger National Park, South Africa

Concept 52.4 The logistic growth model includes the concept of carrying capacity

Transparencies
Figure 52.11   Influence of population size (N) on per capita rate of increase (r)
Table 52.3   A hypothetical example of logistic population growth, where $K = 1,000$ and $r_{max} = 0.05$ per individual per year
Figure 52.12   Population growth predicted by the logistic model
Figure 52.13   How well do these populations fit the logistic growth model?

Concept 52.5 Populations are regulated by a complex interaction of biotic and abiotic influences

Transparencies
Figure 52.14   Determining equilibrium for population density
Figure 52.15   Decreased reproduction at high population densities
Figure 52.18   How stable is the Isle Royale moose population?
Figure 52.19   Extreme population fluctuations
Figure 52.20   Song sparrow populations and immigration

Student Media Resource
Biology Labs On-Line: PopulationEcologyLab

Concept 52.6 Human population growth has slowed after centuries of exponential increase

Transparencies
Figure 52.21   Population cycles in the snowshoe hare and lynx
Figure 52.22   Human population growth
Figure 52.23   Percent increase in the global human population

Figure 52.24   Demographic transition in Sweden and Mexico, 1750–2050

Figure 52.25   Age-structure pyramids for the human population of three countries

Figure 52.26   Infant mortality and life expectancy at birth in developed and developing countries

Figure 52.27   Ecological footprint in relation to available ecological capacity

Student Media Resources

Activity: Human population growth

Activity: Analyzing age-structure pyramids

Biology Labs On-Line: DemographyLab

For additional resources such as digital images and lecture outlines, go to the Campbell Media Manager or the Instructor Resources section of **www.campbellbiology.com.**

Key Terms

age structure	emigration	metapopulation
big-bang reproduction	exponential population growth	population
carrying capacity		population dynamics
cohort	immigration	population ecology
demographic transition	infant mortality	repeated reproduction
	iteroparity	reproductive table
demography	*K*-selection	*r*-selection
density	life expectancy at birth	semelparity
density dependent	life history	survivorship curve
density independent	life table	territoriality
dispersion	logistic population growth	zero population growth (ZPG)
ecological capacity		
ecological footprint	mark-recapture method	

Word Roots

co- = together (*cohort:* a group of individuals of the same age, from birth until all are dead)

demo- = people; **-graphy** = writing (*demography:* the study of statistics relating to births and deaths in populations)

itero- = to repeat (*iteroparity:* a life history in which adults produce large numbers of offspring over many years; also known as repeated reproduction)

semel- = once; **-parity** = to beget (*semelparity:* a life history in which adults have but a single reproductive opportunity to produce large numbers of offspring, such as the life history of the Pacific salmon; also known as "big-bang reproduction")

CHAPTER 53

Community Ecology

Teaching Objectives

Interspecific Interactions and Community Structure

1. List the categories of interspecific interactions and explain how each interaction may affect the population densities of the two species involved.
2. State the competitive exclusion principle.
3. Define an ecological niche and restate the competitive exclusion principle using the niche concept.
4. Distinguish between fundamental and realized niche.
5. Explain how interspecific competition may lead to resource partitioning.
6. Define and compare *predation, herbivory,* and *parasitism.*
7. Give specific examples of adaptations of predators and prey.
8. Explain how cryptic coloration and warning coloration may aid an animal in avoiding predators.
9. Distinguish between Batesian mimicry and Müllerian mimicry.
10. Describe how predators may use mimicry to obtain prey.
11. Distinguish among endoparasites, ectoparasites, and parisitoids.
12. Distinguish among parasitism, mutualism, and commensalism.
13. Explain the relationship between species richness and relative abundance and explain how both contribute to species diversity.
14. Distinguish between a food chain and a food web.
15. Describe two ways to simplify food webs.
16. Summarize two hypotheses that explain why food chains are relatively short.
17. Explain how dominant and keystone species exert strong control on community structure. Describe an example of each.
18. Describe and distinguish between the bottom-up and top-down models of community organization. Describe possible features of a model that is intermediate between these two extremes.

Disturbance and Community Structure

19. Define *stability* and *disturbance.*
20. Provide examples of how disturbance may increase or decrease species diversity.
21. Give examples of humans as widespread agents of disturbance.

22. Distinguish between primary and secondary succession.

23. Describe how species that arrive early in succession may facilitate, inhibit, or tolerate later arrivals.

24. Explain why species richness declines along an equatorial-polar gradient.

25. Explain the significance of measures of evapotranspiration to species richness.

Biogeographic Factors Affect Community Biodiversity

26. Define the *species-area curve.*

27. Explain how species richness on islands varies according to island size and distance from the mainland.

28. Define and contrast the following pairs of hypotheses:

    a. *interactive hypothesis* versus *individualistic hypothesis*

    b. *rivet model* versus *redundancy model*

Student Misconceptions

1. Many students do not fully appreciate the complexity of interactions between populations in a food web. Some students do not understand the link between population growth and environmental constraints and think of populations as essentially independent. Other students recognize the importance of direct interactions between species that interact as predators and prey, but do not recognize that changes in abundance of species also impact other species that do not directly interact with them. Use examples of successful biomanipulation to illustrate that indirect effects may be as important as direct interactions in a food web.

2. Clarify to students that competition may lead to extinction of local populations but may also be an important factor in speciation as species partition resources by modifying their functional niches.

3. Students may have an exaggerated respect for the "balance of nature" and may think that a community maintains a stable and relatively constant composition of species despite disturbance. Clarify to your students that communities are not necessarily stable or static, and that change in community structure following disturbance is a natural event. Small-scale or moderate levels of disturbance may play an important role in maintaining or enhancing species diversity in a healthy community.

Further Reading

D'Avanzo, C. 2003. Research on learning: potential for improving college ecology teaching. *Front Ecol Environ 1(10):* 533–540.

Munson, B. H. 1994. Ecological misconceptions. *Journal of Environmental Education 25(4):* 30–34.

Odum, E. P. 1992. Great ideas in ecology for the 1990s. *BioScience 42(7):* 542–545.

Chapter Guide to Teaching Resources

Overview: What is a community?

Concept 53.1 A community's interactions include competition, predation, herbivory, symbiosis, and disease

Transparencies

Figure 53.2   Can a species' niche be influenced by interspecific competition?

Figure 53.3   Resource partitioning among Dominican Republic lizards

Figure 53.4   Character displacement: Indirect evidence of past competition

Instructor and Student Media Resources

Video: Whale eating a seal

Video: Clownfish and anemone

Video: Sea horses

Activity: Interspecific interactions

Biology Labs On-Line: PopulationEcologyLab

Concept 53.2 Dominant and keystone species exert strong controls on community structure

Transparencies

Figure 53.11   Which forest is more diverse?

Figure 53.12   Examples of terrestrial and marine food chains

Figure 53.13   An antarctic marine food web

Figure 53.14   Partial food web for the Chesapeake Bay estuary on the U.S. Atlantic coast

Figure 53.15   Test of the energetic hypothesis for the restriction of food chain length

Figure 53.16   Testing a keystone predator hypothesis

Figure 53.17   Sea otters as keystone predators in the North Pacific

Figure 53.19   Facilitation by black rush (*Juncus gerardi*) in New England salt marshes

Figure 53.20   Relationship between rainfall and herbaceous plant cover in a desert shrub community in Chile

Page 1171   Biomanipulation diagram

Student Media Resources

Activity: Food webs

Investigation: How are impacts on community diversity measured?

Concept 53.3 Disturbance influences species diversity and composition

Transparencies

Figure 53.23   A glacial retreat in southeastern Alaska

Figure 53.24   Changes in plant community structure and soil nitrogen during succession at Glacier Bay, Alaska

Student Media Resource

Activity: Primary succession

Concept 53.4 Biogeographic factors affect community biodiversity

Transparencies

Figure 53.25   Energy, water, and species richness

Figure 53.26   Species-area curve for North American breeding birds

Figure 53.27   The equilibrium model of island biogeography

Figure 53.28   How does species richness relate to area?

Student Media Resource

Activity: Exploring island biogeography

Concept 53.5 Contrasting views of community structure are the subject of continuing debate

Transparency

Figure 53.29   Testing the integrated and individualistic hypotheses of communities

Review

Transparency

Table 53.1   Interspecific interactions

For additional resources such as digital images and lecture outlines, go to the Campbell Media Manager or the Instructor Resources section of **www.campbellbiology.com.**

Key Terms

aposematic coloration
Batesian mimicry
biomanipulation
biomass
bottom-up model
character displacement
coevolution
commensalism
community
competitive exclusion
cryptic coloration
disturbance
dominant species
dynamic stability
  hypothesis
ecological niche
ecological succession
ectoparasite
endoparasite

energetic hypothesis
evapotranspiration
facilitator
food chain
food web
herbivory
host
individualistic
  hypothesis
integrated hypothesis
intermediate
  disturbance
  hypothesis
interspecific
  interaction
interspecific
  competition
invasive species
keystone species

Müllerian mimicry
mutualism
nonequilibrium model
parasite
parasitism
parasitoidism
pathogen
predation
primary succession
redundancy model
relative abundance
resource partitioning
rivet model
secondary succession
species diversity
species richness
species-area curve
top-down model
trophic structure

Word Roots

crypto- = hidden, concealed (*cryptic coloration:* a type of camouflage that makes potential prey difficult to spot against its background)

ecto- = outer (*ectoparasites:* parasites that feed on the external surface of a host)

endo- = inner (*endoparasites:* parasites that live within a host)

herb- = grass; **-vora** = eat (*herbivory:* the consumption of plant material by an herbivore)

hetero- = other, different (*heterogeneity:* a measurement of biological diversity considering richness and relative abundance)

inter- = between (*interspecific competition:* competition for resources between plants, between animals, or between decomposers when resources are in short supply)

mutu- = reciprocal (*mutualism:* a symbiotic relationship in which both the host and the symbiont benefit)

CHAPTER 54

Ecosystems

Teaching Objectives

Ecosystems, Energy, and Matter

1. Describe the fundamental relationship between autotrophs and heterotrophs in an ecosystem.
2. Explain how the first and second laws of thermodynamics apply to ecosystems.
3. Explain how decomposition connects all trophic levels in an ecosystem.

Primary Production in Ecosystems

4. Explain why the amount of energy used in photosynthesis is so much less than the amount of solar energy that reaches Earth.
5. Define and compare *gross primary production* and *net primary production.*
6. Define and compare net primary production and standing crop.
7. Compare primary productivity in specific marine, freshwater, and terrestrial ecosystems.

Secondary Production in Ecosystems

8. Explain why energy is said to flow rather than cycle within ecosystems.
9. Explain what factors may limit production in aquatic ecosystems.
10. Describe an experiment that provided evidence that iron availability limits oceanic primary production in some regions. Explain how iron availability is related to nitrogen availability in these regions.
11. Explain why areas of upwelling in the ocean have exceptionally high levels of primary production.
12. Distinguish between each of the following pairs of terms:
    a. primary and secondary production
    b. production efficiency and trophic efficiency
13. Explain why the production efficiency of a human is much less than the production efficiency of a mosquito.
14. Distinguish among pyramids of net production, pyramids of biomass, and pyramids of numbers.
15. Explain why aquatic ecosystems may have inverted biomass pyramids.
16. Explain why worldwide agriculture could feed more people if all humans consumed only plant material.
17. Explain the green-world hypothesis. Describe five factors that may act to keep herbivores in check.

The Cycling of Chemical Elements in Ecosystems

18. Describe the four nutrient reservoirs and the processes that transfer the elements between reservoirs.

19. Name the main processes driving the water cycle.

20. Name the major reservoirs of carbon.

21. Describe the nitrogen cycle and explain the importance of nitrogen fixation to all living organisms. Name three other key bacterial processes in the nitrogen cycle.

22. Describe the phosphorus cycle and explain how phosphorus is recycled locally in most ecosystems.

23. Explain how decomposition affects the rate of nutrient cycling in ecosystems.

24. Describe how net primary production and the rate of decomposition vary with actual evapotranspiration.

25. Describe the experiments at Hubbard Brook that revealed the key role that plants play in regulating nutrient cycles.

Human Impact on Ecosystems and the Biosphere

26. Describe how agricultural practices can interfere with nitrogen cycling.

27. Explain how "cultural eutrophication" can alter freshwater ecosystems.

28. Describe the causes and consequences of acid precipitation.

29. Explain why toxic compounds usually have the greatest effect on top-level carnivores.

30. Describe how increased atmospheric concentrations of carbon dioxide could affect Earth.

31. Describe the causes and consequences of ozone depletion.

Student Misconceptions

1. The pyramid of numbers refers to the number of organisms at each trophic level of a food web; the pyramid of biomass refers to the biomass of organisms at each trophic level of a food web. Students may generalize and think that the pyramid of production is based on the energy "stored" in organisms at each trophic level of a food web. Point out to your students that the pyramid of production is based on the production of each trophic level, measured in energy per unit area per unit time or in biomass added to the ecosystem per unit area per unit time. Explain the importance of the inclusion of time in the measure of production, and clarify why time is not a unit in measure of biomass or numbers.

2. Students may view biogeochemical cycles as confusing and boring abstractions. Discuss the crucial role of prokaryotes, especially in the nitrogen cycle, and point out that life on Earth would end without prokaryotic nitrogen fixation. Point out that nutrients may change in chemical form as they move through food webs. Look for interesting and locally relevant examples to illustrate the effects of nutrient availability on community structure and to clarify the concept of limiting factors.

3. Emphasize to students that ecosystems are open systems, and that they are not self-sufficient or self-contained. Students know that energy in the form of sunlight enters ecosystems. They are less likely to realize that an area of high productivity may feed an adjacent area of low productivity or to recognize that a population with a high reproductive rate may be a source of recruits for an adjacent population with a lower reproductive rate.

Chapter Guide to Teaching Resources

Overview: Ecosystems, energy, and matter

Concept 54.1 Ecosystem ecology emphasizes energy flow and chemical cycling

Transparency

Figure 54.2   An overview of energy and nutrient dynamics in an ecosystem

Concept 54.2 Physical and chemical factors limit primary production in ecosystems

Transparencies

Figure 54.4   Net primary production of different ecosystems

Figure 54.5   Regional annual net primary production for Earth

Figure 54.6   Which nutrient limits phytoplankton production along the coast of Long Island?

Table 54.1   Nutrient enrichment experiment for Sargasso Sea samples

Figure 54.8   Actual evapotranspiration (temperature and moisture) related to terrestrial net primary production in selected ecosystems

Figure 54.9   Is phosphorus or nitrogen the limiting nutrient in a Hudson Bay salt marsh?

Instructor and Student Media Resources

Investigation: How do temperature and light affect primary production?

Video: Cyanobacteria

Concept 54.3 Energy transfer between trophic levels is usually less than 20% efficient

Transparencies

Figure 54.10   Energy partitioning within a link of the food chain

Figure 54.11   An idealized pyramid of net production

Figure 54.12   Pyramids of biomass (standing crop)

Figure 54.13   A pyramid of numbers

Figure 54.14   Relative food energy available to the human population at different trophic levels

Student Media Resources
Activity: Pyramids of production
Graph It: Animal food production efficiency and food policy

Concept 54.4 Biological and geochemical processes move nutrients between organic and inorganic parts of the ecosystem

Transparencies
Figure 54.16   A general model of nutrient cycling
Figure 54.17   Nutrient cycles: The water cycle
Figure 54.17   Nutrient cycles: The carbon cycle
Figure 54.17   Nutrient cycles: The nitrogen cycle
Figure 54.17   Nutrient cycles: The phosphorus cycle
Figure 54.18   Review: Generalized scheme for biogeochemical cycles
Figure 54.19   Nutrient cycling in the Hubbard Brook
Experimental Forest: An example of long-term ecological research

Student Media Resources
Activity: Energy flow and chemical cycling
Activity: The carbon cycle
Activity: The nitrogen cycle

Concept 54.5 The human population is disrupting chemical cycles throughout the biosphere

Transparencies
Figure 54.21   Distribution of acid precipitation in North America and Europe, 1980
Figure 54.22   Average pH for precipitation in the contiguous United States in 2002
Figure 54.23   Biological magnification of PCBs in a Great Lakes food web
Figure 54.24   The increase in atmospheric carbon dioxide at Mauna Loa, Hawaii, and average global temperatures over land from 1958 to 2004
Figure 54.26   Thickness of the ozone layer over Antarctica in units called Dobsons
Figure 54.27   How free chlorine in the atmosphere destroys ozone

Student Media Resources
Activity: Water pollution from nitrates
Activity: The greenhouse effect
Graph It: Atmospheric CO_2 and temperature changes

For additional resources such as digital images and lecture outlines, go to the Campbell Media Manager or the Instructor Resources section of **www.campbellbiology.com.**

Key Terms

actual
  evapotranspiration
biogeochemical cycle
biological
  magnification
critical load
decomposer
detritivore
detritus

ecosystem
eutrophication
greenhouse effect
green world hypothesis
gross primary
  production (GPP)
limiting nutrient
net primary
  production (NPP)

primary consumer
primary producer
primary production
production efficiency
secondary consumer
secondary production
tertiary consumer
trophic efficiency
turnover time

Word Roots

auto- = self; **-troph** = food, nourishment (*autotroph:* an organism that obtains organic food molecules without eating other organisms)

bio- = life; **geo-** = the Earth (*biogeochemical cycles:* the various nutrient circuits which involve both biotic and abiotic components of ecosystems)

de- = from, down, out (*denitrification:* the process of converting nitrate back to nitrogen)

detrit- = wear off; **-vora** = eat (*detritivore:* a consumer that derives its energy from nonliving organic material)

hetero- = other, different (*heterotroph:* an organism that obtains organic food molecules by eating other organisms or their by-products)

CHAPTER 55

Conservation Biology and Restoration Ecology

Teaching Objectives

The Biodiversity Crisis

1. Distinguish between conservation biology and restoration biology.
2. Describe the three levels of biodiversity.
3. Explain why biodiversity at all levels is vital to human welfare.
4. List the four major threats to biodiversity and give an example of each.

Conservation at the Population and Species Levels

5. Define and compare the small-population approach and the declining-population approach.
6. Explain how an extinction vortex can lead to the extinction of a small population. Describe how a greater prairie chicken population was rescued from an extinction vortex.
7. Describe the basic steps that are used to analyze declining populations and determine possible interventions in the declining-population approach. Describe the case of the red-cockaded woodpecker to illustrate this approach.
8. Describe the conflicting demands that accompany species conservation.

Conservation at the Community, Ecosystem, and Landscape Levels

9. Explain how edges and corridors can strongly influence landscape biodiversity.
10. Define *biodiversity hot spots* and explain why they are important.
11. Explain why natural reserves must be functional parts of landscapes.
12. Define *zoned reserves* and explain why they are important.
13. Define *restoration ecology* and describe its goals.
14. Explain the importance of bioremediation and biological augmentation of ecosystem processes in restoration efforts.
15. Describe the process of adaptive management.
16. Describe the concept of sustainable development.
17. Explain the goals of the Sustainable Biosphere Initiative.
18. Define *biophilia* and explain why the concept gives some biologists hope.

Student Misconceptions

1. Students may not realize that much environmental damage is reversible. Some students think of ecosystems as static and unchanging, and do not appreciate that natural disturbance is part of the dynamics of many ecosystems. Use local examples to teach your students how ecosystems can recover from moderate levels of human-caused disturbance or degradation.

2. Some students exaggerate the ability of humans to act as stewards of the Earth. Such students do not appreciate the complexity of the living world. It is important to convey to our students the excitement of recent dramatic advances in biological understanding. It is equally important to impress upon them how much remains unknown.

3. Bioremediation, the use of living organisms to detoxify polluted ecosystems, offers an excellent lesson to students on the diversity, power, and promise of the metabolic pathways of living organisms.

Chapter Guide to Teaching Resources

Overview: The biodiversity crisis

Concept 55.1 Human activities threaten Earth's biodiversity

Transparency
Figure 55.2   Three levels of biodiversity

Instructor and Student Media Resources
Activity: Madagascar and the biodiversity crisis
Activity: Introduced species: Fire ants
Graph It: Forestation changes
Graph It: Global fisheries and overfishing
Graph It: Municipal solid waste trends in the U.S.
Video: Coral reef

Concept 55.2 Population conservation focuses on population size, genetic diversity, and critical habitat

Transparencies
Figure 55.9   Processes culminating in an extinction vortex
Figure 55.10   What caused the drastic decline of the Illinois greater prairie chicken population?
Figure 55.12   Growth of the Yellowstone grizzly bear population, as indicated by the number of females observed with cubs and the number of cubs

Concept 55.3 Landscape and regional conservation aim to sustain entire biotas

Transparencies

Figure 55.17   Earth's terrestrial biodiversity hot spots

Figure 55.18   The legal (green border) and biotic (red borders) boundaries for grizzly bears in Yellowstone and Grand Teton National Parks

Figure 55.19   Zoned reserves in Costa Rica

Concept 55.4 Restoration ecology attempts to restore degraded ecosystems to a more natural state

Transparencies

Figure 55.21   The size-time relationship for community recovery from natural and human-caused disasters

Figure 55.22   Restoration ecology worldwide

Student Media Resource

Investigation: How are potential prairie restoration sites analyzed?

Concept 55.5 Sustainable development seeks to improve the human condition while conserving biodiversity

Transparency

Figure 55.23   Infant mortality and life expectancy at birth in Costa Rica

Student Media Resources

Activity: Conservation biology review

Graph It: Global freshwater resources

Graph It: Prospects for renewable energy

For additional resources such as digital images and lecture outlines, go to the Campbell Media Manager or the Instructor Resources section of **www.campbellbiology.com.**

Key Terms

biodiversity hot spot	endangered species	population viability
biological	extinction vortex	analysis (PVA)
augmentation	introduced species	restoration ecology
bioremediation	landscape ecology	sustainable
conservation biology	minimum viable	development
ecosystem services	population (MVP)	threatened species
effective population	movement corridor	zoned reserve
size		

Word Roots

bio- = life (*biodiversity hot spot:* a relatively small area with an exceptional concentration of species)